McGraw-Hill Electrical and Electronic Engineering Series

FREDERICK EMMONS TERMAN, *Consulting Editor*

SERVOMECHANISM ANALYSIS

McGraw-Hill Electrical and Electronic Engineering Series

FREDERICK EMMONS TERMAN, *Consulting Editor*

BAILEY AND GAULT · Alternating-current Machinery

BERANEK · Acoustics

BRUNS AND SAUNDERS · Analysis of Feedback Control Systems

CAGE · Theory and Application of Industrial Electronics

CUCCIA · Harmonics, Sidebands, and Transients on Communication Engineering

EASTMAN · Fundamentals of Vacuum Tubes

EVANS · Control-system Dynamics

FITZGERALD AND HIGGINBOTHAM · Basic Electrical Engineering

FITZGERALD AND KINGSLEY · Electric Machinery

GEPPERT · Basic Electron Tubes

GLASFORD · Fundamentals of Television Engineering

HAPPELL AND HESSELBERTH · Engineering Electronics

HARMAN · Fundamentals of Electronic Motion

HESSLER AND CAREY · Fundamentals of Electrical Engineering

HILL · Electronics in Engineering

JOHNSON · Transmission Lines and Networks

KRAUS · Antennas

KRAUS · Electromagnetics

LEPAGE · Analysis of Alternating-current Circuits

LEPAGE AND SEELY · General Network Analysis

MILLMAN AND SEELY · Electronics

MILLMAN AND TAUB · Pulse and Digital Circuits

ROGERS · Introduction to Electric Fields

RÜDENBERG · Transient Performance of Electric Power Systems

RYDER · Engineering Electronics

SEELY · Electronic Engineering

SEELY · Electron-tube Circuits

SEELY · Radio Electronics

SISKIND · Direct-current Machinery

SKILLING · Electric Transmission Lines

SKILLING · Transient Electric Currents

SPANGENBURG · Fundamentals of Electronic Devices

SPANGENBURG · Vacuum Tubes

STEVENSON · Elements of Power System Analysis

TERMAN · Electronic and Radio Engineering

TERMAN AND PETTIT · Electronic Measurements

THALER · Elements of Servomechanism Theory

THALER AND BROWN · Servomechanism Analysis

THOMPSON · Alternating-current and Transient Circuit Analysis

TRUXAL · Automatic Feedback Control System Synthesis

SERVOMECHANISM
ANALYSIS

George J. Thaler; B.E., Dr. Eng.

Associate Professor, Department of Electrical Engineering
U.S. Naval Postgraduate School, Monterey, Calif.

Robert G. Brown; B.S. in E.E., M.S. in E.E.

Senior Project Engineer, A.C. Spark Plug Division
General Motors Corp., Milwaukee

New York   Toronto   London

McGRAW-HILL BOOK COMPANY, INC.

1953

SERVOMECHANISM ANALYSIS

Library of Congress Catalog Card Number: 52–6005

v

PREFACE

The material in this text has been taught for four years at the University of Notre Dame in a course offered at the postgraduate level. Most of it has also been used for three years at the University of North Dakota in a course given at the undergraduate level.

The material is not original, all of it being available elsewhere in the literature, as evidenced by the numerous bibliographical references. Such merits as the text may have lie in the arrangement and detail of the presentation, which the authors have found well suited to teaching the subject, and which have been well received by the students.

Chapter 1 is an introduction to the basic principles of the subject and the basic concepts involved. Chapters 2 and 3 are intended as review material for postgraduate students but contain sufficient detail for presentation to undergraduate students who may not have previous introduction to the subject material. Chapters 4 through 12 contain the principal tools for the analysis and design of servomechanisms. The presentation is from the point of view of analysis, since the authors believe that analysis must precede design. Those items which are basic are treated in considerable detail. More specialized topics, where presented, are discussed briefly, and the details are left to the initiative of the student.

Chapter 13 has been introduced because of the growing importance of relay servomechanisms in many fields. Chapter 14 presents the fundamental principles of the root-locus method, not only because this method provides a convenient means of computing the transient response from the transfer-function equation, but also because the concept of pole and zero configurations seems to offer great promise for future developments in the analysis and design of dynamic systems.

The appendixes, while admittedly abbreviated, contain a good deal of factual information about components which, as far as the authors know, cannot be found under any other single cover. The purpose of this material is to provide the student with a concept of the physical nature of the systems which are discussed quite abstractly in the bulk of the text.

The names of those whose work has contributed to the preparation of this text might well be listed by referring to the bibliography. While this is manifestly impractical, the authors wish to offer their sincere thanks to all those whose writings have influenced the contents, arrangement, and presentation used in this text. Special thanks are due to J. A. Northcott, head of the Electrical Engineering Department at the

University of Notre Dame, and to Keith B. MacKichan, head of the Electrical Engineering Department at the University of North Dakota, for their wholehearted cooperation in many of the details; to Miss Fern Bosard for typing the original notes which were used in class to develop the material further, and to Mrs. Margaret Dineen for typing the final manuscript.

GEO. J. THALER
ROBERT G. BROWN

MONTEREY, CALIF.
MILWAUKEE, WIS.
   August, 1952

CONTENTS

CHAPTER 1

GENERAL BACKGROUND

1-1. Introduction. In the past decade the importance of automatic controls has grown tremendously in almost every field of technical endeavor. The normal advances in theory and practice have been greatly accelerated by the high performance requirements of military equipments using automatic-control systems. As the need for speed and accuracy grew, so too did the complexity of the control system. In many cases combinations of hydraulic, pneumatic, mechanical, and electrical components were required to meet the performance specifications. Such combinations, owing to their complexity, made empirical, or trial-and-error, design methods unsatisfactory. Thus new design methods had to be developed to meet the need for precise automatic controls. This text is devoted to a study of the mathematical and graphical methods developed for one type of automatic-control system—servomechanisms.

The term *servomechanism*, though relatively new, has become widely known in engineering fields, but a clear concept of the meaning of this term seems to be limited to the few who are closely associated with the subject. Hazen[1],* originally defined a servomechanism as "a power amplifying device in which the amplifier element driving the output is actuated by the difference between the input to the servo and its output." While it is doubtful whether this definition includes all of the systems now classified as servomechanisms, this text will not attempt a better definition but will clarify the meaning of the term by discussion and illustration. In general, it may be said that all servomechanisms are automatic-control systems but not all automatic controls are servomechanisms. The following classification of automatic-control systems is intended to illustrate the place of servomechanisms in the field of automatic control.

1-2. Automatic-control Systems. *Open-loop.* In general, there are two types of automatic-control systems, open-loop and closed-loop. In an open-loop system an input signal, or command, is applied, amplified (usually), and a power output is obtained. The location of the power-output device is frequently remote from the input station. The input

* Superior numbers, when they appear in the text, are the numbers of references given in the Bibliography.

1

may be applied manually, as by turning a dial. The expected output is normally predetermined by calibration, and the input control may be accompanied by some sort of calibration chart. The actual output obtained depends on the validity of the calibration, and if the components of the system are affected by time, temperature, humidity, lubrication, etc., the actual output may vary from the expected output.

An open-loop control usually has the basic components indicated in the block diagram of Fig. 1-1. An example might be a temperature control for a high-temperature electric furnace. Such a control may be obtained with a saturable reactor as shown in the schematic diagram of Fig. 1-2. Here the input is a variable resistor in the grid circuit of a

```
┌────────┐      ┌───────────┐      ┌────────────┐      ┌────────────┐
│ Input  ├─────▶│ Amplifier ├─────▶│ Controller ├─────▶│   Power    │
│        │      │           │      │            │      │   output   │
└────────┘      └───────────┘      └────────────┘      │   (load)   │
                                                        └────────────┘
```

Fɪɢ. 1-1. Block diagram of an open-loop system.

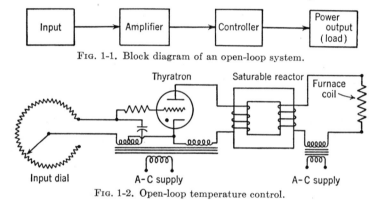

Fɪɢ. 1-2. Open-loop temperature control.

thyratron and would undoubtedly be calibrated. The thyratron and the reactor act as amplifier and controller. The output is the power loss in the furnace coil, and the controlled quantity, or load, is the temperature of the furnace. It is apparent that the calibration is affected by tube aging, voltage variations in the a-c source, the physical condition of the furnace coil, and possibly by ambient conditions at the furnace location.

Closed-loop Systems. Closed-loop automatic-control systems have the same basic components shown in Fig. 1-1 but also have additional features. The actual output is measured, and a signal corresponding to this measurement is fed back to the input station, where it is compared with the input (desired output). This comparison is effected in some device* which produces a signal proportional to the difference between input and output. The *error* thus determined is used to drive the system, *i.e.*, the command signal is obtained from the error rather than from a calibrated input. Such a system automatically attempts to correct any discrepancy between desired and actual output and thus is relatively independent of calibration and of fluctuations in system parameters, though proper design is prerequisite to good performance.

* See appendix on Error Detectors.

Closed-loop control systems may be classified according to the manner in which the error signal is used to control the power output. The most common classifications are:

1. On-off controllers
2. Step controllers
3. Servomechanisms

Each of these will now be discussed in some detail.

1-3. On-Off Controllers. In this type of automatic-control system the function of the error (difference between input and output) is to turn the power on or off. Once this switching is accomplished, there is no further control of the system. Typical examples are thermostatic control of room temperature or of an electric refrigerator. In each case an error detector (thermostat) measures the output (temperature) continuously. No signal is sent to the power unit until the output reaches the preset value; then full power is applied to regain the desired output temperature. In the case of room-temperature control, power is *on* when the temperature is too low and *off* after the desired temperature has been reached, while for refrigeration control the power is *on* when the temperature is too high and is turned *off* as the temperature drops to the preset value.

1-4. Step Controllers. Occasionally, a type of on-off control may be combined with one or more timing mechanisms to obtain a step controller. This name arises from the fact that the desired output is obtained by applying power in steps. As an example, consider a high-temperature furnace in which the temperature is to be raised to the desired value with minimum overshoot. The temperature is measured continuously and compared continuously with the desired condition. The error is used to adjust the power input only at preset time intervals, perhaps once every 5 min. If the temperature is below the desired value, the power is turned on when the error is applied to the controller. The power remains on for a definite time, less than the interval used for error checking. As an additional refinement, the duration of the power application may be made a function of the magnitude of the error. Thus the power is applied in pulses, and the temperature rises in *steps*, rather than continuously.

1-5. Servomechanisms. Those closed-loop systems which not only measure the output and compare it with the reference but which also use the error (or some function of the error) to control the magnitude and/or the direction of the power applied to the output are called servomechanisms.

One class of servomechanisms, which were in existence long before the term "servomechanisms" was coined, are those devices known as regulators.

Many regulatory systems are on-off mechanisms, but far more have continuous control. Some examples are generator voltage regulators, speed regulators, turbine governors, and temperature and pressure regulators. Although most regulators have been designed by other methods, they can be analyzed and designed by the methods of servomechanism theory.[2] Regulators are normally designed to compensate for load or output disturbances with the input held fixed, and this restriction is not normally applicable to other types of servomechanisms.

Most servomechanisms have continuous control and are designed to obey accurately a command signal as well as regulate against output disturbances. They are used in almost every field in which accurate controls are necessary. Examples are radar-antenna sweeping controls, gun directors, constant-tension control of sheet rolls in paper mills, controlling sheet-metal thickness in hot-rolling mills, and controlling concentrations of chemical-process materials. It is important to note that the servomechanism is the entire system, not a component part. Since the bulk of this text is devoted to the analysis of this class of automatic controllers, a more detailed general treatment follows.

1-6. Basic Equation of a Servomechanism. Servomechanism systems are not limited as to the type or nature of their component parts or as to the number of such parts. They may contain electrical, pneumatic, mechanical, hydraulic, optical, or chemical units in any sequence and number. Despite this variety, the mathematical equations which express system characteristics are of the same form for all servomechanisms. Hence, the solutions of these equations will be of the same form. It is this similarity which justifies the use of a common method for analysis. The basic equation for any servomechanism is an integrodifferential equation such as (1-1),*

$$A_n \frac{d^n\theta_o}{dt^n} + \cdots + A_2 \frac{d^2\theta_o}{dt^2} + A_1 \frac{d\theta_o}{dt} + A_0\theta_o + A + \int \theta_o \, dt = F(\varepsilon) \quad (1\text{-}1)$$

where
θ_o = output quantity
ε = error = $(\theta_i - \theta_o)$
θ_i = input quantity
$A_n, \ldots, A$ = coefficients which are functions of the system parameters

In Eq. (1-1) the assumption is usually made that the system is linear. This is equivalent to saying that the coefficients $A_n, \ldots, A$ are constants or functions of time. In physical terminology all fixed parameters such as inertia, friction, inductance, capacitance, etc., are assumed to maintain constant values under operating conditions, and the dynamic parameters of such system components as springs, amplifiers, motors,

---

* This is the equation of motion of the system and may be arrived at in any specific case by applying Newton's laws of motion.

generators, etc., are assumed to maintain linear relationships during operation: *i.e.*, a spring is assumed to produce a deflection exactly proportional to the applied force regardless of the magnitude of the force; an amplifier is assumed to maintain constant gain and zero phase shift regardless of the input-signal amplitude or frequency; an electric motor is assumed to produce a torque proportional to the applied voltage; a generator is assumed to produce an output voltage proportional to its field current; etc. Of course it is known that none of these assumptions is exactly true; and occasionally, a system is sufficiently nonlinear to make such assumptions badly in error. However, the assumption of linearity in servomechanisms is a desirable starting point for three reasons:

1. Many servomechanisms are essentially linear under normal operating conditions.

2. Slightly nonlinear systems usually may be approximated with sufficient accuracy by assuming linearity.

3. At present the mathematical methods for solving nonlinear equations have not been developed sufficiently for practical use.

1-7. Transient Analysis. The simplest type of servomechanism contains components with inertia, friction, and elasticity or their equivalents, and therefore the simplest equation of motion for a servomechanism is at least a second-order linear differential equation. The solution to the equation may therefore show oscillatory or nonoscillatory characteristics depending on the damping. Because of the feedback loop in a servomechanism it is possible that the solution of the differential equation may show sustained as well as transient oscillations. The oscillatory characteristics of the system depend only upon system parameters, which thus determine the system response to a disturbance or specific input signal. If the specific signal can be expressed mathematically and used in the differential equation, the resulting solution expresses the exact performance of the system, within the limits of accuracy of the differential equation itself. When the input signal is not known exactly, it is general practice to assume more severe input (or output) conditions than will be met in actual operation in order to obtain slightly pessimistic results. Therefore, in analyzing servomechanism systems, the obvious approach is to write the differential equation of motion of the system and solve for its roots. The performance may then be predicted by plotting the appropriate curves and inspecting them. A portion of this text is devoted to such procedures.

The analysis of servomechanisms by solution of their differential equations does not satisfactorily fulfill all the aims of engineering studies. Solutions of the differential equations specify the performance of a system and so will indicate whether or not improvement is needed, but in general such solutions do not indicate a direct means of altering the system to obtain the desired improvements. Transient analysis predicts (among other things), the response time of the system, which is the time required for the system to regain steady-state conditions after a disturbance, the maximum deviation of the output from the desired condition, and the frequency of transient oscillation. This information permits a ready comparison with specifications if the problem is one of design. When such a comparison shows a need for improvement of the system, the designer must return to the equations of the system. In the differential equation the effective inertias, friction coefficients, and stiffness of all system components are lumped in the equation coefficients $(A_n, \ldots, A)$. As a result, the effect of the inertia, friction, or stiffness of any component of the system is not easily determined. The alteration in system performance which is produced by changing or modifying a system component usually cannot be predicted by inspection of the equations, so that an entire new solution is necessitated.

Thus design procedures based on transient-analysis methods have the following inherent disadvantages:

1. The excessive labor of repeated solutions of the equations.

2. Trial-and-error methods in changing components, since it is difficult to establish a trend.

3. A final result which may be satisfactory without being the most desirable solution.

It is evident that a method of analysis which lends itself more readily to design work is highly desirable. Such a method has been developed and is generally known as the transfer-function method.

1-8. Transfer-function Analysis. The transfer-function method is based on ordinary transmission-network theory. In brief, it postulates that the transfer of signal through any component, as expressed by the amplitude and phase relationships between input and output, completely describes the characteristics of the component. Once the characteristics of components are known and expressed mathematically, they may be combined in series or parallel (depending on the system arrangement) and the performance of the over-all system may be arrived at by simple algebraic combination of the equations of the component parts. The advantage of this method of analysis is that the effect of each component of the system is expressed separately in the equation, and therefore the effect of changes in specific components may be readily calculated. The net result is a considerable saving in labor.

It should not be assumed that the transfer-function method is in itself sufficient for servomechanism analysis and design. Several important characteristics of servomechanism performance, such as the response time and the maximum deviation of the output, cannot be calculated with great accuracy except from the differential equation, though they may be estimated fairly well from the transfer-function data. Thus, for complete quantitative information on a servomechanism both the differential-equation solution and the transfer-function solution are desirable: the transfer function for ease in calculation and design, the differential equation for exact performance data on several important characteristics of the system. The transfer-function approach is normally the best starting point, since it permits rapid calculation of most of the desired information within reasonably close limits. The differential-equation solution would be attempted only if the specifications of the system required the information or if the desired performance could not be checked closely enough from the transfer-function data.

1-9. The Laplace Transformation. Before design problems may be considered, it is apparent that a thorough study must be made of servomechanism analysis. Such a study must include both the differential-equation and the transfer-function approach. While many mathematical methods are available for such work, considerable simplification may be obtained by using one form of operational calculus, the Laplace transformation. This tool is used almost exclusively in this text, for a number of reasons. It is suitable both for the solution of differential equations and for the construction of transfer functions. The transfer function of a system may be arrived at very simply from the Laplace transform of the differential equation by assuming the system to be initially at rest and thus providing for all initial conditions to be zero. In doing this, one eliminates much intermediate labor if both transfer-function data and differential-equation data are desired. Finally, the Laplace-transform method is entirely suited to certain necessary excursions into complex-variable theory associated with the Nyquist stability criterion.

1-10. Sequence of Text Material. Since the main purpose of this text is to present methods for analyzing servomechanisms, with limited reference to design, the tools required for the analysis must first be developed. Hence, the first topics discussed are the direct and inverse Laplace transformations. A generalized treatment is then made of means of setting up the differential equations which define the motion of elementary systems, with some examples of applications to more complex systems. Having established the necessary mathematical background, the transient analysis of servomechanisms is undertaken. Only simpler cases are considered, since they illustrate the principles involved without unnecessary mathematical complications, but most of the important variations are treated in detail. The remainder of the text is devoted to an intensive development of the transfer-function approach, including mechanical procedures in manipulation, mathematical theory, and graphical aids to analysis and design. The transient analysis is undertaken first because it is felt that it promotes a better physical understanding of servomechanism systems in the minds of most students and so makes the transfer-function analysis easier to comprehend.

CHAPTER 2

THE LAPLACE TRANSFORMATION

2-1. Introduction. In engineering analysis and design, modern practice leans heavily on mathematical methods, especially those methods which are of an operational, or transform, nature. The Laplace transformation is an operational method which seems best suited to the analysis and design of servomechanisms. The scope of this text does not permit a detailed discussion of operational methods in general or of all the extensions of the Laplace transformation. Therefore only the mechanics of applying the Laplace transform are treated in this chapter, together with such definitions and explanations as are thought necessary. Since full use of any tool is obtained only if its possibilities and limitations are known, it is recommended that the student acquire additional information from a more authoritative text.[3-6,*]

The Laplace transformation, which leads to a modern yet mathematically sound form of the operational calculus, is based on the use of the Laplace integral. In servomechanisms, when an equation expressed in terms of time (t) is operated on by the Laplace integral, a new, or "transformed," equation results which is expressed in terms of an arbitrary complex variable of the form $\sigma + j\omega$. The above process is known as taking the direct Laplace transform of the equation. The transformed equation as a rule is in purely algebraic terms and so may be manipulated algebraically to solve for the desired quantity. This is one of the principal advantages of the Laplace-transform method. Of course, the solution obtained is an explicit function of the complex variable; it is therefore necessary to perform the inverse process to replace the complex variable with t. This latter process is called "taking the inverse Laplace transform."

It is probably true that the use of a classical or other direct method of solving first- and second-order differential equations does involve less labor than employing both a direct and inverse transformation, especially if boundary conditions are simple, but for solving higher-order equations it is a decided advantage to limit the mathematics to purely algebraic manipulation of the transformed equation. Moreover, for equations

---

* Superior numbers, when they appear in the text, are the numbers of references given in the Bibliography.

8

relating to physical systems, boundary conditions are more readily handled with the Laplace transform than with other mathematical methods. These facts will become more evident as the manipulations are carried out and explained.

2-2. The Laplace Transformation. The defining equations and symbols of Laplace-transform mathematics as applied to servomechanisms are:

$f(t)$ = any function of time

s = a complex variable having the form $\sigma + j\omega$

$F(s)$ = the resulting equation in the transform variable, s, when $f(t)$ has been operated on by the Laplace integral

$\mathcal{L}$ = an operational symbol indicating that the quantity which it prefixes is to be transformed by the Laplace integral

Thus

$$F(s) \triangleq \mathcal{L}[f(t)] \tag{2-1}$$

where the symbol $\triangleq$ means "equal to by definition." Equation (2-1) states that an equation $F(s)$ results from applying the Laplace transformation to another equation $f(t)$. The Laplace integral, which has been represented symbolically by $\mathcal{L}$, is defined as

$$\mathcal{L} \triangleq \int_0^\infty e^{-st}\, dt \tag{2-2}$$

Therefore

$$\mathcal{L}[f(t)] = \int_0^\infty e^{-st}\, dt[f(t)] = \int_0^\infty f(t)e^{-st}\, dt \tag{2-3}$$

Thus the Laplace transform of any equation or term in an equation (in which the variable is t) may be obtained by multiplying by e^{-st} and then integrating the product from $t = 0$ to $t = \infty$. Of course the same general procedure applies for any other variable. The variable t is used here because it is the common variable in servomechanism theory. The following paragraphs illustrate the procedure followed in obtaining the transformed equation.

2-3. Illustrative Direct Transforms. The following illustrations of Laplace transformations, together with the symbols used, are typical of those met in servomechanism analysis and design:

1. Let $f(t) = A$ (a constant). Then, applying the Laplace integral,

$$\mathcal{L}[f(t)] = \mathcal{L}(A) = \int_0^\infty A e^{-st}\, dt$$

$$= A \int_0^\infty e^{-st}\, dt = A \left(-\frac{1}{s}\right) e^{-st}\Big|_0^\infty$$

$$= -\frac{A}{s}(e^{-\infty} - e^0) = +\frac{A}{s} \tag{2-4}$$

$$\therefore\ \mathcal{L}(A) = \frac{A}{s} \tag{2-5}$$

A function similar to that above—the unit step function—is met so often in servomechanism work that it is discussed here in detail. When a quantity changes instantaneously from one constant value to a second constant value but makes only one such change in the period

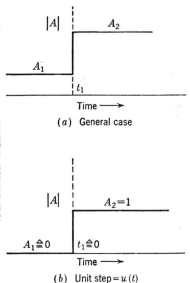

(a) General case

(b) Unit step $= u(t)$

Fig. 2-1. Step-functions plot.

$-\infty < t < +\infty$, such a change is known as a step variation, or step function. An illustration of a step function is given in Fig. 2-1a. Such a function has two nominal values, A_1 and A_2; but the transition at t_1 cannot be readily defined mathematically. However, if the value A_1 is chosen as a reference, so that $A_1 = 0$, it is possible to describe the step function variation as, for $t < 0$,

$$f(t) = f(0)$$

and

$$\mathcal{L}[f(t)] = \mathcal{L}(0) = 0 \qquad (2\text{-}6)$$

for $t \geq 0$,

$$f(t) = f(A_2)$$

and

$$\mathcal{L}[f(t)] = \mathcal{L}(A_2) = \frac{A_2}{s} \qquad (2\text{-}7)$$

Furthermore, if the amplitude of the step is restricted to $A_2 = 1$, then the step function becomes the familiar step function $f(t) = u(t)$ as shown in Fig. 2-1b and

$$\mathcal{L}[u(t)] = \mathcal{L}(1) = \int_0^\infty e^{-st}\, dt = \frac{1}{s} \qquad (2\text{-}8)$$

2. Let $f(t) = e^{-\alpha t}$. Then

$$\mathcal{L}[f(t)] = \mathcal{L}(e^{-\alpha t}) = \int_0^\infty e^{-\alpha t} e^{-st}\, dt$$

$$= \int_0^\infty e^{-(\alpha+s)t}\, dt = -\frac{1}{\alpha+s} e^{-(\alpha+s)t}\Big|_0^\infty \qquad (2\text{-}9)$$

$$\therefore \mathcal{L}(e^{-\alpha t}) = \frac{1}{\alpha+s} \qquad (2\text{-}10)$$

3. Let $f(t) = A e^{-\alpha t}$. Then

$$\mathcal{L}[f(t)] = \mathcal{L}(A e^{-\alpha t}) = \int_0^\infty A e^{-\alpha t} e^{-st}\, dt$$

$$= A \int_0^\infty e^{-\alpha t} e^{-st}\, dt \qquad (2\text{-}11)$$

$$\therefore \mathcal{L}(A e^{-\alpha t}) = \frac{A}{\alpha+s} \qquad (2\text{-}12)$$

In general it may be stated that $\mathcal{L}[Af(t)] = A\mathcal{L}[f(t)]$ where A is a constant.

4. Let $f(t) = Ae^{-\alpha t} + e^{-\beta t}$. Then

$$\mathcal{L}[f(t)] = \mathcal{L}(Ae^{-\alpha t} + e^{-\beta t})$$

$$= \int_0^\infty (Ae^{-\alpha t} + e^{-\beta t})e^{-st}\, dt$$

$$= \int_0^\infty Ae^{-\alpha t}e^{-st}\, dt + \int_0^\infty e^{-\beta t}e^{-st}\, dt \qquad (2\text{-}13)$$

$$\therefore \mathcal{L}[f(t)] = \frac{A}{\alpha + s} + \frac{1}{\beta + s} \qquad (2\text{-}14)$$

In general it may be said that $\mathcal{L}[Af(t) + Bg(t)] = A\mathcal{L}[f(t)] + B\mathcal{L}[g(t)]$, where A and B are constants.

5. Let $f(t) = \sin \beta t$. Then

$$\mathcal{L}[f(t)] = \mathcal{L}(\sin \beta t) = \int_0^\infty \sin \beta t e^{-st}\, dt \qquad (2\text{-}15)$$

but

$$\sin \beta t = \frac{e^{j\beta t} - e^{-j\beta t}}{2j} \qquad (2\text{-}16)$$

$$\therefore \mathcal{L}(\sin \beta t) = \frac{1}{2j} \int_0^\infty (e^{j\beta t} - e^{-j\beta t})e^{-st}\, dt \qquad (2\text{-}17)$$

$$\mathcal{L}(\sin \beta t) = \frac{1}{2j}\left(\frac{-1}{s - j\beta}\right)e^{(-s+j\beta)t}\Big|_0^\infty - \frac{1}{2j}\left(\frac{-1}{s + j\beta}\right)e^{(-s-j\beta)t}\Big|_0^\infty$$

$$= \frac{1}{2j}\left(\frac{1}{s - j\beta}\right) - \frac{1}{2j}\left(\frac{1}{s + j\beta}\right)$$

$$= \frac{1}{2j}\left(\frac{1}{s - j\beta} - \frac{1}{s + j\beta}\right) = \frac{1}{2j}\left(\frac{s + j\beta - s + j\beta}{s^2 + \beta^2}\right) \qquad (2\text{-}18)$$

$$\therefore \mathcal{L}(\sin \beta t) = \frac{\beta}{s^2 + \beta^2} \qquad (2\text{-}19)$$

6. Let $f(t) = \cos \beta t$.

$$\mathcal{L}(\cos \beta t) = \int_0^\infty \cos \beta t e^{-st}\, dt \qquad (2\text{-}20)$$

but

$$\cos \beta t = \frac{e^{j\beta t} + e^{-j\beta t}}{2} \qquad (2\text{-}21)$$

$$\therefore \mathcal{L}(\cos \beta t) = \frac{1}{2} \int_0^\infty (e^{j\beta t} + e^{-j\beta t})e^{-st}\, dt$$

$$= \frac{1}{2}\left(\frac{1}{j\beta - s}\right)e^{(j\beta - s)t}\Big|_0^\infty + \frac{1}{2}\left(\frac{1}{-j\beta - s}\right)e^{(-j\beta - s)t}\Big|_0^\infty$$

$$= \frac{1}{2}\left(\frac{1}{s - j\beta}\right) + \frac{1}{2}\left(\frac{1}{s + j\beta}\right)$$

$$= \frac{s}{s^2 + \beta^2} \qquad (2\text{-}22)$$

7. Let $f(t) = t$. Then

$$\mathcal{L}[f(t)] = \mathcal{L}(t) = \int_0^\infty t e^{-st} \, dt \tag{2-23}$$

Let $u = t$; $dv = e^{-st} \, dt$. Then

$$du = dt \qquad v = \frac{e^{-st}}{-s} \tag{2-24}$$

and

$$\int_{v_1}^{v_2} u \, dv = uv \Big|_{u_1}^{u_2} - \int_{u_1}^{u_2} v \, du = \frac{t e^{-st}}{-s} \Big|_0^\infty - \int_0^\infty \frac{e^{-st} \, dt}{-s} \tag{2-25}$$

$$\therefore \mathcal{L}(t) = 0 - \frac{e^{-st}}{s^2} \Big|_0^\infty = \frac{1}{s^2} \tag{2-26}$$

8. Let $f(t) = t^2$.

$$\mathcal{L}[f(t)] = \mathcal{L}(t^2) = \int_0^\infty t^2 e^{-st} \, dt \tag{2-27}$$

Applying integration by parts, as in 7,

$$\mathcal{L}(t^2) = \frac{2}{s^3} \tag{2-28}$$

9. Let $f(t) = t^n$. Then

$$\mathcal{L}(t^n) = \frac{n!}{s^{n+1}} \tag{2-29}$$

The preceding examples have shown the result of applying the Laplace integral to a few of the commoner functions. It should be noted that exponential and harmonic time functions become algebraic in form when expressed as functions of the transformed variable, s. The succeeding pages include the derivation of a real differentiation and a real integration theorem which establish and justify a standard procedure for handling the derivatives and integrals that appear in servomechanism equations. The examples chosen present sufficient variety to allow the student to develop for himself any other transforms needed. As a further aid, a short table of the more frequently used transforms may be found in Appendix A.

2-4. Direct Transforms of Derivatives and Integrals. *Real Differentiation Theorem.* The Laplace transform of the derivative of a function is given by

$$\mathcal{L}\left\{ \frac{d}{dt} [f(t)] \right\} = sF(s) - f(0+) \tag{2-30}$$

where s = transform variable

$F(s)$ = Laplace transform of $f(t)$

$f(0+)$ = initial value of $f(t)$, evaluated as $t \to 0$ from positive values

Figures 2-2a and b illustrate the meaning of $f(0+)$. For a step function of amplitude A, Fig. 2-2a shows that $f(0-) = 0$ and $f(0+) = A$. For a cosine function having an amplitude M, Fig. 2-2b shows that $f(0-) = M$ and also $f(0+) = M$.

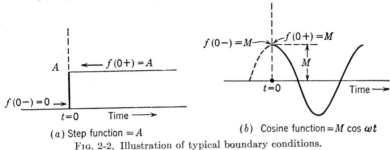

(a) Step function $= A$ (b) Cosine function $= M \cos \omega t$

Fig. 2-2. Illustration of typical boundary conditions.

Proof of Real Differentiation Theorem. Let the chosen time function be

$$\frac{d}{dt}[f(t)] = f'(t) \tag{2-31}$$

Then

$$\mathcal{L}[f'(t)] = \int_0^\infty f'(t)e^{-st}\,dt \tag{2-32}$$

Using the form for integrating by parts, let

$$f(t) = u \qquad \text{and} \qquad e^{-st}\,dt = dv \tag{2-33}$$

Then

$$f'(t)\,dt = du \qquad \text{and} \qquad \frac{e^{-st}}{-s} = v$$

$$\int_0^\infty f(t)e^{-st}\,dt = f(t)\frac{e^{-st}}{-s}\Big|_0^\infty - \frac{1}{-s}\int_0^\infty e^{-st}f'(t)\,dt \tag{2-34}$$

from which

$$\int_0^\infty f'(t)e^{-st}\,dt = s\left[\int_0^\infty f(t)e^{-st}\,dt - \frac{f(t)e^{-st}}{-s}\Big|_0^\infty\right]$$

$$= s\left[F(s) + \frac{0}{s} - \frac{f(0+)}{s}\right] \tag{2-35}$$

$$\therefore \mathcal{L}[f'(t)] = sF(s) - f(0+) \tag{2-36}$$

Example 1. Find $\mathcal{L}\left[\dfrac{d}{dt}(M \cos \beta t)\right]$ (see Fig. 2-2b). This problem can be treated as the transform of a derivative, in which case the real differentiation theorem is applied, or the derivative of the function may be taken first and the transform of the resulting trigonometric function found. Both methods are used here to show their equivalence.

1. Using the real differentiation theorem,

$$\mathcal{L}[f'(t)] = s[F(s)] - f(0+)$$

$$\mathcal{L}\left[\frac{d}{dt}(M \cos \beta t)\right] = s\left(\frac{Ms}{s^2 + \beta^2}\right) - M$$

$$= \frac{s^2 M - s^2 M - \beta^2 M}{s^2 + \beta^2}$$

$$= \frac{-\beta^2 M}{s^2 + \beta^2}$$

2. Simplifying first,

$$\frac{d}{dt}(M \cos \beta t) = -M\beta \sin \beta t$$

$$\mathcal{L}(-M\beta \sin \beta t) = -M\beta\left[\frac{\beta}{s^2 + \beta^2}\right] = \frac{-M\beta^2}{s^2 + \beta^2}$$

from which it is seen that the real differentiation theorem gives the correct result.

For transforms of derivatives of higher order essentially the same procedure may be followed as in the proof of Eq. (2-30). The result for second derivatives is, for example,

$$\mathcal{L}[f''(t)] = s^2 F(s) - sf(0+) - f'(0+) \tag{2-37}$$

The Laplace transforms of the above derivatives were obtained by formal substitution in the Laplace integral. They are not necessarily correct* for all possible functions, $f(t)$. In particular they are not correct when $f(t)$ has discontinuities. In most servomechanisms, however, particularly continuous-control systems, $f(t)$ is continuous, and the results of (2-30) and (2-37) may be used directly.

Real Integration Theorem. The Laplace transform of the integral of a function is given by

$$\mathcal{L}\left[\int f(t) \, dt\right] = \frac{F(s)}{s} + \frac{f^{-1}(0+)}{s} \tag{2-38}$$

where $f^{-1}(0+) = \int f(t) \, dt$, evaluated as $t \to 0$ from positive values.

Proof of Real Integration Theorem. Let the chosen time function be

$$\int f(t) \, dt$$

$$\mathcal{L}\left[\int f(t) \, dt\right] = \int_0^\infty e^{-st}\left[\int f(t) \, dt\right] dt \tag{2-39}$$

Using forms for integrating by parts, let

$$\int f(t) \, dt = u \qquad \text{and} \qquad e^{-st} \, dt = dv \tag{2-40}$$

* See Churchill, Ref. 4, p. 6.

Then

$$f(t)\,dt = du \qquad \text{and} \qquad \frac{e^{-st}}{-s} = v$$

Therefore

$$\int_0^\infty \left[\int f(t)\,dt\right] e^{-st}\,dt = \int f(t)\,dt\,\frac{e^{-st}}{-s}\bigg|_0^\infty - \int_0^\infty \frac{e^{-st}}{-s} f(t)\,dt$$

$$= \left[0 + \int_{0+} \frac{f(t)\,dt}{s}\right] + \frac{1}{s}\int_0^\infty f(t)e^{-st}\,dt \quad (2\text{-}41)$$

$$\therefore\ \mathfrak{L}\left[\int f(t)\,dt\right] = \frac{f^{-1}(0+)}{s} + \frac{F(s)}{s} \qquad (2\text{-}42)$$

Example 2. Find $\mathfrak{L}[\int M \cos \beta t\,dt]$ (see Fig. 2-2b). This transform may be found by using the real integration theorem or by integrating the function and then transforming the result. Both methods are used to show their equivalence.

1. Using the integration theorem,

$$\mathfrak{L}\left[\int M \cos \beta t\,dt\right] = \frac{F(s)}{s} + \frac{f^{-1}(0+)}{s}$$

$$= \frac{1}{s}\left(\frac{Ms}{s^2 + \beta^2}\right) + 0$$

$$= \frac{M}{s^2 + \beta^2}$$

2. Integrating first,

$$\int M \cos \beta t\,dt = \frac{M}{\beta} \sin \beta t$$

$$\mathfrak{L}\left[\int M \cos \beta t\,dt\right] = \mathfrak{L}\left[\frac{M}{\beta} \sin \beta t\right] = \int_0^\infty \frac{M}{\beta} \sin \beta t e^{-st}\,dt$$

$$= \frac{M}{\beta}\left(\frac{\beta}{s^2 + \beta^2}\right) = \frac{M}{s^2 + \beta^2}$$

2-5. The Inverse Laplace Transformation. Once an equation has been transformed, an explicit solution for the unknown may be determined through algebraic simplification. (Ordinarily, in servomechanisms, the original equation of motion involves differentials, and the desired unknown is either the output quantity or the error.) The solution obtained is expressed in terms of the complex variable, s. In some cases the solution in s is sufficient, but in other cases it is desired to retransform the equation so that the solution is expressed in terms of time. The mathematical process of passing from the complex-variable expression to that of time is called an inverse transformation and may be denoted symbolically as

$$\mathcal{L}^{-1}F(s) = f(t) \tag{2-43}$$

The relation between direct and inverse Laplace transforms is similar to that between functions and integrals in calculus, except that the transforms have a property of uniqueness. That is, for any given $f(t)$ there is only one direct transform, $F(s)$; and for any given $F(s)$ there is only one inverse transform, $f(t)$. The sensible method for determining inverse transformations is therefore to use a table of transforms, just as it is common practice to use tables of integrals. The few illustrations presented below may be verified from the direct transforms derived at the beginning of this chapter.

1. If $F(s) = A/s$, then

$$\mathcal{L}^{-1}\left(\frac{A}{s}\right) = A \tag{2-5}$$

2. If $F(s) = 1/s$, then

$$\mathcal{L}^{-1}\left(\frac{1}{s}\right) = 1 \tag{2-8}$$

3. If $F(s) = 1/\alpha + s$, then

$$\mathcal{L}^{-1}\left(\frac{1}{\alpha + s}\right) = e^{-\alpha t} \tag{2-10}$$

4. If $F(s) = A/\alpha + s$, then

$$\mathcal{L}^{-1}\left(\frac{A}{\alpha + s}\right) = Ae^{-\alpha t} \tag{2-12}$$

5. If $F(s) = \beta/s^2 + \beta^2$, then

$$\mathcal{L}^{-1}\left(\frac{\beta}{s^2 + \beta^2}\right) = \sin \beta t \tag{2-19}$$

Where the form of the solution in s cannot be reduced to the form of any of the transform pairs in the table, it is necessary to resort to Heaviside's expansion theorem. Briefly, the theorem makes it possible to expand the algebraic equation into a series of simpler terms whose transforms are normally available in a transform table. Then, the inverse transformation of the original algebraic expression can be found by adding together the inverse transformations of the terms of the Heaviside expansion. Symbolically, *if $F(s)$ is the original algebraic expression, and $F_1(s)$, $F_2(s)$, $F_3(s)$, . . . , $F_n(s)$ are terms in the partial fraction expansion of $F(s)$, then*

$$\mathcal{L}^{-1}[F(s)] = \mathcal{L}^{-1}[F_1(s)] + \mathcal{L}^{-1}[F_2(s)] + \cdots + \mathcal{L}^{-1}[F_n(s)] \tag{2-44}$$

2-6. Solution of Differential Equations with the Laplace Transform. The transform fundamentals which have been presented will now be used to obtain the solutions of a few differential equations. The first few examples consider ordinary circuit equations whose solutions are well known, while the final example will be concerned with the equation of a simple servomechanism.

Example 1. Find the equation for the current variation in the circuit of Fig. 2-3 after the switch is closed. E, R, and C are constants, and there is no initial charge on C. The equilibrium equation is

$$E = iR + \int \frac{i \, dt}{C} \qquad (2\text{-}45)$$

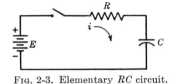

Fig. 2-3. Elementary RC circuit.

It is often advantageous, in more complex expressions, to add a parenthetical notation indicating that a symbol or a term is a function of some variable (such as time) and is not a constant. For example, i becomes $i(t)$, etc. Thus the equilibrium equation may be written as

$$E = i(t)R + \int \frac{i(t) \, dt}{C} \qquad (2\text{-}45a)$$

Transforming both sides,

$$\mathcal{L}(E) = \mathcal{L}[i(t)R] + \mathcal{L}\left[\int \frac{i(t) \, dt}{C}\right]$$

$$\frac{E}{s} = I(s)R + \frac{I(s)}{sC} + \frac{f^{-1}(0+)}{s} \qquad (2\text{-}46)$$

since there is no initial charge on C; $f^{-1}(0+)/s = 0$;

$$\therefore \frac{E}{s} = I(s)\left(R + \frac{1}{sC}\right) \qquad (2\text{-}47)$$

Solving,

$$I(s) = \frac{E}{s(R + 1/sC)} = \frac{E}{R}\frac{1}{s + 1/RC} = \frac{E/R}{s + 1/RC} \qquad (2\text{-}48)$$

$$i(t) = \mathcal{L}^{-1}[I(s)] = \mathcal{L}^{-1}\left(\frac{E/R}{s + 1/RC}\right) = \frac{E}{R} e^{-t/RC} \qquad (2\text{-}49)$$

since $\dfrac{E/R}{s + 1/RC}$ is of the form $\dfrac{A}{s + \alpha}$.

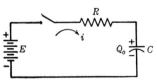

Fig. 2-4. RC circuit with capacitor initially charged.

Example 2. In Fig. 2-4 the capacitor has an initial charge Q_0 with polarity as indicated. Find the equation for the current variation. The equilibrium equation is

$$E = iR + \int \frac{i \, dt}{C} \qquad (2\text{-}50)$$

Transforming,

$$\frac{E}{s} = I(s)R + \frac{I(s)}{sC} + \frac{f^{-1}(0+)}{s} \tag{2-51}$$

but $f^{-1}(0+) = Q_0/C$;

$$\therefore \frac{E}{s} = I(s)R + \frac{I(s)}{sC} + \frac{Q_0}{sC} \tag{2-52}$$

[It may be noted here that the boundary conditions of the problem are inserted in this case by evaluating $f^{-1}(0+)$, that is, the boundary conditions are automatically taken care of in the process of transformation. The advantages of this are apparent.]

$$I(s) = \frac{E/s - Q_0/Cs}{R + 1/sC} \tag{2-53}$$

$$I(s) = \frac{E - Q_0/C}{s(R + 1/sC)} = \frac{(E - Q_0/C)/R}{s + 1/RC} \tag{2-54}$$

$$i(t) = \mathcal{L}^{-1}[I(s)] = \mathcal{L}^{-1}\left[\frac{(E - Q_0/C)/R}{s + 1/RC}\right] = \left(\frac{E - Q_0/C}{R}\right)e^{-t/RC} \tag{2-55}$$

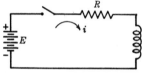

FIG. 2-5. Elementary RL circuit.

Example 3.   In Fig. 2-5, E, R, and L are constants.   Find the equation for the current flow after the switch is closed.   The equilibrium equation is

$$E = iR + L\frac{di}{dt} = i(t)R + L\frac{di(t)}{dt} \tag{2-56}$$

Transforming,

$$\frac{E}{s} = I(s)R + LsI(s) - Lf(0+) \tag{2-57}$$

at $t = 0$, $i = 0$;

$$\therefore f(0+) = 0$$

Then

$$\frac{E}{s} = I(s)R + LsI(s) \tag{2-58}$$

and

$$I(s) = \frac{E}{s(R + Ls)} \tag{2-59}$$

None of the transforms derived in previous examples have the form of the solution for $I(s)$.   A table could be consulted to obtain the inverse transform, but in this case a general method will be followed for reducing the transform to a series of terms whose inverse transforms are known.

In terms of the partial fraction expansion, the preceding equation becomes

$$I(s) = \frac{E}{s(Ls + R)} = \frac{A(s)}{B(s)} = \frac{K_1}{s - s_1} + \frac{K_2}{s - s_2} \tag{2-60}$$

Where s_1 and s_2 are the roots of the polynomial,

$$B(s) = s(Ls + R) = 0$$

It is apparent that these roots are $s_1 = 0$ and $s_2 = -R/L$ so that

$$I(s) = \frac{E}{s(Ls + R)} = \frac{K_1}{s} + \frac{K_2}{s + R/L} \tag{2-61}$$

There are several ways of evaluating the coefficients K_1 and K_2. One method is used in this example, another in the next. To determine K_1, multiply both sides of the equation by the denominator of the K_1 term, $s - s_1(= s - 0 = s)$.

$$\frac{Es}{s(Ls + R)} = \frac{K_1 s}{s} + \frac{K_2 s}{s + R/L} \tag{2-62}$$

$$\frac{E}{Ls + R} = K_1 + \frac{K_2 s}{s + R/L} \tag{2-63}$$

Next let this same term $(s - s_1) \to 0$; in this case $s \to 0$; then

$$\frac{E}{R} = K_1 \tag{2-64}$$

Having evaluated K_1, repeat the same process with the denominator of the K_2 term. Multiplying,

$$\frac{E}{s(Ls + R)}\left(s + \frac{R}{L}\right) = \frac{K_1}{s}\left(s + \frac{R}{L}\right) + K_2 \tag{2-65}$$

which reduces to

$$\frac{E}{Ls} = \frac{K_1}{s}\left(s + \frac{R}{L}\right) + K_2 \tag{2-66}$$

Letting $(s + R/L) \to 0$, $s = -R/L$, and substituting,

$$\frac{E}{L(-R/L)} = 0 + K_2 \tag{2-67}$$

$$K_2 = -\frac{E}{R}$$

Hence

$$I(s) = \frac{E/R}{s} + \frac{-E/R}{s + R/L} \tag{2-68}$$

$$\therefore i(t) = \frac{E}{R} - \frac{E}{R} e^{-Rt/L} \tag{2-69}$$

Example 4.   The block diagram of Fig. 2-6 shows the basic components of a simple servomechanism.   The symbols used represent the
following quantities:

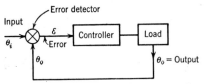

Fig. 2-6. Block diagram of a servomechanism.

θ_i = input quantity

θ_o = output quantity

$\mathcal{E} = \theta_i - \theta_o$ = error quantity

In this case it is desired to obtain an
equation expressing the variation
of the error, $\mathcal{E}$, for a given input
signal, θ_i, to be specified later.   The differential equation, describing the
motion of the system is

$$\frac{d^2\mathcal{E}}{dt^2} + 2\,\zeta\omega_n\,\frac{d\mathcal{E}}{dt} + \omega_n{}^2\mathcal{E} = \frac{d^2\theta_i}{dt^2} + 2\,\zeta\omega_n\,\frac{d\theta_i}{dt} \qquad (2\text{-}70)$$

where ζ and ω_n are constants depending on the parameters of the system.
The physical system will not be discussed at this time, since the purpose
of the example is to illustrate Laplace-transform methods.

The Laplace transform of the differential equation may be obtained
term for term from a table of transforms or from the examples at the
beginning of this chapter.

$$\mathcal{L}\left[\frac{d^2\mathcal{E}}{dt^2}\right] = s^2 E(s) - s\mathcal{E}(0+) - \frac{d\mathcal{E}(0+)}{dt} \qquad (2\text{-}71)$$

$$\mathcal{L}\left[2\zeta\omega_n\,\frac{d\mathcal{E}}{dt}\right] = 2\zeta\omega_n[sE(s) - \mathcal{E}(0+)] \qquad (2\text{-}72)$$

$$\mathcal{L}\left[\omega_n{}^2\mathcal{E}\right] = \omega_n{}^2 E(s) \qquad (2\text{-}73)$$

$$\mathcal{L}\left[\frac{d^2\theta_i}{dt^2}\right] = s^2\Theta_i(s) - s\theta_i(0+) - \frac{d\theta_i}{dt}(0+) \qquad (2\text{-}74)$$

where $\Theta_i(s)$ symbolizes the Laplace transform of the input signal.

$$\mathcal{L}\left[2\zeta\omega_n\,\frac{d\theta_i}{dt}\right] = 2\zeta\omega_n[s\Theta_i(s) - \theta_i(0+)] \qquad (2\text{-}75)$$

Therefore

$$s^2 E(s) - s\mathcal{E}(0+) - \frac{d\mathcal{E}}{dt}(0+) + 2\zeta\omega_n[sE(s) - \mathcal{E}(0+)] + \omega_n{}^2 E(s)$$

$$= s^2\Theta_i(s) - s\theta_i(0+) - \frac{d\theta_i}{dt}(0+) + 2\zeta\omega_n[s\Theta_i(s) - \theta_i(0+)] \quad (2\text{-}76)$$

Before manipulating the equation algebraically some simplification is
achieved by evaluating the initial condition terms.   Normally this
requires knowledge of the physical conditions existing at $t = 0$.   To

avoid a discussion of the significance of these conditions at this point, the initial conditions, for this illustration, are arbitrarily stated as, at $t = 0$,

$$\mathcal{E}(0+) = 0 \qquad \frac{d\mathcal{E}}{dt}(0+) = |\omega_i|$$

$$\theta_i(0+) = 0 \qquad \frac{d\theta_i}{dt}(0+) = |\omega_i| \qquad (2\text{-}77)$$

Substituting these conditions,

$$s^2 E(s) - |\omega_i| + 2\zeta\omega_n s E(s) + \omega_n{}^2 E(s) = s^2\Theta_i(s) - |\omega_i| + 2\zeta\omega_n s\Theta_i(s)$$
$$(2\text{-}78)$$

Solving for $E(s)$,

$$E(s) = \frac{s(s + 2\zeta\omega_n)}{s^2 + 2\zeta\omega_n s + \omega_n{}^2} \Theta_i(s) \qquad (2\text{-}79)$$

Thus the transformed equation for the error is expressed as the product of two terms, one of which is a generalized input function, $\Theta_i(s)$. If it is desired to obtain a quantitative solution to the differential equation for the time function, $E(t)$, the explicit equation for $\theta_i(t)$ must be known. For this example assume that $\theta_i(t) = |\omega_i|t$. Then

$$\mathcal{L}[\theta_i(t)] = \Theta_i(s) = \mathcal{L}(|\omega_i|t) = \frac{|\omega_i|}{s^2} \qquad (2\text{-}80)$$

Therefore

$$E(s) = \frac{s(s + 2\zeta\omega_n)}{s^2 + 2\zeta\omega_n s + \omega_n{}^2} \frac{|\omega_i|}{s^2} = \frac{(s + 2\zeta\omega_n)|\omega_i|}{s(s^2 + 2\zeta\omega_n s + \omega_n{}^2)} \qquad (2\text{-}81)$$

Inspection of this equation shows that it is different from any of the transforms encountered thus far. Therefore the partial fraction expansion is applied, resulting in

$$\frac{s|\omega i| + 2\zeta\omega_n|\omega_i|}{s(s^2 + 2\zeta\omega_n s + \omega_n{}^2)} = \frac{A_1}{s - s_1} + \frac{A_2}{s - s_2} + \frac{A_3}{s - s_3} \qquad (2\text{-}82)$$

where s_1, s_2, and s_3 are roots of the cubic denominator. Applying the usual algebraic methods, these roots are found to be

$$s_1 = 0$$
$$s_2 = -\zeta\omega_n + j\omega_n\sqrt{1 - \zeta^2} \qquad (2\text{-}83)$$
$$s_3 = -\zeta\omega_n - j\omega_n\sqrt{1 - \zeta^2}$$

so that

$$\frac{s|\omega_i| + 2\zeta\omega_n|\omega_i|}{s(s^2 + 2\zeta\omega_n s + \omega_n{}^2)} = \frac{A_1}{s} + \frac{A_2}{s + \zeta\omega_n - j\omega_n\sqrt{1 - \zeta^2}}$$
$$+ \frac{A_3}{s + \zeta\omega_n + j\omega_n\sqrt{1 - \zeta^2}} \qquad (2\text{-}84)$$

To evaluate the coefficients A_1, A_2, and A_3, the method of equating coefficients of like powers may be used. (Note that this method is different from the one used in Example 3.) This approach requires that the right-hand side of the equation be collected, resulting in

$$\frac{s|\omega_i| + 2\zeta\omega_n|\omega_i|}{s(s^2 + 2\zeta\omega_n s + \omega_n{}^2)} =$$
$$\frac{\left\{ \begin{array}{l} A_1 s^2 + A_1 2\zeta\omega_n s + A_1\omega_n{}^2 + A_2 s^2 + A_2\zeta\omega_n s + A_2 s j\omega_n \sqrt{1 - \zeta^2} + A_3 s^2 \\ \qquad\qquad + A_3\zeta\omega_n s - A_3 s j\omega_n \sqrt{1 - \zeta^2} \end{array} \right\}}{s(s^2 + 2\zeta\omega_n s + \omega_n{}^2)}$$

$$(2\text{-}85)$$

If a true equality exists, then the coefficients of like terms must be equal; therefore the terms having like powers are considered, and their coefficients equated.

s^2 terms: $\qquad\qquad\qquad 0 = A_1 + A_2 + A_3$

s terms: $\quad |\omega_i| = 2\zeta\omega_n A_1 + \zeta\omega_n A_2 + j\omega_n \sqrt{1 - \zeta^2}\, A_2$
$$\qquad\qquad\qquad\qquad + \zeta\omega_n A_3 - j\omega_n \sqrt{1 - \zeta^2}\, A_3 \qquad (2\text{-}86)$$

Constant terms: $\qquad\quad 2\zeta\omega_n|\omega_i| = A_1\omega_n{}^2$

Solving simultaneously,

$$A_1 = \frac{2\zeta|\omega_i|}{\omega_n}$$

$$A_2 = \frac{(1 - 2\zeta^2) - 2j\zeta \sqrt{1 - \zeta^2}}{2j\omega_n \sqrt{1 - \zeta^2}}|\omega_i| \qquad (2\text{-}87)$$

$$A_3 = \frac{-(1 - 2\zeta^2) - 2j\zeta \sqrt{1 - \zeta^2}}{2j\omega_n \sqrt{1 - \zeta^2}}|\omega_i|$$

The transformed equation for the error in terms of the partial fraction expansion is then

$$E(s) = \frac{\dfrac{2\zeta|\omega_i|}{\omega_n}}{s} + \frac{\dfrac{(1 - 2\zeta^2) - 2j\zeta \sqrt{1 - \zeta^2}}{2j\omega_n \sqrt{1 - \zeta^2}}|\omega_i|}{s + \zeta\omega_n + j\omega_n \sqrt{1 - \zeta^2}}$$

$$+ \frac{\dfrac{-(1 - 2\zeta^2) - 2j\zeta \sqrt{1 - \zeta^2}}{2j\omega_n \sqrt{1 - \zeta^2}}|\omega_i|}{s + \zeta\omega_n - j\omega_n \sqrt{1 - \zeta^2}} \qquad (2\text{-}88)$$

Inspection shows that this equation is of the form

$$E(s) = \frac{A}{s} + \frac{B}{s + \alpha_1} + \frac{C}{s + \alpha_2} \qquad (2\text{-}89)$$

and the inverse transform of such terms is readily obtained. The result is

$$\mathcal{E}(t) = A + Be^{-\alpha_1 t} + Ce^{-\alpha_2 t}$$

$$\mathcal{E}(t) = \frac{2\zeta|\omega_i|}{\omega_n} + \left[\frac{(1 - 2\zeta^2) - 2j\zeta\sqrt{1 - \zeta^2}}{2j\omega_n\sqrt{1 - \zeta^2}}|\omega_i|\right]e^{-(\zeta\omega_n + j\omega_n\sqrt{1-\zeta^2})t}$$

$$+ \left[\frac{-(1 - 2\zeta^2) - 2j\zeta\sqrt{1 - \zeta^2}}{2j\omega_n\sqrt{1 - \zeta^2}}|\omega_i|\right]e^{-(\zeta\omega_n - j\omega_n\sqrt{1-\zeta^2})t} \quad (2\text{-}90)$$

PROBLEMS

2-1: Derive the transform of the following expressions by applying the Laplace integral:

  a. $\theta(t) = 0.02\,u(t)$, where $u(t)$ is the unit step function
  b. $\theta(t) = 5t$ c. $\theta(t) = 6e^{-3t}$
  d. $\theta(t) = 4(0.3 + 0.1e^{-0.2t})$ e. $\theta(t) = 5 - e^{-0.06t}$
  f. $\theta(t) = 5t + e^{-0.5t}$ g. $\theta(t) = 2\sin 20t$
  h. $\theta(t) = 4\sin(2 - 4t)$ i. $\theta(t) = 8\cos(6t - \pi/4)$
  j. $\theta(t) = 7e^{-0.2t}\sin 10.5t$

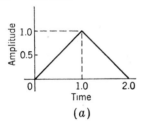

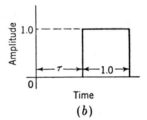

(a)   (b)

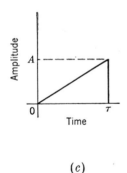

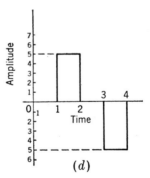

(c)   (d)

Fig. 2P-1

2-2. Transform the following equations, using standard forms and theorems. Assume initial conditions are all zero.

  a. $L\,d^2i/dt^2 + R\,di/dt + \int i\,dt/C = 0$
  b. $(J_1 + N^2J_2)\,d^2\theta/dt^2 + B\,d\theta/dt + C\theta = D$
  c. $3\,d\theta/dt + 8\theta + j\int\theta\,dt = 16$
  d. $d^2\theta/dt^2 + 3\,d\theta/dt + 4\theta + 5\int\theta\,dt = 10$

   e. $2\, d^2\theta/dt^2 + 3\, d\theta/dt + 5\theta = 7e^{-(t/\tau)}$

   f. $5\, dx/dt + 6x + 12\int x\, dt = te^{-3t}$

   g. $d^2\, x/dt^2 + 9\, dx/dt + 16x = 27$

   h. $F\, dy/dz + G\int y\, dz = Hy^2$

   i. $0.002\, d^2\theta/dt^2 + 0.135\, d\theta/dt + 1.6\theta = 3.2e^{-0.001t}$

2-3. Find the inverse Laplace transforms of the following:

   a. $\theta(s) = 6/s^4$

   b. $\theta(s) = \dfrac{2s + 10}{s^2 + 10s + 24}$

   c. $Y(s) = 1/(s + 3)(s + 4)$

   d. $X(s) = \dfrac{3s^2 + 12s + 11}{s^3 + 6s^2 + 11s + 6}$

   e. $Z(s) = \dfrac{s + 2}{(s + 1)^2(s + 3)}$

   f. $Q(s) = \dfrac{s + 1}{s^3(s + 3)}$

   g. $\theta(s) = \dfrac{s + 2}{s(s + 1)(s^2 + 9)}$

   h. $Y(s) = \dfrac{5s^2 + 8}{s^3 + 2s}$

   i. $\theta(s) = \dfrac{s^3 + 9s^2 + 9s + 36}{s^4 + 13s^2 + 36}$

   j. $G(s) = \dfrac{1}{s^3 + 7s^2 + 25s + 39}$

2-4. Find the Laplace transforms of the following (see Fig. 2P-1):

   a. $y = t$ for $0 < t < 1$

       $y = 2 - t$ for $1 \leqq t < 2$

       $y = 0$ for $t > 2$

   b. $y = 0$ for $0 < t \leqq \tau$

       $y = 1$ for $\tau \leqq t < \tau + 1$

       $y = 0$ for $t > \tau + 1$

   c. $y = (A/\tau)\, t$ for $0 < t < \tau$

       $y = 0$ for $t > \tau$

   d. $y = 0$ for $0 < t \leqq 1$

       $y = 5$ for $1 < t \leqq 2$

       $y = 0$ for $2 \leqq t \leqq 3$

       $y = -5$ for $3 \leqq t \leqq 4$

CHAPTER 3

EQUATIONS OF PHYSICAL SYSTEMS

3-1. Introduction. In general, the analysis and design of servomechanisms must be carried out on a mathematical basis in order that time may be saved in reaching an optimum design. This implies that all the physical elements which constitute the servo system must be described in some mathematical form before their contributions to system performance can satisfactorily be related to determine the over-all system response.[7-10,*]

Mathematical expressions can be found relating significant factors for each of the system components through the application of one or more fundamental formulas, peculiar to the physical nature of the component. For example, ordinary electric-circuit problems can be analyzed through the application of Kirchhoff's and Ohm's laws; the performance of simple mechanical translational and rotational systems can be found by applying Newton's laws of motion or d'Alembert's principle; a few basic laws of heat transfer, such as Fourier's conduction law and Newton's law for cooling, can be directed toward determination of mathematical expressions for thermal system and component operation; for hydraulic components possibly Darcy's law for linear flow or the continuity law can be employed to derive the necessary equations.

Primary consideration in this chapter is given to general methods of formulating the mathematical equations for dynamic equilibrium for selected mechanical systems whose counterparts are often found in a servomechanism. The methods for handling thermal, mechanical, hydraulic, electrical, and pneumatic units are discussed, but not at great length.

Because of the growing importance of the electrical-analogy approach in the investigation of performance of a nonelectrical system, a goodly portion of the chapter is devoted to setting up electrical analogues of mechanical, thermal, hydraulic, and pneumatic systems and electromechanical machinery. It should also be kept in mind that often the complete solution of the derived system equations (as evidenced in Chap. 4) is tedious to arrive at and, in some instances, the complexity of

* Superior numbers, when they appear in the text proper, are the numbers of references given in the Bibliography.

the equations effectively prohibits attaining a satisfactory solution.   For such cases, much can be gained through the use of electrical analogues of the actual system, which may be set up on analogue computer boards.[11-13]

3-2. Mechanical Systems—Translational.   *Spring-mass Type.*   Consider the elementary system shown in Fig. 3-1, consisting of a mass of M units suspended by a spring from a stationary wall.   The system has but a single degree of freedom.*

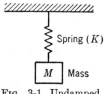

FIG. 3-1. Undamped
spring-mass system.

The spring is assumed to have negligible mass and a spring-deflection constant of K (units of K are force per unit displacement, for example, pounds per inch).   It is further assumed that there is no effective damping of the system.   Of interest will be the equation of motion which defines the system, and the mode of vibration of the entire system.   Several methods are available for determining the equation of motion, but that chosen here is most applicable to elementary systems.

The equations can be obtained through the application of Newton's second law of motion, which states:

$$\Sigma \text{ forces acting on body} = (\text{mass of body})(\text{acceleration})$$

The summation of the forces must, of course, be algebraic, and thus considerable care must be taken in writing the mathematical expression so that proper signs prefix the forces.   One method of determining the proper sign is outlined in this and the following examples.

Outline of Procedure:

1. Assume that the system originally is in equilibrium.   In this way the often troublesome effect of gravity is eliminated.

2. Assume then that the system is given some arbitrary displacement if no disturbing force is present.

3. Draw a free-body diagram of the forces exerted on each mass in the system.   There should be a separate diagram for each mass.

4. Apply Newton's law of motion to each diagram, using the convention that any force acting in the direction of the assumed displacement is positive.

5. Rearrange the equation in suitable form to solve by any convenient mathematical means.

In Figs. 3-2a and b the original nonequilibrium and equilibrium positions of the mass are shown.   Following the method outlined, assume that the mass M is displaced some distance Y from its equilibrium position (see Fig. 3-2c).   In Fig. 3-2d is shown the free-body diagram of the forces exerted on the mass for the assumed displacement.   The sum-

---

* A mechanical system has a single degree of freedom if its geometrical position can be expressed at any instant by a single number.

mation of forces is

$$-Ky = \text{spring-restoring force}$$

Hence

$$-Ky = M\frac{d^2y}{dt^2}$$

or

$$M\frac{d^2y}{dt^2} + Ky = 0 \qquad (3\text{-}1)$$

Equation (3-1) is the equation of motion of the spring-mass system.

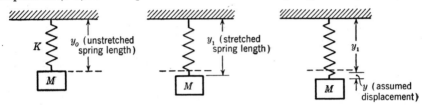

(a) System not at equilibrium   (b) System at equilibrium   (c) System with assumed displacement

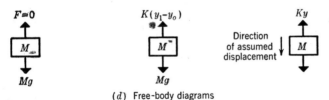

(d) Free-body diagrams

Fig. 3-2. Pictorial representation of spring-mass system and corresponding free-body diagrams.

The solution to Eq. (3-1) is obtained by classical methods or by using the Laplace transform. The latter method is chosen for illustrative purposes, though it is not necessarily any simpler than the direct approach.

$$\mathcal{L}\left(M\frac{d^2y}{dt^2} + Ky\right) = M[s^2Y(s) - sy(0+) - y'(0+)] + KY(s) \quad (3\text{-}2)$$

Obviously before a complete solution can be carried out the initial conditions must be known.

Let it be assumed that

$$y(0+) = 0$$
$$y'(0+) = 5 \qquad (3\text{-}3)$$

If these initial conditions are substituted in (3-2), then

$$M[s^2Y(s) - 5] + KY(s) = 0 \qquad (3\text{-}4)$$

Dropping the parenthetical notation,

$$M[s^2Y - 5] + KY = 0$$

where $\mathcal{L}[y(t)] = Y(s) = Y$.

Rearranging (3-4),

$$Y = \frac{5M}{Ms^2 + K} = \frac{5}{s^2 + K/M} \tag{3-5}$$

The inverse Laplace transformation may be applied to Eq. (3-5) to obtain Y as a function of time, after using the partial fraction expansion. The final solution to (3-5) is

$$y = \frac{5}{\sqrt{K/M}} \sin \sqrt{\frac{K}{M}}\, t \tag{3-6}$$

Spring-mass-damping Type. A more practical version of the same system is shown in Fig. 3-3a, with a damping device added. The damper might be an ordinary fluid-filled dashpot, or equivalent viscous damping

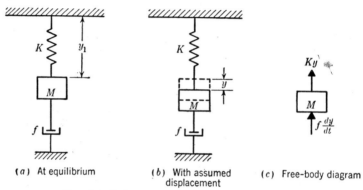

(a) At equilibrium   (b) With assumed displacement   (c) Free-body diagram

FIG. 3-3. Spring-mass system with viscous damper.

may be set up because of the suspension of the mass in a fluid as air or oil. It is assumed here that the damping force does vary directly with the velocity of the mass and that the viscous-damping coefficient, denoted by f, is constant. (Units of f are force per unit velocity, for example, pounds per foot per second.)

Assume that a displacement of y is given to the mass from its equilibrium position as shown in Fig. 3-3b. The free-body diagram depicted in Fig. 3-3c will result. The summation of forces is

$$-Ky = \text{retarding-spring force}$$

$$-f\frac{dy}{dt} = \text{viscous-damping force}$$

Then, applying Newton's second law of motion,

$$-Ky - f\frac{dy}{dt} = M\frac{d^2y}{dt^2} \tag{3-7}$$

Rearranging

$$M \frac{d^2y}{dt^2} + f \frac{dy}{dt} + Ky = 0 \qquad (3\text{-}7a)$$

Equation 3-7(a) is the equation of motion for the system.

To find the time variation of the displacement, the Laplace transform is again applied, and Eq. 3-7(a) becomes

$$M[s^2Y - sy(0+) - y'(0+)] + KY + f[sY - y(0+)] = 0 \qquad (3\text{-}8)$$

Before the solution can be completed, initial conditions $y(0+)$ and $y'(0+)$ must be specified. Assume that

$$y(0+) = 0$$
$$y'(0+) = \frac{dy}{dt}(0+) = 5 \qquad (3\text{-}9)$$

Then Eq. (3-8) becomes

$$M(s^2Y - 0 - 5) + f(sY - 0) + KY = 0 \qquad (3\text{-}10)$$

which may be solved algebraically for

$$Y = \frac{5M}{Ms^2 + Fs + K} \qquad (3\text{-}11)$$

Using the partial fraction expansion and the inverse Laplace transform, the solution is

$$y = \frac{5M}{\sqrt{KM - f^2/4}} e^{-ft/2M} \sin \sqrt{\frac{K}{M} - \frac{f^2}{4M^2}} t \qquad (3\text{-}12)$$

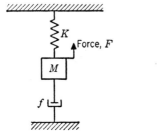

(a) System diagram   (b) Free-body diagram

FIG. 3-4. Forced vibration of damped spring-mass system.

Spring-mass-damping System (with Forced Vibration). The procedure for determining the equation of motion of a translational system when there is a forced vibration is much the same as for the previous cases. For the system shown in Fig. 3-4a, which is at equilibrium, assume a constant force of F lb is suddenly applied.

The resultant free-body diagram is shown in Fig. 3-4b. Here, the recommended convention for determining the sign of the active forces is to regard any force which acts in the direction of the applied force as positive. Then the summation of forces is

$$+F = \text{applied disturbing force}$$
$$-Ky = \text{spring force}$$
$$-f\frac{dy}{dt} = \text{viscous-damping force}$$

and Newton's law becomes

$$+F - Ky - f\frac{dy}{dt} = M\frac{d^2y}{dt^2} \qquad (3\text{-}13)$$

Rearranging,

$$M\frac{d^2y}{dt^2} + f\frac{dy}{dt} + Ky - F = 0 \qquad (3\text{-}13a)$$

which may be solved for

$$y = \frac{F}{K}\left[1 - \frac{\sqrt{K/M}}{\sqrt{K/M - f^2/4M^2}}e^{-ft/2M}\right.$$
$$\left. \cos\left(\sqrt{\frac{K}{M} - \frac{f^2}{4M^2}}\,t - \tan^{-1}\frac{f/2M}{\sqrt{K/M - f^2/4M^2}}\right)\right] \qquad (3\text{-}14)$$

Multi-spring-mass-dashpot Combination. Often the mechanical system is made up of a fairly complex arrangement of masses, springs, and damping devices. The problem of determining the dynamic-equilibrium equations for these is only slightly longer. But solving these equations may be quite difficult. Where possible, simplifying assumptions are made which allow reduction in the number of elements or the replacement of an array of elements by an equivalent single element. Generally, if the resultant equations are of higher than the second order, referral of the problem to an analogue board is worth while, especially if the problem is basically one of design.

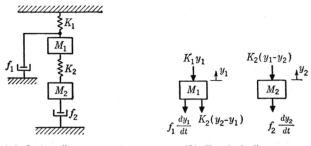

(a) System diagram   (b) Free-body diagrams

Fig. 3-5. Complex translational system.

In Fig. 3-5 is illustrated a fairly complex translational mechanical system. Completely to define the dynamic equilibrium for this system, it would be necessary to write two equations of motion, one for each mass, and then solve these simultaneously. The free-body diagrams are drawn assuming that the displacement of M_1 is y_1 and that of M_2 is y_2.

The equations of motion which can be written are

$$-K_1y_1 - K_2(y_1 - y_2) - f_1\frac{dy_1}{dt} = M_1\frac{d^2y_1}{dt^2} \tag{3-15}$$

$$K_2(y_1 - y_2) - f_2\frac{dy_2}{dt} = M_2\frac{d^2y_2}{dt^2} \tag{3-16}$$

The above equations would be solved simultaneously to obtain a solution.

3-3. Rotational Mechanical Systems. The equations of motion for rotational systems can be written by following the steps outlined for translational systems. The only modification necessary is that the polar form of Newton's second law of motion be used,

$$\Sigma T = J\alpha \tag{3-17}$$

where ΣT = algebraic summation of all torques exerted on the rotational
body
J = polar moment of inertia of system
α = angular acceleration = $d^2\theta/dt^2$
θ = angular displacement
The following examples will serve to illustrate the manner of handling this type of mechanical system.

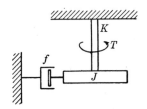
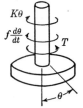

(a) Pictorial diagram   (b) Free-body diagram

FIG. 3-6. Forced vibration of elementary rotational system.

Spring-mass-damping System. Consider the system shown in Fig. 3-6a, which is assumed to be originally at equilibrium. The shaft is fixed at one end and is assumed to have a constant torsional stiffness of K units. The shaft stiffness corresponds to the spring constant in translational systems. The shaft and the damping devices are assumed to have negligible inertia so that the total inertia of the system is the inertia of the disk alone. The damping device is assumed to set up an equivalent viscous-friction force.

Figure 3-6b is the free-body diagram of the system, assuming that an angular displacement of θ is given to the inertia. The summation of torques is

$$-K\theta = \text{retarding torque due to shaft stiffness}$$

$$-f\frac{d\theta}{dt} = \text{retarding torque due to the torsional damper}$$

where f is the viscous-damping coefficient in units of foot-pounds per mechanical radian, etc.

Substituting in Newton's law,

$$-K\theta - f\frac{d\theta}{dt} = J\frac{d^2\theta}{dt^2} \tag{3-18}$$

Rearranging,

$$J\frac{d^2\theta}{dt^2} + f\frac{d\theta}{dt} + K\theta = 0 \tag{3-18a}$$

The solution may be obtained in much the same fashion as for the translational system described by Eq. (3-7a) and is for the same initial conditions,

$$\theta = \frac{5J}{\sqrt{KJ - f^2/4}} e^{-ft/2J} \sin\sqrt{\frac{K}{J} - \frac{f^2}{4J^2}}\, t \tag{3-19}$$

Spring-mass-damping System (Forced Vibration). The equation of motion for the rotational system in Fig. 3-6a, when subjected to a sudden applied torque T, is easily determined by referring to the free-body diagram in Fig. 3-6b. The torques are

$$-K\theta = \text{shaft-stiffness torque}$$

$$-f\frac{d\theta}{dt} = \text{viscous-damping torque}$$

$$T = \text{constant disturbing torque}$$

Substituting in Newton's law of motion,

$$-K\theta - f\frac{d\theta}{dt} + T = J\frac{d^2\theta}{dt^2} \tag{3-20}$$

Rearranging,

$$J\frac{d^2\theta}{dt^2} + f\frac{d\theta}{dt} + K\theta - T = 0 \tag{3-20a}$$

Solving for θ with initial conditions zero,

$$\theta = \frac{T}{K}\left[1 - \frac{\sqrt{K/J}}{\sqrt{K/J - f^2/4J^2}} e^{-ft/2J}\right.$$
$$\left. \cos\left(\sqrt{\frac{K}{J} - \frac{f^2}{4J^2}}\, t - \tan^{-1}\frac{f/2J}{\sqrt{K/J - f^2/4J^2}}\right)\right] \tag{3-21}$$

Complex Rotational System. For the multiple-inertia system shown in Fig. 3-7 the equation of motion can be written by considering each inertia individually.

Applying Newton's law to each inertia,

$$K_1(\theta_2 - \theta_1) - K_2(\theta_3 - \theta_4) = J_1 \frac{d^2\theta_2}{dt^2}$$

$$J_1 \frac{d^2\theta_2}{dt^2} + K_2(\theta_3 - \theta_4) - K_1\theta_2 = 0 \qquad (3\text{-}22)$$

and

$$-K_2(\theta_3 - \theta_4) + K_3(\theta_6 - \theta_5) = J_2 \frac{d^2\theta_4}{dt^2}$$

$$J_2 \frac{d^2\theta_4}{dt^2} + K_2(\theta_3 - \theta_4) - K_3(\theta_6 - \theta_5) = 0 \qquad (3\text{-}23)$$

Finally

$$-K_3(\theta_6 - \theta_5) = J_3 \frac{d^2\theta_6}{dt^2}$$

or

$$J_3 \frac{d^2\theta_6}{dt^2} + K_3(\theta_6 - \theta_5) = 0 \qquad (3\text{-}24)$$

Geared Rotational System. In many servo systems the output member, or *load*, is not driven off a shaft common with the power member but is coupled to the drive through a gear train as shown in Fig. 3-8a. The power member (here signified by a motor armature) and the load generally have inertia and probably exhibit approximate viscous-damping characteristics. The manner in which "coupled" rotational systems should be handled is of interest for these reasons.

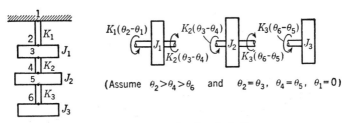

(Assume $\theta_2 > \theta_4 > \theta_6$ and $\theta_2 = \theta_3$, $\theta_4 = \theta_5$, $\theta_1 = 0$)

(a) System diagram   (b) Free-body diagrams

FIG. 3-7. Complex rotational system.

Several mathematical approaches may be used to take into account such combinations. Newton's law of motion can be applied to each mass, the equations of motion determined separately, and the solutions of these equations reached by solving the equations simultaneously; or the two members of the rotational system can be reduced to a less complicated equivalent system before carrying out the work of a complete solution. In the latter instance a simplifying assumption that all shafts have infinite stiffness must be made, but as a rule the results obtained are still satisfactory. This latter approach considerably lessens the work entailed in arriving at a solution as it reduces the problem to a single degree of freedom.

With a steady torque T developed by the power member (here a motor armature), the following equations of motion can be derived (see Fig. 3-8b for free-body diagrams of the system). The summation of torques is

T = torque applied to J_m

$-f\dfrac{d\theta_m}{dt}$ = viscous-damping torque on motor side

$-T_1$ = restraining torque exerted on gear train by output member

Applying Newton's law,

$$\sum T = T - T_1 - f_m \frac{d\theta_m}{dt} = J_m \frac{d^2\theta_m}{dt^2} \tag{3-25}$$

Rearranging,

$$J_m \frac{d^2\theta_m}{dt^2} + f_m \frac{d\theta_m}{dt} + T_1 - T = 0 \tag{3-25a}$$

Referring now to the free-body diagram in Fig. 3-8c, let θ_2 be the angular displacement of the output member as a result of the torque

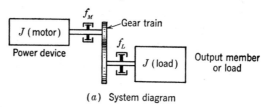

(a) System diagram

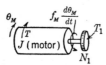

(b) Motor free-body diagrams
(steady applied torque)

(c) Load free-body diagram

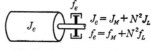

(d) Equivalent system diagram

Fig. 3-8. Output and powering elements coupled by a gear train.

applied to N_1. The summation of torques is

$+T_2$ = torque exerted by motor on gear, N_2

$-f_L\dfrac{d\theta_L}{dt}$ = viscous-damping torque exerted by output member

Newton's law of motion becomes

$$T_2 - f_L \frac{d\theta_L}{dt} = J_2 \frac{d^2\theta_L}{dt^2} \tag{3-26}$$

Rearranging,

$$J_2 \frac{d^2\theta_L}{dt} + f_L \frac{d\theta_L}{dt} - T_2 = 0 \tag{3-26a}$$

The equations of motion for the two systems can be combined when T_1, T_2, θ_m, and θ_L are properly related.

It can be shown that

$$\theta_L = \frac{N_1}{N_2} \theta_m = N\theta_m \tag{3-27}$$

where N_1 = number of teeth on gear 1
N_2 = number of teeth on gear 2
$\dfrac{N_1}{N_2} = N$

It may also be shown that

$$T_2 = \frac{N_2 T_1}{N_1} = \frac{T_1}{N} \tag{3-28}$$

Equation (3-26a) can then be written as

$$J_L \frac{d\theta_L{}^2}{dt^2} + f_L \frac{d\theta_L}{dt} = \frac{T_1}{N} \tag{3-29}$$

or

$$T_1 = NJ_L \frac{d^2\theta_L}{dt^2} + Nf_L \frac{d\theta_L}{dt} \tag{3-29a}$$

Substituting (3-29a) in (3-25a),

$$J_m \frac{d^2\theta_m}{dt^2} + f_m \frac{d\theta_m}{dt} + NJ_L \frac{d^2\theta_L}{dt^2} + Nf_L \frac{d\theta_L}{dt} = T \tag{3-30}$$

and using relation (3-27),

$$J_m \frac{d^2\theta_m}{dt^2} + f_m \frac{d\theta_m}{dt} + N^2 J_2 \frac{d^2\theta_m}{dt^2} + N^2 f_L \frac{d\theta_m}{dt} = T \tag{3-31}$$

Simplifying,

$$(J_m + N^2 J_L) \frac{d^2\theta_m}{dt^2} + (f_m + N^2 f_L) \frac{d\theta_m}{dt} = T \tag{3-32}$$

Thus, for the two mass systems, an equivalent system can be substituted if the inertia of the output member and the viscous-friction constant are altered by a factor of N^2. The equivalent system is shown in Fig. 3-8d. In conclusion, the solution for θ_m can be found by the usual transform methods. Should θ_L be desired, then the solution for θ_m need be altered only by the ratio $1/N$.

Multiple-gear System. The multiple-gear system in Fig. 3-9 can be reduced to an equivalent single inertia-friction system using the procedure outlined in the previous section. Assuming it is desired to find the equivalent system referred to the motor shaft, the equivalent inertia of the system can be written as

$$J_e = J_m + N_a{}^2[J_1 + N_b{}^2(J_2 + N_c{}^2J_L)] \qquad (3\text{-}33)$$

where $N_a = N_1/N_2$, $N_b = N_3/N_4$, and $N_c = N_5/N_6$ and J_m, J_1, J_2, and J_L are respective inertias of the motor, coupling members 1 and 2, and the load.

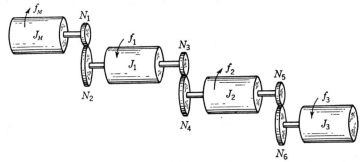

Fɪɢ. 3-9. Multiple-gear system.

Similarly it can be shown that

$$f_e = f_m + N_a{}^2[f_1 + N_b{}^2(f_2 + N_c{}^2f_L)] \qquad (3\text{-}34)$$

When Eqs. (3-33) and (3-34) are expanded,

$$\begin{aligned} J_e &= J_m + N_a{}^2J_1 + (N_aN_b)^2J_2 + (N_aN_bN_c)^2J_L \\ f_e &= f_m + N_a{}^2f_1 + (N_aN_b)^2f_2 + (N_aN_bN_c)^2f_L \end{aligned} \qquad (3\text{-}35)$$

Thus the equivalent inertia of a system referred to a common shaft is found by multiplying each inertia by the square of the total gear reduction seen by individual inertias. The same generalization can be made for the viscous-friction coefficients. It can be noted from the equations in (3-35), for the multigear system illustrated, that the further removed the member is from the referral shaft, the less effective are the inertia and friction of the remote member.

3-4. Electrical Analogue of Physical Systems. In most cases the determination of mathematical expressions which adequately relate the factors influencing the characteristics of mechanical, thermal, hydraulic, pneumatic, and electrical systems is more difficult than those presented thus far. In some instances, though the equation determination is relatively simple, attaining a satisfactory solution of the equation is extremely difficult or impossible. (This is especially true where nonlinearities of any extent exist.) For these reasons it is often of great advantage to use the electrical-analogy method of determining the system equations. The system equation may then be solved by experimental methods, *i.e.*, by an analogue computer.

It is possible, with the aid of electronic summing, integrating, and differentiating devices, coordinated by servomechanism guide loops, to set up a miniature "electrical model" of the system or component which poses the problem. By means of ordinary electrical indicating instruments, determination of modes of vibration, temperature variation, fluid flow, etc., is readily accomplished. It is not the purpose here to discuss the operation of the analogue computer, but it should be noted that the use of such computing devices and electrical counterparts of a physical system makes possible the rapid solution (with reasonable accuracies) of most types of problems which center on automatic control.

Of primary concern, here, is the manner in which electrical-analogy methods make possible the determination of defining equations and their ultimate solutions for the more complex physical systems. The advantages of the analogue approach are most apparent when several degrees of freedom are known to exist.

Basically, the analogy of mechanical, thermal, hydraulic, and pneumatic systems with electrical systems rests upon the similarity of the mathematical laws which govern mechanical motion, heat transfer, fluid flow, and electron flow. Early papers by Baker and Paschkis[14] have done much to develop the analogy method of obtaining analytical and experimental solutions.

Table 3-1 summarizes the electrical and analogous units which are generally covered in the analogue treatment. Interrelationships, where they exist, are shown.

3-5. Electrical Analogue of Mechanical Systems. The displacement-charge method of setting up electrical analogues of mechanical systems will be used in the following examples. This is only one of the various approaches which may be followed. In Table 3-1 are shown the analogous mechanical and electrical elements.

3-6. Outline of General Procedure in Applying Electrical-analogy Methods.

1. Draw the complete mechanical system, including all elements showing inertia, spring, and damping characteristics.

2. Label the junctions between elements to facilitate identification and location of analogous electrical units.

3. Determine the number of electrical components required. This will depend upon the number of individual mechanical elements.

4. Assume that a displacement is given to the mechanical system, and note the displacement of all junctions in the diagram.

TABLE 3-1

TABLE OF ANALOGOUS ELEMENTS

	Electrical resistor	Electrical capacitor	Electrical inductor
Electrical elements	 $E_R = R\dfrac{d(Q_1 - Q_2)}{dt}$ R = resistance; Q = charge	 $E_C = \dfrac{1}{C}(Q_1 - Q_2)$ C = capacitance	 $E_L = L\dfrac{d^2Q}{dt^2}$ L = inductance
	Viscous damper	Spring	Inertia
Mechanical elements (translational)	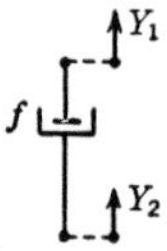 $F = f\dfrac{d(Y_1 - Y_2)}{dt}$ Y = displacement f = damping coefficient	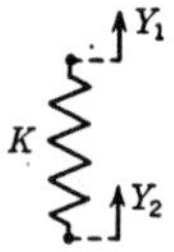 $F = K(Y_1 - Y_2)$ K = spring constant	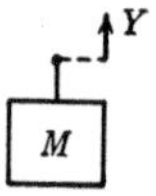 $F = M\dfrac{d^2Y}{dt^2}$ M = inertia
	Torsional damper	Shaft stiffness	Inertia
Mechanical elements (rotational)	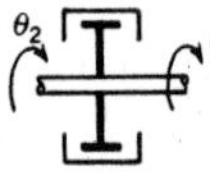 $T = f\dfrac{d(\theta_1 - \theta_2)}{dt}$ f = damping coefficient	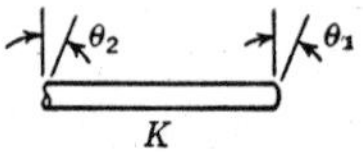 $T = K(\theta_1 - \theta_2)$ K = stiffness coefficient	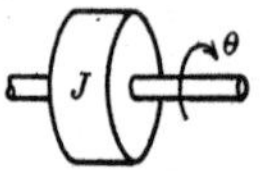 $T = J\dfrac{d^2\theta}{dt^2}$ J = moment of inertia
	Fluid resistance	Fluid capacity	
Hydraulic elements	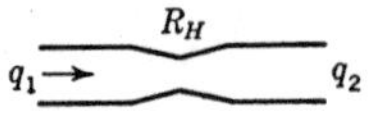 $F = R_h q = R_h\dfrac{dQ}{dt}$ $q = q_1 = q_2$ R_H = hydraulic resistance q = rate of flow Q = quantity of flow ($Q_2 = 0$ in electrical analogue)	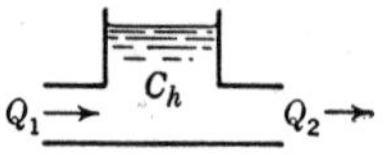 $F = \dfrac{Q_1 - Q_2}{C_h}$ C_h = hydraulic capacity Q_1 = quantity of inflow Q_2 = quantity of outflow	

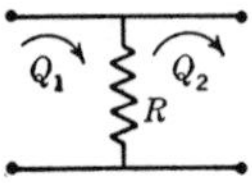

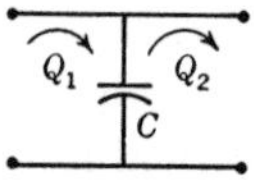

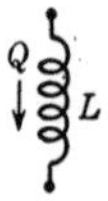

5. Connect analogous electrical units together, keeping in mind the displacement-charge relationship.

3-7. Electrical Analogue for Displacement Systems. *Simple Spring-mass System.* For the system in Fig. 3-10a, two electrical elements will be required, a capacitor, for the spring, and an inductance, for the mass as shown in Fig. 3-10a. Assuming that the mass M is given an arbitrary displacement, it is obvious that points 2 and 3 will be displaced the same amount, that is, $Y_2 = Y_3$. This means that, in the analogous electric circuit, Q_2 must be the same as Q through the inductance. Thus the L and C can be combined as shown by the dotted line in Fig. 3-10b.

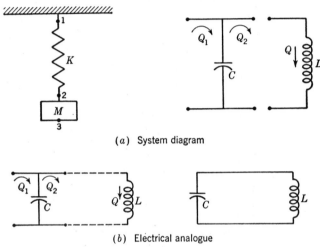

(*a*) System diagram

(*b*) Electrical analogue

FIG. 3-10. Electrical analogue of spring-mass system.

To complete the analogous electrical circuit, it is necessary to note that the spring is fixed at the wall; therefore, $Y_1 = 0$, and in the analogous circuit $Q_1 = 0$. Hence the left-hand terminals of the capacitor can be removed, leaving the analogous circuit illustrated in Fig. 3-10b.

As a check on the validity of the analogue, a Kirchhoff voltage equation may be written about the loop of the analogue and the result compared with the application of Newton's law to the original mechanical system. The equilibrium equation of the analogue is

$$L\frac{di}{dt} + \frac{1}{C}\int i\,dt = 0$$
$$L\frac{d^2Q}{dt^2} + \frac{Q}{C} = 0$$

(3-36)

while the equilibrium equation of the mechanical system is

$$M\frac{d^2Y}{dt^2} + KY = 0$$

Spring-mass-damping System (Free Vibration). For the system shown in Fig. 3-11a, three elements will be required. To determine the manner of connection, associate

1. Q_1 and Q_2 of capacitor with Y_1 and Y_2 of the spring
2. Q_3 and Q_4 of resistance with Y_3 and Y_4 of the damper

Assuming that the mass is displaced, then it follows that

$$Y_2 = Y_3 \qquad \therefore Q_2 = Q_3 = Q_m$$
$$Y_1 = Y_4 = 0 \qquad \therefore Q_1 = Q_4 = 0$$

This means that all portions of circuit must be connected in series (see dotted lines in Fig. 3-11b) because the same charge is common to all components and since one side of the damper and spring are fixed, a pair of terminals on R and C must be omitted. Thus the analogous electric circuit is shown in Fig. 3-11b.

To check the analogy, the equilibrium equation of the electrical circuit is

$$L\frac{di}{dt} + Ri + \frac{1}{C}\int i\,dt = 0$$

or   (3-37)

$$L\frac{d^2Q}{dt^2} + R\frac{dQ}{dt} + \frac{Q}{C} = 0$$

The equilibrium equation of the mechanical system is

$$M\frac{d^2y}{dt^2} + f\frac{dy}{dt} + Ky = 0$$

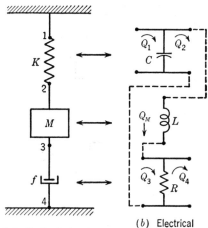

(a) Mechanical system   (b) Electrical analogue

FIG. 3-11. Electrical analogue of three-element mechanical system.

Spring-mass-damping System (Forced Vibration). Where the mechanical system is subjected to a forced vibration, an electrical analogue can still be set up. The only modification necessary is that a voltage (having the same time variation) must be substituted appropriately in the electrical circuit. In Fig. 3-12a is shown such a system, while in Fig. 3-12b the necessary elements with appropriate charge subscripts are noted.

Assuming the mass is displaced, in the mechanical system,

$$Y_2 = Y_3 = Y_m$$

while in the electrical system,

$$Q_2 = Q_3 = Q_m$$

Thus connections can be made as indicated in Fig. 3-12c by dotted lines. In the mechanical system, Y_1 and $Y_4 = 0$ so that Q_1 and Q_4 in the analogue can be left open or ignored.

The final step in completing the analogue is the location of the voltage analogous to the applied force (a d-c voltage is used because F = constant). Since the force is applied at point 2 of the spring, the voltage should be included in series with the branch where Q_2 flows. The completed electrical analogue is drawn in Fig. 3-12d.

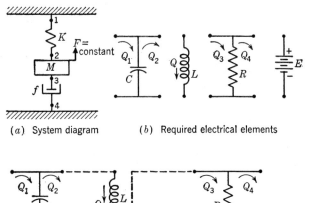

(a) System diagram   (b) Required electrical elements

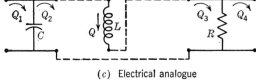

(c) Electrical analogue

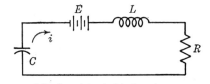

(d) Complete electrical analogue

FIG. 3-12. Electrical analogue of system with suddenly applied force.

The equilibrium equation of the electrical analogue is

$$L\frac{di}{dt} + Ri + \frac{1}{C}\int i\,dt - E = 0$$
$$L\frac{d^2Q}{dt^2} + R\frac{dQ}{dt} + \frac{Q}{C} - E = 0$$

(3-38)

while the equilibrium equation of the original mechanical system is

$$M\frac{d^2Y}{dt^2} + f\frac{dY}{dt} + KY - F = 0$$

Complex Mechanical System. The number of elements required for the electrical analogue of the system in Fig. 3-13a would be six. The manner of connection of these elements may be determined if mechanical displacements of the masses M_1 and M_2 are assumed.

By observation of the displaced mechanical system it is found that $Y_1 = Y_6 = Y_7 = 0$, because the system is fastened at the walls, and $Y_2 = Y_3$, $Y_4 = Y_5$.

By analogy then, $Q_1 = 0$, $Q_6 = 0$, $Q_7 = 0$. Therefore pairs of terminals for C_1, R_1, R_2 can be left open. Also $Q_2 = Q_3 = Q_{m1}$ so that C_1, L_1, and R_1 are in series. Because $Q_4 = Q_5 = Q_{m2}$, C_2, L_2, and R_2 are all in series. Redrawing the circuit, the analogue is completed as shown in Fig. 3-13c.

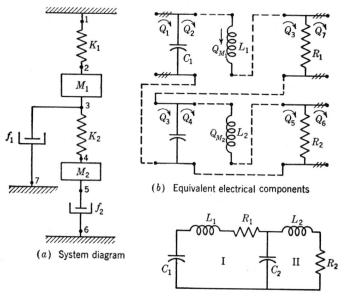

(a) System diagram

(b) Equivalent electrical components

(c) Completed analogue

FIG. 3-13. Complex mechanical system and its analogue.

The equilibrium equations of the mechanical system are

$$M_1 \frac{d^2 y_2}{dt^2} + f_1 \frac{dy_1}{dt} + K_1 y_1 + K_2 (y_1 - y_2) = 0$$

and

$$M_2 \frac{d^2 y_2}{dt^2} + f_2 \frac{dy_2}{dt} + K_2 (y_2 - y_1) = 0$$

For the electrical analogue, around loop 1 (calling the charge Q_a),

$$L_1 \frac{d^2 Q_a}{dt^2} + R_1 \frac{dQ_a}{dt} + \frac{Q_a}{C} + \frac{1}{C_2} (Q_a - Q_b) = 0 \qquad (3\text{-}39)$$

and around loop 2,

$$L_2 \frac{d^2 Q_b}{dt^2} + R_2 \frac{dQ_b}{dt} + \frac{1}{C_2} (Q_b - Q_a) = 0 \qquad (3\text{-}40)$$

3-8. Electrical Analogue of Rotational Systems. The analogy methods applied to the translational systems are readily extended to rotational mechanical systems. Table 3-1 includes rotational components and their respective equivalents.

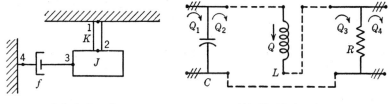

(a) System diagram   (b) Electrical analogue

FIG. 3-14. Electrical analogue of rotational system.

Spring-mass-damping System (Rotational). The rotational system shown in Fig. 3-14a would require three elements for its electrical analogue. These are shown in Fig. 3-14b. Assuming an angular displacement given to the inertia, then $\theta_2 = \theta_3$ so that $Q_2 = Q = Q_3$ in the analogous circuit. Thus C, L, and R may be connected in series (indicated by dotted lines). Since $\theta_1 = \theta_4 = 0$, then Q_1 and Q_4 must be zero.

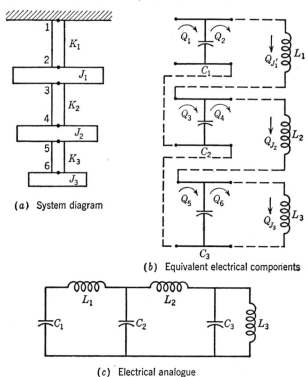

(a) System diagram

(b) Equivalent electrical components

(c) Electrical analogue

FIG. 3-15. Complex rotational system and its electrical analogue.

Complex Rotational System. For a multiinertia system as in Fig. 3-15a, the number of components would, of course, be six. Assuming displacements are given to the individual inertias, it is possible to make the dotted connections shown in Fig. 3-15b.

Since $\theta_1 = 0$, then Q_1 must be zero, and $\theta_2 = \theta_3 = \theta$ of inertia, J_1, so that Q_1, Q_{m1}, Q_3 must be the same; hence C_1, L_1, and C_3 must be in series. The displacement $\theta_4 = \theta_5 =$ displacement of inertia J_2; therefore $Q_4 = Q_5 = Q_{m2}$, and the dotted connection connecting C_2, L_2, and C_3 in series must be made.

Finally, the displacement of J_3 must be same as θ_3 so that, on the analogous electrical circuit, $Q_6 = Q_{m3}$. Redrawing the circuit accordingly, the result is shown in Fig. 3-15c.

3-9. Electrical Analogue of General Systems.[17–26] The mathematical expressions which describe the operation of thermal, hydraulic, and pneumatic components of a servomechanism can usually be found by direct application of fundamental laws for the specific type of system. As with complex mechanical systems, an equally effective means of determining the desired relations is through the use of electrical-analogy methods. Once the electrical analogues have been established, rapid solutions to the specific problems may be attained through the use of analogue computers. In the following paragraphs is outlined a somewhat generalized approach to handling some common nonmechanical and nonelectrical components and processes which often form part of a servomechanism loop. Of particular interest are those units which may be used as sensing devices in servos.

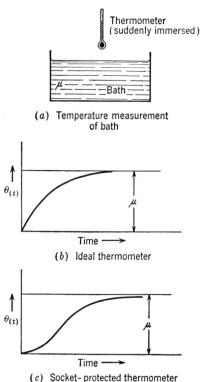

(a) Temperature measurement of bath

(b) Ideal thermometer

(c) Socket-protected thermometer

FIG. 3-16. Response characteristics of resistance thermometer.

3-10. Electrical Analogue of Elementary Thermometer. The many types of temperature-measuring elements which may be used with automatic temperature controllers have similar characteristics. In all cases the temperature-sensitive device introduces some time lag into the control system, though the time lag varies considerably, depending upon the type of measuring device and its heat-transfer characteristics. These lags must, of course, be taken into consideration in undertaking the design of a controller.

The response characteristics of the temperature-measuring device (a resistance thermometer) discussed here can be found by using Newton's law for cooling or through analogy methods. Newton's law for cooling states that the rate of change of temperature is proportional to the difference between the bath temperature and the measured temperature (assuming that the thermometer is suddenly immersed in the bath whose temperature is to be measured).

Mathematically,

$$\frac{d\theta}{dt} = \frac{1}{T}(\mu - \theta) \tag{3-41}$$

where θ is indicated temperature and μ is bath temperature (constant). T is the lag coefficient, which is a function of the heat-transfer characteristics of the bath and the temperature-measuring element, and t is, of course, time.

Newton's equation for cooling can be solved for the measured temperature variation by transform methods. Rearranging,

$$T\frac{d\theta}{dt} + \theta = \mu$$

$$\mathcal{L}\left(T\frac{d\theta}{dt} + \theta\right) = \mathcal{L}(\mu) \tag{3-42}$$

$$T[s\Theta(s) - \theta(0+)] + \Theta(s) = \frac{\mu}{s} \tag{3-43}$$

Then, to simplify the algebra in this illustration, assume $\theta(0+) = 0$, where $\theta(0+)$ is the initial temperature of the thermometer.

$$\Theta(s)(sT + 1) = \frac{\mu}{s}$$

Solving for $\Theta(s)$,

$$\Theta(s) = \frac{\mu}{s(sT + 1)} = \frac{\mu/T}{s(s + 1/T)} \tag{3-43a}$$

The partial fraction expansion can be used in carrying out the inverse transformation.

$$\Theta(s) = \frac{A_1}{s - s_1} + \frac{A_2}{s - s_2} \tag{3-44}$$

where $s_1 = 0$ and $s_2 = -1/T$.

$$\therefore \Theta(s) = \frac{A_1}{s} + \frac{A_2}{s + 1/T} \tag{3-45}$$

To evaluate A_1 and A_2, obtain a common denominator.

$$A_1\left(s + \frac{1}{T}\right) + A_2 s = \frac{\mu}{T} \tag{3-46}$$

$$\therefore A_1 s + A_2 s = 0$$

and

$$\frac{A_1}{T} = \frac{\mu}{T}$$

Hence

$$A_1 = \mu$$

and

$$A_2 = -A_1 = -\mu$$

Substituting in Eq. (3-45),

$$\Theta(s) = \frac{\mu}{s} - \frac{\mu}{s + 1/T} \tag{3-47}$$

$$\mathcal{L}^{-1}[\Theta(s)] = \theta(t) = \mu - \mu e^{-t/T} = \mu(1 - e^{-t/T}) \tag{3-48}$$

In Fig. 3-16b is shown a typical response curve of an elementary resistance thermometer. Figure 3-16c shows the effect on response of additional lag due to the protective metal socket.

An alternate means of determining the equation is through the use of the electrical analogue of a thermal system. Early work done on this is credited to Baker and Paschkis;[14] many recent papers are concerned with this method. Only brief justification of the analogy with thermal systems is included here; for more complete studies the literature[15] should be consulted.

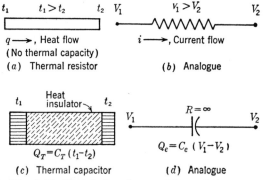

FIG. 3-17. Electrical analogues of thermal elements.

Thermal-resistance Concept. A concept of thermal resistance and thermal capacitance can be formed because of the similarity of heat-flow and current-flow equations. If one compares the flow of heat through a metal rod, as in Fig. 3-17a, the ends of which are maintained at different temperatures, with the current flow through a resistance whose terminals are maintained at different potentials, the concept can be deduced.

For the thermal system,

$$q = \frac{t_1 - t_2}{R} \tag{3-49}$$

where ς = heat flow, Btu/min

t_1, t_2 = temperatures of either end of rod

R = thermal resistance, °F/Btu/min

For the electrical system,

$$i = \frac{V_1 - V_2}{R} \tag{3-50}$$

where i = current, coulombs/sec

V_1, V_2 = potentials at either end of resistor

R = electrical resistance, ohms

The concept of thermal resistance can be applied equally well to surface films and heat insulators.

Thermal-capacitance Concept. In a practical situation when there is a flow of heat through a body, there will be some storage of heat, resulting in an increase in the temperature of the body which serves as a heat conductor. This is much the same as the storage of charge on the plates of a capacitor, which increases the voltage across the terminals.

Better to visualize the concept of thermal capacitance, consider the highly idealized case in Figs. 3-17c and d. The two bodies shown in the figures are separated by an insulator whose thermal resistance is infinite and are maintained at temperatures t_1 and t_2. The amount of heat that would be stored in such a system, provided storage is possible, can be found from

$$Q_T = C_T(t_1 - t_2) \tag{3-51}$$

where Q_T = quantity of heat stored, Btu

t_1, t_2 = temperatures of bodies, °F

C_T = thermal capacitance, Btu/°F

Compare Eq. (3-51) with that for finding the total charge on the plates of the capacitor in Fig. 3-17d.

$$Qe = Ce(V_1 - V_2) \tag{3-52}$$

where Qe = total quantity of electricity stored, coulombs

V_1, V_2 = potentials of either plate

Ce = electrical capacitance, farads

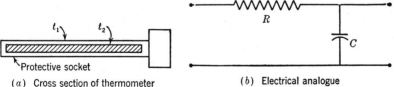

(a) Cross section of thermometer   (b) Electrical analogue

FIG. 3-18. Electrical analogue of a thermometer.

The analogy approach will now be applied to the ideal resistance thermometer. Assume that the sensitive element is completely enclosed and at a uniform temperature t_2, also that heat transfer takes place at the outer jacket primarily by convection (heat transfer by conduction and radiation negligible). Then the enclosing jacket can be considered to have thermal capacity only. The electrical analogue will be a series combination of resistor and capacitor, as in Fig. 3-18b.

The thermal resistance, simulated by R, is the opposition to heat flow offered by the film adjacent to the enclosing jacket. The capacitance, C, corresponds to the thermal capacity of the jacket itself (the film has negligible heat capacity). The combination is connected in series because all of the heat which is stored in the jacket must first flow through the film; and since the heat flow through each must be the same, in the electrical analogue the current flow must be the same.

3-11. Electrical Analogue of Thermal Processes. Those thermal processes which are of interest in automatic control are usually classified as single- or multiple-capacity systems. A single-capacity system is one in which there is only one independent energy-storage element, etc. The quantitative analysis of either type of process can be followed through by setting up ordinary heat balances or, again, by analogy methods. Both approaches are used here to illustrate their correspondence.

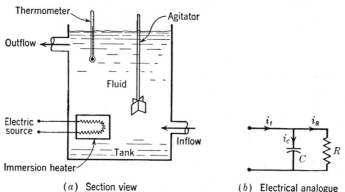

(a) Section view   (b) Electrical analogue

FIG. 3-19. Single-capacity process and its analogue.

Single-capacity Thermal Process. In Fig. 3-19a is shown a simple continuous process. It is assumed that a constant fluid flow in and out of the container is maintained. The fluid is heated as it passes through the container by an immersion type of heater. The complete mathematical analysis is not presented here but can be found in the literature.[204] The manner in which a solution is obtained and the solution itself are of primary interest here. Given the following:

q_e = heat supplied by electrical source, Btu/min
q_o = heat carried away in fluid, Btu/min
q_i = heat carried in by fluid, Btu/min

(For a given set of inflow conditions let it be assumed that the heat carried in by the fluid is zero.)

C_T = thermal capacity of tank, Btu/°F

θ = instantaneous tank temperature (uniform temperature distribution assumed because of agitator action)

θ_F = final steady-state tank temperature after a disturbance

A heat balance can be set up for the process for any set of inflow and outflow conditions.

$$q_e + q_i = q_o + q \text{ (stored)} \tag{3-53}$$

which reduces to

$$q_e = q_o + q \text{ (stored)} \tag{3-54}$$

since

$$q_i = 0$$

To facilitate arriving at a solution, it is convenient to define a "fictitious" thermal resistance and then redefine thermal capacity as applied to a process.

$$R \text{ (thermal)} \triangleq \frac{\theta \text{ (deg)}}{q \text{ (Btu/min)}}, \qquad R \text{ (elec.)} = \frac{E \text{ (volts)}}{I \text{ (amp)}} \tag{3-55}$$

The heat-flow potential in (3-55) is analogous to voltage, while the heat flow, itself, is analogous to current. Thermal resistance is a fictitious quantity since it is just the ratio of the temperature and flow rate at a point.

$$C \text{ (thermal)} = \frac{Q \text{ (Btu)}}{\theta \text{ (deg)}} \qquad \text{(for unit mass)} \tag{3-56}$$

$$C \text{ (elec.)} = \frac{q \text{ (coulombs)}}{E \text{ (volts)}}$$

Here the total quantities of heat and charge are analogous; and heat-flow potential is again analogous to voltage. Then Eq. (3-53) can be written as

$$q_e = C_T \underbrace{\frac{d\theta}{dt}}_{q\text{(stored)}} + \underbrace{\frac{\theta}{R_T}}_{q \text{ (out)}} \tag{3-53a}$$

Rearranging (3-53a),

$$\frac{d\theta}{dt} = \frac{R_T q_e - \theta}{R_T C_T} \tag{3-53b}$$

Solving by classical or transform methods, an explicit relation for θ can be found,

$$\theta = R_T q_e + (\theta - R_T q_e)_o e^{-t/R_T C_T} \tag{3-57}$$

where $R_T q_e = \theta_F$ and $(\theta - R_T q_e)_o$ is the indicated temperature difference before any disturbance.   Obviously, if the original temperature is assumed to be zero (this merely changes the temperature datum line), Eq. (3-57) becomes

$$\theta = R_T q_e (1 - e^{-t/R_T C_T}) = \theta_F (1 - e^{-t/R_T C_T}) \qquad (3\text{-}58)$$

The electrical analogue of the process requires that a resistance and capacitance be used.   The manner of connection of these can be deduced from the heat-balance equation (3-53).

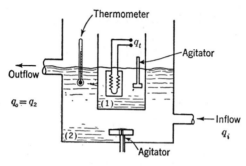

(a) System diagram

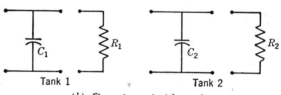

Tank 1   Tank 2
(b) Elements required for analogue

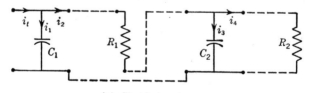

(c) Electrical analogue
FIG. 3-20. Electrical analogue of multiple-capacity process.

Since $q_e = q$ (stored) $+ q$ (out), in the electric circuit,

$$i \text{ (total)} = i \text{ (capacitor)} + i \text{ (resistor)} \qquad (3\text{-}59)$$

Thus R and C must be connected in parallel in the analogous circuit. This is shown in Fig. 3-19b.   As a check on the validity of the analogue,

Kirchhoff's current law may be written as

$$i_t = C \frac{de_c}{dt} + \frac{e}{R} \tag{3-60}$$

while for the actual thermal system,

$$q_e = C \frac{d\theta}{dt} + \frac{\theta}{R}$$

Electrical Analogue of Multiple-capacity Thermal Process. In Fig. 3-20a a simple multiple-capacity process is illustrated. In this instance, the fluid in tank 2 is not heated directly by the immersion heater; rather, the fluid in tank 1 is heated by the resistance heater, and the temperature of tank 2 is raised by the outflow of heat from tank 1. Thus an additional lag is introduced. Again, the complete mathematical analysis is not presented but can be found in the literature.[204]

A mathematical analysis of the multiple-capacity process requires that a number of simplifying assumptions be made and a number of defining terms summarized. Assumptions are:

1. No delay is introduced in transferring heat from the immersion heater to tank 1.

2. The thermometer measures the instantaneous bath temperature in tank 2.

3. The fluid in both tanks is agitated so that temperatures are uniform throughout each tank.

4. The heat carried in by the liquid and the heat supplied by the immersion unit remain constant.

Defining terms are:

q_e = heat supplied by immersion heater, Btu/min
Q_{1s} = heat stored in tank 1, Btu
q_1 = heat flow from tank 1 to tank 2, Btu/min
Q_{2s} = heat stored in tank 2, Btu
q_i = heat carried into tank 2 by fluid, Btu/min
q_2 = heat flow out of tank 2, Btu/min
C_1 = thermal capacity of tank 1
C_2 = thermal capacity of tank 2
R_1 = thermal resistance of tank 1 = $(\theta_1 - \theta)/q_1$
$\quad \theta_1$ = temperature of tank 1
$\quad \theta$ = temperature of tank 2
$\quad \theta_F$ = maximum final temperature of tank 2 for a given set of conditions = $(q + q_i)R_2$
R_2 = thermal outflow resistance of tank 2 = θ/q_2

The following heat balances can be set up for the multiple-capacity process. For tank 1,

$$q_e = q_{1s} + q_1 \tag{3-61}$$

Equation (3-61) states that the rate of heat supplied equals rate of storage plus rate of heat outflow.   For tank 2,

$$q_1 + q_i = q_{2s} + q_2 \tag{3-62}$$

Equation (3-61) can be rewritten in terms of thermal capacity and resistance since

$$Q_{1s} = C_1 \theta_1$$
$$\therefore \frac{dQ_{1s}}{dt} = q_{1s} = C_1 \frac{d\theta_1}{dt} \tag{3-63}$$

which when substituted in (3-61) becomes

$$q_e = C_1 \frac{d\theta_1}{dt} + q_1 \tag{3-64}$$

Solving for the rate of temperature change in tank 1 yields

$$\frac{d\theta_1}{dt} = \frac{q_e - q_1}{C_1} \tag{3-65}$$

The rate of temperature change in tank 2 can be found similarly.

$$Q_{2s} = C_2 \theta$$
$$\therefore q_{2s} = C_2 \frac{d\theta}{dt}$$

and

$$\frac{d\theta}{dt} = \frac{q_1 + q_i - q_2}{C_2} = \frac{q_1 + q_i - \theta/R_2}{C_2} \tag{3-66}$$

It can be shown that Eqs. (3-65) and (3-66) combine to give

$$C_2 R_2 C_1 R_1 \frac{d^2\theta}{dt} + (C_2 R_2 + C_1 R_2 + C_1 R_1) \frac{d\theta}{dt} + \theta - R_2(q_e + q_i) = 0 \tag{3-67}$$

which may then be directly solved for θ by transform methods if initial conditions are known.   The most general solution will be

$$\theta = R_2(q_i + q_e) + A_1 e^{\alpha_1 t} + A_2 e^{\alpha_2 t} \tag{3-68}$$

where

$$\alpha_1 = -\frac{a}{2b} - \sqrt{\left(\frac{a}{2b}\right)^2 - \frac{1}{b}}$$

and

$$\tag{3-69}$$

$$\alpha_2 = -\frac{a}{2b} + \sqrt{\left(\frac{a}{2b}\right)^2 - \frac{1}{b}}$$

in which

$$a = C_2 R_2 + C_1 R_2 + C_1 R_1$$
$$b = C_2 R_2 C_1 R_1 \tag{3-70}$$

and

$$A_1 = \frac{\dfrac{d\theta}{dt}(0+) - \alpha_1(\theta - \theta_F)_{0+}}{\alpha_1 - \alpha_2} \qquad (3\text{-}71)$$

$$A_2 = (\theta - \theta_F)_{0+} - C_2 \qquad (3\text{-}72)$$

Both (3-71) and (3-72) are functions of the process initial conditions.

The electrical analogue of the multiple-capacity process, just discussed, will now be set up. To simulate the thermal resistances and capacitances of the process, a separate RC combination is required for tank 1 and for tank 2. These are shown in Fig. 3-20b. The manner of interconnection of the elements can be derived from the original heat balances [Eqs. (3-61) and (3-62)], which are rewritten here for convenience.

$$q_e = q_{1s} + q_1 \qquad (3\text{-}61)$$
$$q_1 + q_i = q_{2s} + q_2 \qquad (3\text{-}62)$$
$$i_t = i_1 + i_2 \qquad (3\text{-}73)$$
$$i_2 + i_0 = i_3 + i_4 \qquad (3\text{-}74)$$

Equations (3-73) and (3-74) would be the necessary electrical equivalents for the process heat balance. From Eq. (3-73) it is obvious that i_1 is current flow to capacitor C_1 and i_2 is current flow to R_1. The current through R_1 must also flow through C_2 and R_2 according to Eq. (3-74). If i_0 is neglected (this corresponds to current that would flow because of an initial charge on C_2) then the elements can be connected together as shown in Fig. 3-20c. The electrical equivalent of the immersion heater would be some current source which has the same characteristics as the heater; i.e., if $q_s =$ constant, then the analogue would have to be supplied by a constant-current source.

3-12. Electrical Analogue of a Hydraulic System. Frequently the problem of fluid-flow control necessitates the addition of automatic-control equipment to a hydraulic system. Again, the design of the automatic controller will be a function of the nature of the process as well as other factors so that any quantitative analysis will require a mathematical description of the process characteristics. Instead of a direct solution which may be achieved through use of well-known hydraulic formulas, the electrical-analogue approach is utilized here.

Assume that the hydraulic system under consideration can be reduced to that shown in Fig. 3-21a. The hydraulic system consists of two tanks, or capacity elements, connected together by either a valve and piping or a length of piping alone. A second valve, which may represent the flow-control element, is shown at the output of tank 2. In the diagram, the flow resistance of the interconnecting piping (and valve if present) is represented symbolically by valve 1.

To set up the analogue, it is fairly obvious that the electrical equivalents are resistive and capacitive elements. The analogy between hydraulic and electrical systems is well known to most readers, but to define the mathematical similarity more closely, hydraulic elements are included in Table 3-1.

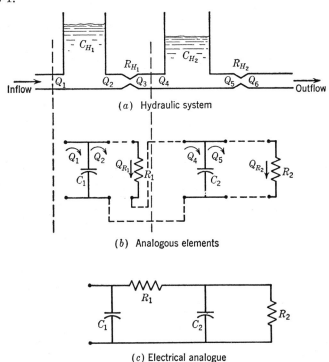

(a) Hydraulic system

(b) Analogous elements

(c) Electrical analogue

Fig. 3-21. Electrical analogue of hydraulic system.

Placing corresponding electrical analogues below each element of Fig. 3-21a results in Fig. 3-21b. By observation, the equivalent of the displacement-charge method used for the mechanical system can be applied to the above figure and the following relations noted:

$$Q_1 \text{ (ft}^3 \text{ entering tank 1)} > Q_2 \text{ (ft}^3 \text{ leaving tank 1)}$$
$$Q_3 = Q_2 \triangleq Q_{R_1}$$
$$Q_4 > Q_5$$
$$Q_5 = Q_6 \triangleq Q_{R_2}$$

Since the charge is analogous to the total fluid flow, the RC elements can be combined as shown by the dotted lines. The resulting analogous circuit is shown in Fig. 3-21c. The dynamic-equilibrium flow equations may be written for the hydraulic system and its electrical analogue to prove the validity of the analogue.

3-13. Electrical Analogue of Pressure-measuring Device. In Fig. 3-22a is shown a typical pressure-measuring device. The equation of equilibrium can be obtained by applying Newton's second law of motion to the system. The forces acting are:

$+p$ = active pressure being measured

$-f\dfrac{d\theta}{dt}$ = viscous friction or damping force set up by rack and pinion and other moving parts

$-K\theta$ = effective spring force set up by the elliptical tube (this linearity is an approximation)

Hence

$$J\frac{d^2\theta}{dt^2} = +p - f\frac{d\theta}{dt} - K\theta \quad (3\text{-}75)$$

where θ is pressure or motion actually recorded and J is the inertia of the moving parts referred to the proper shaft.

When (3-75) is rewritten as

$$J\frac{d^2\theta}{dt^2} + f\frac{d\theta}{dt} + K\theta = p \quad (3\text{-}76)$$

the solution for the measured pressure can be found by applying transform methods. The solution thus found may have several forms, depending upon whether friction effects are excessive or not and upon the initial conditions. If the oscillatory case results, then

$$\theta = \frac{p}{K}\left[1 - e^{-ft/2J}\right.$$
$$\left.\left(\cos\sqrt{\frac{K}{J} - \frac{f^2}{4J^2}}\,t\right)\right] \quad (3\text{-}77)$$

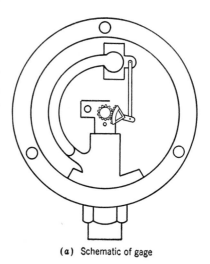

(a) Schematic of gage

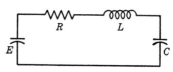

(b) Electrical analogue (constant pressure)

Fig. 3-22. Electrical analogue of bourdon gage.

When (3-77) is compared with similar equations previously developed, it is apparent that the electrical analogue of this system will be an RLC series circuit excited by a d-c source (corresponds to p = constant). The analogous circuit is shown in Fig. 3-22b. As a check on the analogy, the equilibrium equation of the circuit is

$$L\frac{d^2Q}{dt^2} + R\frac{dQ}{dt} + \frac{Q}{C} = E \quad (3\text{-}78)$$

and, comparing Eqs. (3-76) and (3-78),

$$L \propto J \quad R \propto f \quad \frac{1}{C} \propto K \quad \text{and} \quad E \propto p$$

all of which agree with the table of analogous units.

3-14. Electrical Analogue of Electrical Machines. The electrical components of a servomechanism, such as generators, amplidynes, two-phase a-c motors, shunt- and series-wound d-c motors, transformers, and electrical error detectors, can also be replaced by simpler equivalent or analogous electric circuits and ordinary electronic amplifiers. Replacement by these analogous circuits is of great value during preliminary studies of a servomechanism's performance or early design procedures as these studies can then be carried out on analogue computers. Often it may be necessary (possibly owing to system complexity or to nonlinearities that are present) to refer to analogue studies of an equivalent of the proposed system before even a satisfactory first design is obtained. Considerable work has been done on analogue treatment of nonelectrical as well as electrical systems.[10,14,17,19,22,23] Of particular interest in this section are electrical analogues of some of those electrical components which are often found in a servo system. The analogues subsequently developed assume that operation of equipment does not extend into nonlinear or saturated zones of component characteristics, though many new techniques have been developed to simulate these nonlinearities.[205]

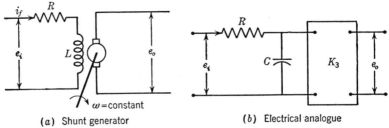

(a) Shunt generator   (b) Electrical analogue

FIG. 3-23. Electrical analogue of shunt generator.

Analogue of Generators. For the ordinary shunt generator shown in Fig. 3-23a the electrical analogue of Fig. 3-23b may be substituted. The following assumptions are made in proving the equivalence of the generator and its analogue: The generator is driven at constant speed; armature voltage losses are negligible;* hysteresis effects are neglected, and the operation of the generator is along the straight-line portion of its saturation curve.

---

* The inductance and series resistance of the generator armature generally are combined with the resistance and inductance of the motor, which is supplied by the generator.

The generator-field-circuit voltage-equilibrium equation can be written and transformed.

$$e_i = Ri_f + L\frac{di_f}{dt} \tag{3-79}$$

$$E_i(s) = RI(s) + sLI(s) \tag{3-80}$$

The output voltage may be expressed as

$$e_o = ki_f \tag{3-81}$$

where k is dependent upon the units and the slope of the saturation curve. When transformed, this becomes

$$E_o(s) = kI_f(s) = kI(s) \tag{3-82}$$

Then, dividing Eq. (3-82) by (3-80) to get an expression for the ratio of output to input voltage,

$$\frac{E_o}{E_i}(s) = \frac{k}{R + sL} = \frac{k/R}{s\tau + 1} = \frac{k_1}{s\tau + 1} \tag{3-83}$$

where $k_1 = k/R$
$\quad \tau = L/R$

The expression derived in Eqs. (3-83) is commonly called the transfer function of the generator, since it is the relationship between the output and input of the component.

The expression of the output-input voltage (or transfer function) of the generator analogue is now derived. The voltage-equilibrium equations are

$$e_i = iR + \frac{1}{C}\int i\,dt$$
$$e_o = \frac{K_3}{C}\int i\,dt \tag{3-84}$$

and when transformed become

$$E_i(s) = I(s)R + \frac{I(s)}{Cs} \tag{3-85}$$

$$E_o(s) = K_3\frac{I(s)}{Cs}$$

Hence

$$\frac{E_o(s)}{E_i(s)} = \frac{K_3/Cs}{R + 1/Cs} = \frac{K_3}{s\tau + 1} \tag{3-86}$$

The output-input voltage ratio for the generator and analogue are seen to be the same if equivalence of K_1 with K_3 and L/R with RC is obtained. It should be noted here that the electronic amplifier may necessarily have to be phase-sensitive in order that voltages of reversible polarity be produced, if such voltages normally are expected for the generator.

Analogue of Dynamoelectric Amplifier (Amplidyne). Essentially the same analogue may be used for the amplidyne as for the shunt generator just considered. However, special design features of amplidynes which result in high amplification (with relatively rapid speed of response) require that an additional time-lag network be added to the analogue. In Fig. 3-24a is shown the schematic drawing of an amplidyne used in servomechanism applications. Though the operation of the amplidyne

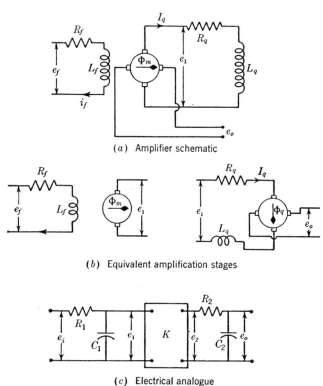

(*a*) Amplifier schematic

(*b*) Equivalent amplification stages

(*c*) Electrical analogue

FIG. 3-24. Electrical analogue of dynamoelectric amplifier.

is not explained here, it can be said that the rotating amplifier is equivalent to a two-stage amplifier. The first stage of voltage amplification e_i/e_f is dependent on the shunt-field flux, Φ_m. This flux is not in time phase with e_f because of the delay caused by the shunt-field inductance L_f. However, by design this delay is only a fraction of that for an ordinary generator.

The second stage of voltage amplification, e_o/e_i, is produced by the flux set up along the quadrature axis by the short-circuit current I_q. (Ordinarily the shorted brushes are connected through an auxiliary field to increase the effective amplification.) The flux produced by this short-circuit current is delayed in time by the inductance of the armature and the auxiliary field, if used.   Thus in setting up the electrical analogue of an amplidyne two time delays, for the shunt field and the quadrature field, must be reckoned with.

It is again assumed that the amplidyne is driven at constant speed, etc., and that the effective inductance and resistance in series with the amplidyne output circuit is to be combined with the following component and so can be neglected.*

The voltage equations can then be written as

$$e_f = i_f R_f + L_f \frac{di_f}{dt}$$
$$e_1 = k i_f$$
$$e_1 = i_q R_q + L_q \frac{di_q}{dt} \tag{3-87}$$
$$e_o = k_1 i_q$$

Transforming the above equations and combining to find the ratio of output-input voltage yields

$$\frac{E_o}{E_f}(s) = \frac{kk_1}{(R_f + sL_f)(R_q + sL_q)} = \frac{K_2 K_3}{(s\tau_f + 1)(s\tau_q + 1)} \tag{3-88}$$

where $K_2 = k/R_f$
$\quad\;\; K_3 = k_1/R_q$
$\quad\;\; \tau_f = L_f/R_f$
$\quad\;\; \tau_q = L_q/R_q$

The electrical analogue may be shown to require two RC networks and an electronic amplifier as indicated in Fig. 3-24c.   The transformed voltage-equilibrium equations for the analogue are

$$\frac{E_1}{E_i} = \frac{1}{s\tau_1 + 1} \quad\text{and}\quad \frac{E_o}{E_2} = \frac{1}{s\tau_2 + 1} \tag{3-89}$$

and since E_2 and E_1 are related by the amplifier gain constant, K, the output-input voltage expression for the analogue becomes

$$\frac{E_o}{E_i} = \frac{E_1}{E_i}\frac{E_2}{E_1}\frac{E_o}{E_2} = \frac{K}{(s\tau_1 + 1)(s\tau_2 + 1)} \tag{3-90}$$

The correspondence of Eqs. (3-89) and (3-90) proves the analogue.

Electrical Analogue of D-C Motors.   In determining the analogues of d-c or a-c motors, which are utilized as power members in servo systems, it is generally necessary to combine the load characteristics with the

---

* If it is desirable, the analogue can just as conveniently be set up to include the amplidyne output inductance by adding an additional delay circuit.

motor characteristics, though, in some instances, the analogues may be set up independently of each other. The following examples illustrate analogue development for typical motor drives and loading conditions.

Example 1. Field-controlled d-c motor with inertia and friction loading. In Fig. 3-25a are shown the load member and power drive connected by an appropriate gear train. It is assumed that the armature current supplied is constant. The electrical analogue which relates the angular motion of the output member to the voltage applied to the shunt

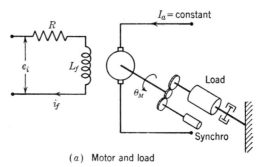

(a) Motor and load

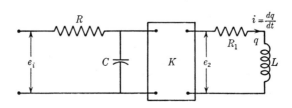

(b) Electrical analogue

Fig. 3-25. Electrical analogue of field-controlled d-c motor.

field is shown in Fig. 3-25b. Referring to Fig. 3-25a, the voltage-equilibrium equation for the field circuit is

$$e_i = i_f R_f + L_f \frac{di_f}{dt} \tag{3-91}$$

The motor developed-torque expression is

$$T_D = k_2 \Phi i_a = K_3 i_f$$
$$T_D(s) = k_3 I_f(s) \tag{3-92}$$

and the load-torque expression is

$$T_L = J \frac{d^2\theta_m}{dt^2} + f \frac{d\theta_m}{dt}$$
$$T_L(s) = Js^2\Theta_m + fs\Theta_m \tag{3-93}$$

J is the inertia of all output members referred to a common shaft (motor shaft), and f is the friction coefficient similarly referred.

The transformed expressions from the previous three equations may be combined, assuming that the developed torque and the load torque are equal.

$$k_3 \left[\frac{E_i(s)}{R_f + sL_f} \right] = \frac{k_3 E_i(s)}{R_f(1 + \tau_f s)} = s^2 J \Theta_m + sf\Theta_m = s\Theta_m f(s\tau_m + 1) \quad (3\text{-}94)$$

where $\tau_m = J/f$

$\quad\quad \tau_f = L_f/R_f$

Solving for the ratio of output to input:

$$\frac{\Theta_m(s)}{E_i(s)} = \frac{k_3 k}{R_f(1 + s\tau_f)sf(1 + s\tau_m)}$$
$$= \frac{K_4}{s(1 + s\tau_f)(1 + s\tau_m)} \quad (3\text{-}94a)$$

where $K_4 = k_3 k/R_f f$

$\quad\quad k = $ gear ratio

The analogue for the system is a series RC network connected to a series RL network by an electronic amplifier. The displacement-charge analogy used for mechanical systems must be kept in mind in mathematically justifying the analogue. For the RC network-amplifier combination it has been shown that

$$\frac{E_o}{E_i}(s) = \frac{K}{s\tau_1 + 1} \quad (3\text{-}94b)$$

while for a series resistance-inductance combination the equilibrium equation is

$$e_o = iR_1 + L\frac{di}{dt}$$
$$= \frac{dq}{dt}R_1 + L\frac{d^2q}{dt^2} \quad (3\text{-}95)$$

Transforming Eq. (3-95) yields

$$E_o(s) = sR_1 Q(s) + s^2 L Q(s) \quad (3\text{-}96)$$

and substituting the equivalent $E_o(s)$ from (3-94) into (3-96) and solving,

$$\frac{Q(s)}{E_i(s)} = \frac{K}{(s\tau_1 + 1)sR(s\tau_2 + 1)} = \frac{k}{s(s\tau_1 + 1)(s\tau_2 + 1)} \quad (3\text{-}97)$$

where $k = K/R$

$\quad\quad \tau_1 = RC$

$\quad\quad \tau_2 = L/R_1$

Upon comparing Eqs. (3-97) and (3-93), the charge variation in the electrical analogue is seen to correspond to positional variation of the output member. The current variation in the RL network would correspond to the instantaneous speed of the output; so the same analogue could be used for studying velocity controllers. The circuit for the analogue is shown in Fig. 3-25b.

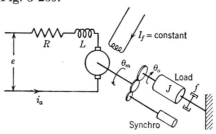

(a) Motor and load

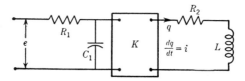

(b) Electrical analogue

FIG. 3-26. Electrical analogue of armature-controlled d-c motor.

Example 2. Armature-controlled d-c motor with inertia and friction loading. In applications where a response more rapid than obtainable with a field-controlled motor is desired, the drive motor is generally armature-controlled as shown in Fig. 3-26a. It is assumed here that the inductance L includes not only the inductance of the motor armature and any other auxiliary series motor windings but also the series inductances neglected in developing the analogues of the supply generator. The resistance R, similarly, includes pertinent series resistances. The voltage-equilibrium equation for Fig. 3-26a is

$$e = i_a R + L\frac{di_a}{dt} + K_b\frac{d\theta_m}{dt} \tag{3-98}$$

Transforming,

$$E(s) = I_a(s)R + sLI_a(s) + sK_b\Theta_m \tag{3-98a}$$

The torque-equilibrium equations are

$$T_d = K\Phi i_a = k_1 I_a(s)$$

$$T_L = J\frac{d^2\theta_m}{dt^2} + f\frac{d\theta_m}{dt} \tag{3-99}$$

$$T_L(s) = Js^2\Theta_m + fs\Theta_m$$

When Eqs. (3-98a) and (3-99) are combined, taking care to include the necessary constant to relate θ_o and θ_m, the ratio of output position to armature applied voltage reduces to

$$\frac{\Theta_o(s)}{E(s)} = \frac{K}{s(\tau_a s^2 + \tau_b s + 1)} \tag{3-100}$$

The same grouping of electric networks can be used for the electrical analogue of an armature-controlled d-c motor as for a field-controlled motor, but obvious changes in circuit parameters must be made. Rewriting the output-input relation established in Eq. (3-97),

$$\frac{Q(s)}{E(s)} = \frac{k}{s(\tau_1 s + 1)(s\tau_2 + 1)}$$

Expanding this leads to

$$\frac{Q(s)}{E(s)} = \frac{k}{s[\tau_1 \tau_2 s^2 + (\tau_1 + \tau_2)s + 1]} \tag{3-101}$$

If correspondence is established between K and k, $\tau_1\tau_2$ and τ_a, and $\tau_1 + \tau_2$ and τ_b, the analogue for an armature-controlled d-c motor with inertia and friction loading consists of series RC and RL networks connected through an electronic amplifier.

Electrical Analogue of Two-phase A-C Motors. For applications with relatively light power requirements, two-phase motor drives, similar to the drive shown in Fig. 3-27a, are often used. The electrical analogue for such a motor is readily derived, assuming that the load is characterized by both inertia and friction. It is also assumed that the steady-state torque-speed curve, drawn in Fig. 3-27b, sufficiently describes the motor operation under transient conditions. The ideal motor-torque expression is

$$T_m = \frac{\partial T}{\partial n} n + \frac{\partial T}{\partial e_i} e_i = \frac{\partial T}{\partial n} \frac{d\theta_o}{dt} + \frac{\partial T}{\partial e_i} e_i \tag{3-102}$$

since the dependence of torque upon both voltage (applied to variable phase) and speed is apparent. Some simplification in the torque expression results if several constants derived from torque-speed characteristics are defined; letting

$$\frac{\partial T}{\partial n} = -K_n \qquad \text{and} \qquad \frac{\partial T}{\partial e_i} = K_e$$

and transforming the resultant motor-torque expression,

$$T_m(s) = -K_n s \Theta_m(s) + K_e E_i(s) \tag{3-103}$$

Again the dynamic load-torque equilibrium equation is

$$T_L = J \frac{d^2\theta_m}{dt^2} + f \frac{d\theta_m}{dt} \tag{3-104}$$

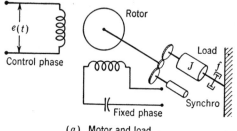

(a) Motor and load

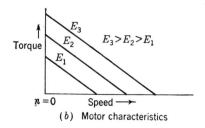

(b) Motor characteristics

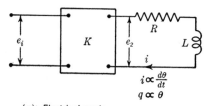

$$i \propto \frac{d\theta}{dt}$$
$$q \propto \theta$$

(c) Electrical analogue

FIG. 3-27. Electrical analogue of a two-phase motor.

And if inertia and friction are referred to a common shaft (here the motor shaft is selected),

$$T_L(s) = Js^2\Theta_m + fs\Theta_m. \tag{3-105}$$

Equating load and developed torques,

$$-K_ns\Theta_m(s) + K_eE_i(s) = Js^2\Theta_m(s) + sf\Theta_m(s) \tag{3-106}$$

Solving for the expression relating the output motion to the voltage applied to the variable phase,

$$\frac{\Theta_m(s)}{E_i(s)} = \frac{K_e}{Js^2 + s(f + K_n)} = \frac{K_m}{s(\tau_b s + 1)} \tag{3-107}$$

where $K_m = K_e/(f + K_n)$
    $\tau_b = J/(f + K_n)$

The electrical analogy of the two-phase motor is described for the characteristics in Fig. 3-27b and for stated loading conditions. The result is a series RL circuit connected to an amplifier as shown in Fig. 3-27c. The ratio of the charge, q, to the amplifier input voltage can be shown to have the same mathematical form as Eq. (3-107). Letting e_2 be the voltage output of the amplifier,

$$e_2 = Ke_i$$

and (3-108)

$$E_2(s) = KE_i(s)$$

A Kirchhoff voltage equation can be written for the series RL circuit in terms of the circuit parameters and the charge,

$$e_2 = R\frac{dq}{dt} + L\frac{d^2q}{dt^2} \tag{3-109}$$

Transforming (3-109) and substituting the equivalent of $E_2(s)$,

$$KE_i(s) = RsQ(s) + s^2LQ(s) \tag{3-110}$$

Rearranging and solving for charge in terms of applied amplifier voltage,

$$\frac{Q(s)}{E_i(s)} = \frac{K}{s(sL + R)} = \frac{K_1}{s(s\tau + 1)} \tag{3-111}$$

Equations (3-111) and (3-107) may be compared to show the equivalence of the analogue.

Electrical Analogue of Transformers. Transformers are used extensively in almost all types of servos for purposes of matching, amplification, isolation, or producing electrical damping. Since transformers are inherently highly inductive, if used for one or more of the first three purposes mentioned, an objectionable delay may be added to the system. This delay, on the other hand, would be desirable when the transformer is intended to provide or augment the system damping. Analogy methods may again be employed to study the effect upon system performance of the transformers used.

An ordinary two-winding transformer is pictured in Fig. 3-28a. Standard engineering practice has indicated that, for purposes of analysis and design, it is accurate to assume that the actual transformer windings with distributed resistance and inductance (stray capacitances can be neglected here) on both primary and secondary can be replaced by an ideal transformer (one which incurs no voltage losses) with the winding impedances lumped together and considered as external to the ideal transformer. The exact equivalent circuit, as such visualization is called, is drawn in Fig. 3-28b. The shunt-exciting branch is normally included in any exact analysis to take care of no-load power requirements. All constants may be determined by standardized test procedures.

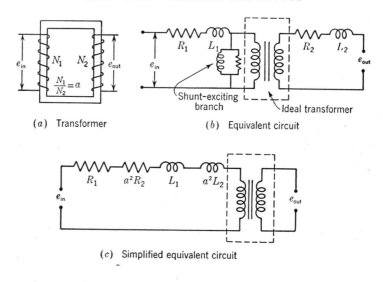

(a) Transformer (b) Equivalent circuit

(c) Simplified equivalent circuit

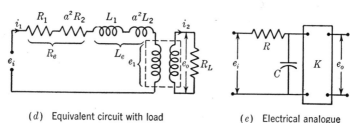

(d) Equivalent circuit with load (e) Electrical analogue

FIG. 3-28. Two-winding transformer: approximate equivalent circuits and electrical analogue.

The exact equivalent circuit of a transformer can be replaced by a simpler circuit (Fig. 3-28c), which allows more convenient calculation of transformer performance. The shunt-exciting branch is neglected, and the secondary-winding parameters are referred to the primary side (in much the same manner as referring inertias and friction coefficients to the common shaft as discussed earlier). If the assumed transformer load is predominantly resistive, then the following derivation can be carried through to obtain the output-input voltage ratio and eventually to derive the electrical analogue.

Referring to Fig. 3-28d, the primary and secondary voltage-equilibrium equations are

$$e_i = i_1 R_e + L_e \frac{di_1}{dt} + e_1$$

$$e_o = i_2 R_L$$

$$\frac{e_1}{e_o} = \frac{n_1}{n_2} = a \qquad (3\text{-}112)$$

Transforming the set of equations given in (3-112),

$$E_i(s) = I_1(s)R_e + sL_eI_1(s) + E_1(s)$$
$$E_o(s) = I_2(s)R_L \qquad\qquad (3\text{-}113)$$
$$\frac{E_1}{E_o(s)} = a$$

The equations in (3-112) may be combined, utilizing the relation $N_1I_1 = N_2I_2$ to yield

$$E_i(s) = \frac{R_e}{aR_L} E_o(s) + \frac{sL_e}{aR_L} E_o(s) + aE_o(s) \qquad (3\text{-}114)$$

and

$$\frac{E_o(s)}{E_i(s)} = \frac{K}{(s\tau + 1)} \qquad (3\text{-}115)$$

where $\tau = L_e/R_t$
$\quad K = aR_L/R_t$
$\quad R_t = R_e + a^2R_L$

As previously, the electrical analogue will be the RC network-amplifier combination of Fig. 3-28e.

3-15. Electrical Analogue of Electrical Error Detectors. A synchro generator and control transformer connected electrically in tandem and mounted on input and output members of a servo, as shown in Fig. 3-29, are often used as error detectors.* The operation of this type of error detector is explained in detail in the appendix; let it suffice to say here that when the rotors of the two transformers are not aligned 90 deg

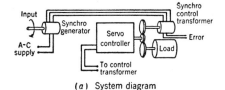

(a) System diagram

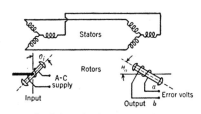

(b) Schematic of error detector

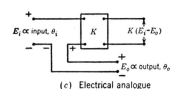

(c) Electrical analogue

Fig. 3-29. Analogue of synchro error detector.

in space from each other (the output rotor lags the input rotor in the diagram above), a voltage appears between terminals a and b whose magnitude and sense are a function of the angular difference between the rotors, $\theta_i - \theta_o$. For small angular differences the voltage developed is directly proportional to the angular difference. If the terminals ab are connected to a suitable controller, the voltage error signal will be amplified, possibly converted to a different form, and will cause some type of powering device to drive the output into alignment with the input.

* See appendix on Error Detectors.

The function of the error detector, to provide a voltage $\varepsilon = K(\theta_i - \theta_o)$, immediately suggests the use of an ordinary amplifier, with dual inputs, as shown in Fig. 3-29c, having an output $K(E_i - E_o)$, as an electrical analogue. It would be necessary that the voltages E_o and E_i, fed inversely into the amplifier, represent the output and input quantities. This might entail some difficulties if one considers that normally the output and input quantities of interest are the mechanical displacements of these members and the rates of change of the displacements. In establishing the electrical analogues of mechanical systems, it has already been found that electrical charge and displacement are analogous; thus accessory devices must be added to the amplifier of Fig. 3-29 to cause the voltages E_o and E_i to correspond to electrical charges related to output and input.

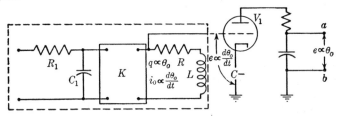

Analogue of motor with inertia and friction load

FIG. 3-30. Electrical means of obtaining a voltage proportional to output charge.

The partial electrical analogue of a positional servomechanism is shown in Fig. 3-30, to illustrate, in principle, one possible method of obtaining the conversion of an electrical charge identified with mechanical output motion to the voltage, E_o. The resistance, R, serves a dual purpose: it represents the friction present in the load and also provides an input signal to tube V_1 which is proportional to $d\theta_o/dt$. When the output of V_1 is picked off the condenser as indicated, the voltage across ab will be proportional, approximately, to θ_o and so to q_o.

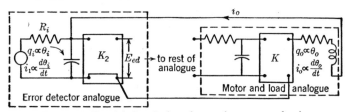

FIG. 3-31. Partial electrical analogue of a servomechanism.

Another method well suited to analogue-computer studies of servomechanisms, drawn in Fig. 3-31, illustrates a means of obtaining the driving voltages E_o and E_i which simulate practical output and input variations of a servo system. Again only a partial electrical analogue is depicted, but the literature[22] can be consulted for a more complete description. The voltage source provides a current flow (and so charge flow) corresponding to desired input conditions. The output current, i_o, is fed in from the output analogue as shown. The condenser voltage is

$$\frac{1}{C} \int i \, dt$$

or

$$\frac{1}{C} \int \left(\frac{d\theta_i}{dt} - \frac{d\theta_o}{dt} \right) dt$$

Therefore the output of amplifier with gain, K_2, will be a voltage which is proportional to the difference between input and output conditions,

$$E_{ed} = \frac{K_2}{C} (\theta_i - \theta_o)$$

Care must be exercised in the choice of the relative size of all components because of the possibility of excessive loading of the load and motor analogue.

PROBLEMS

NOTE: In some of the following problems not all the system parameters are defined, nor are they indicated on the diagrams. It is expected that the student will investigate such details.

3-1. *a.* Write the equation of motion for the system shown in Fig. 3P-1.

b. If M weighs 125 lb, $K = 10$ lb/in., $f = 2$ lb-sec/ft, and assuming an external force of 10 lb applied vertically downward, solve the system equations, using Laplace-transform methods.

3-2. *a.* Write the equation of motion for the torsional system of Fig. 3P-2.

b. If J is made of cast iron, K has a stiffness of 200 lb-ft/deg, $f = 10$ lb-sec/in., and assuming a torque of 1,000 lb-ft applied to J, solve the system equation, using Laplace transforms.

3-3. *a.* Write the equation of motion for the system of Fig. 3P-3, assuming the motor to be frictionless.

b. If $J = 1.0$ slug-ft^2, $f = 10$ in.-lb-sec/radian, and if the motor produces a torque of 5 lb-ft (assume constant at all speeds), find the steady-state rotational velocity of the load and the time required to reach that velocity if started from rest.

3-4. What are the analogous electrical circuits for the systems of Probs. 1 to 3?

3-5. In Fig. 3P-4 water flows into a tank at a rate F_1 and flows out at a rate F_2. Write the system equations for the following conditions:

a. F_2 is constant.

b. $F_2 = AH$, where A is a constant.

Set up an electric-circuit analogue for the system.

3-6. If a float-controlled valve is added to the system of Fig. 3P-4 as shown in Fig. 3P-5,

a. Write the system equations relating F_1, F_2, and H, for F_2 constant.

b. Set up an electric-circuit analogue.

3-7. A force F is applied to a spring bellows as shown in Fig. 3P-6. The needle valve restricts the flow of air from the bellows. Write the equation for the displace-

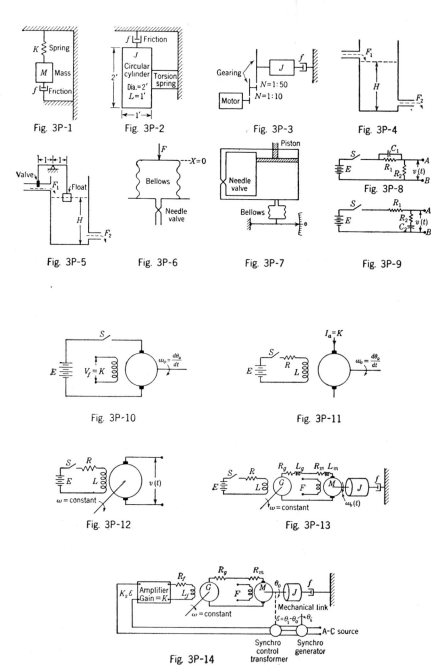

Fig. 3P-1

Fig. 3P-2

Fig. 3P-3

Fig. 3P-4

Fig. 3P-5

Fig. 3P-6

Fig. 3P-7

Fig. 3P-8

Fig. 3P-9

Fig. 3P-10

Fig. 3P-11

Fig. 3P-12

Fig. 3P-13

Fig. 3P-14

ment of the bellows top from $X = 0$ as a function of time. Define all symbols used.

3-8. In Fig. 3P-7, the piston moves downward. The needle valve restricts flow through the by-pass. Write the equations relating pointer deflection to piston movement. Define all symbols used.

3-9. For the circuit of Fig. 3P-8, derive the equation for the voltage across terminals AB as a function of time after the switch, S, is closed.

3-10. For the circuit of Fig. 3P-9, derive the equation for the voltage across terminals AB as a function of time after the switch, S, is closed.

3-11. A separately excited shunt-wound d-c motor is connected as shown in Fig. 3P-10. Define all symbols used. Specify type of loading and any assumptions made, and

a. Derive the equation relating the shaft velocity to the supply voltage after switch S is closed.

b. Set up an electric-circuit analogue.

c. Modify the results of (*a*) and (*b*) to include an external inertia, J_1, connected to the motor shaft.

3-12. A shunt-wound d-c motor is supplied with constant armature current as shown in Fig. 3P-11. Define all symbols used. Specify types of loading and any other assumptions made, and

a. Derive the equation relating the shaft velocity to the field supply voltage after the switch, S, is closed.

b. Set up an electrical-circuit analogue.

c. Modify the results of (*a*) and (*b*) to include the effect of an inertia J_L and a viscous damper, f_L, connected to the motor shaft.

3-13. A generator is driven at constant speed as shown in Fig. 3P-12. Define all symbols used, list any assumptions made, and

a. Derive the equation for the output voltage, V, after the switch, S, is closed.

b. Set up an electric-circuit analogue.

3-14. For Fig. 3P-13, define all symbols used to describe the system, and

a. Write the equation for the output velocity after the switch S is closed.

b. Set up an electric-circuit analogue.

c. Neglect L_g and L_m, and repeat parts *a* and *b*.

3-15. For the system of Fig. 3P-14, define all symbols used, and

a. Write the equation for the output position, θ_o.

b. Set up an electric-circuit analogue.

CHAPTER 4

TRANSIENT ANALYSIS OF SERVOMECHANISMS

4-1. Introduction. A servomechanism may be considered as a dynamic system, and the differential equations describing its performance may be established by the methods presented in Chap. 3. In this chapter the differential equations of some basic servomechanism systems are derived, solved, and the solutions analyzed. Such mathematical treatment is commonly called a transient analysis and is necessary whenever a complete analysis of a servomechanism is required. While a transient study of complex servomechanisms is avoided if possible (because of the labor involved and because the results are not readily applied to design), certain basic concepts regarding system performance are clearly defined in terms of transient considerations and usually must be evaluated even when other analysis methods are used. The following treatment is reasonably thorough, but more detailed studies of the transient behavior of servomechanisms may be found in the literature.[1,2,27–33,*]

Those basic performance criteria which are established from transient consideration are:

1. Speed of response, which is a measure of the time required for a system to reach approximate steady-state conditions after a disturbance.

2. Steady-state error, which is the difference between the actual and the desired output after the system has reached steady state.

3. Maximum overshoot, which is the maximum amount by which the actual output exceeds the desired output during transient conditions.

4. Frequency of system oscillation.

The quantitative meaning of these terms is more readily discovered after specific equations have been derived. They are defined at this point because they influence certain mathematical manipulations and thus permit reduction of results to a desirable form.

4-2. Basic Block Diagram of a Control System. Since actual servo-system components vary in number and physical nature depending on the particular application, and since it is desirable to discuss servo-mechanism principles in general rather than analyzing a special case, the basic control systems will be represented in this text by block dia-

---

* Superior numbers, when they appear in the text proper, are the numbers of references given in the Bibliography.

72

grams.   Figure 4-1a shows the basic block diagram of an open-loop control system.   Each of the blocks represents a property which is required in all control systems.   In any specific system each block may contain a large number of distinct physical components, and it is also possible to have a combined controller-power device which is a single unit physically. In Fig. 4-1a the input and output quantities are symbolized as rotations θ_i and θ_o.   This is merely a convenient notation, and in a particular solution the notation naturally corresponds to the physical nature of the system.

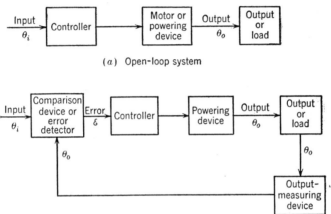

(a) Open-loop system

(b) Servomechanism

FIG. 4-1. Block diagrams of basic control systems.

The differential equation of any such system is obtained by simple application of the principle of dynamic equilibrium at the output location.   That is (for assumed rotational motion) the applied torque at the output shaft is instantaneously equal to the reaction torque,

$$T \text{ (applied)} = T \text{ (reaction)} \tag{4-1}$$

But the applied torque is normally proportional to some function of the input signal, and reaction torque is due to the inertia and damping effects of the systems,

$$T \text{ (applied)} = K'\mathbf{f}(\theta_i)$$

$$T \text{ (reaction)} = J\frac{d^2\theta_o}{dt^2} + f\frac{d\theta_o}{dt} \tag{4-2}$$

$$K'\mathbf{f}(\theta_i) = J\frac{d^2\theta_o}{dt^2} + f\frac{d\theta_o}{dt} \tag{4-3}$$

The function $\mathbf{f}(\theta_i)$ is determined by the characteristics of the controller and powering device.   These may produce an output which is directly proportional to θ_i or may also differentiate or integrate the input.   In the simplest types of control systems the output is proportional only to the controller input, and

$$K'\mathbf{f}(\theta_i) = K\theta_i \qquad (4\text{-}4)$$

$$K\theta_i = J\frac{d^2\theta_o}{dt^2} + f\frac{d\theta_o}{dt} \qquad (4\text{-}5)$$

The physical nature of the inertia effect depends on the application: it may be mass inertia, thermal inertia, etc. Likewise the damping effect varies with the system but is normally a type of viscous friction.

The open-loop control system of Fig. 4-1a may be converted into a servomechanism by adding two interconnected measuring devices as shown in Fig. 4-1b. One measuring device is connected to the output, determines the instantaneous condition of the output, and transmits this information to the second measuring device, which is called a comparison device or error detector. The input signal or command, θ_i, is fed not into the controller but into the error detector, which then compares the input θ_i with the output θ_o, by subtraction, and produces an error signal, ε, such that

$$\varepsilon = \theta_i - \theta_o \qquad (4\text{-}6)$$

Thus the error signal is actually used to command the controller, rather than the input signal, and the basic components of the control system are not changed by conversion into a servomechanism. The equation of the closed system is therefore

$$K'\mathbf{f}(\varepsilon) = J\frac{d^2\theta_o}{dt^2} + f\frac{d\theta_o}{dt} \qquad (4\text{-}7)$$

and for the so-called "proportional-error" servomechanism, in which the applied torque is directly proportional to the error,

$$K\varepsilon = J\frac{d^2\theta_o}{dt^2} + f\frac{d\theta_o}{dt} \qquad (4\text{-}8)$$

Many control problems may be successfully solved with servomechanisms utilizing simple proportional-error control. Much of the remainder of this chapter is therefore limited to such systems. When the performance specifications for a control system cannot be met by a proportional-error system, the controller must be redesigned and in general becomes considerably more complex. This chapter treats several types of more complex servomechanisms and the manner in which modification of components results in a controller with the desired characteristics.

4-3. Proportional-error Servomechanism—General.[28,30,31] The block diagram of a proportional-error servo system is shown in Fig. 4-2. It will be noted that this diagram is the same as Fig. 4-1b except that a special symbol is used for the error detector and the output-measuring device is included in the load block.   If the components are assumed to be linear and ideal,* the differential equation of the system is

$$K\varepsilon = J\frac{d^2\theta_o}{dt^2} + f\frac{d\theta_o}{dt} \tag{4-9}$$

where θ_o = output quantity

K = gain constant of controller–power-device combination

f = viscous-damping coefficient of the system referred to the output shaft

J = inertia of the system referred to the output shaft

ε = instantaneous error = $\theta_i - \theta_o$

t = time

Equation (4-9) may be solved for either θ_o or ε or may be rewritten in terms of θ_o and θ_i and then solved for θ_o.   In practice this latter form is

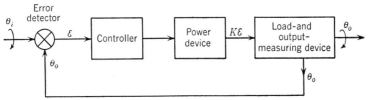

FIG. 4-2. Block diagram of proportional-error servomechanism.

frequently desirable, but the authors prefer to solve for ε because the error is a direct measure of the performance of the control system.   Substituting $\theta_o = \theta_i - \varepsilon$, Eq. (4-9) becomes

$$J\frac{d^2\varepsilon}{dt^2} + f\frac{d\varepsilon}{dt} + K\varepsilon = J\frac{d^2\theta_i}{dt^2} + f\frac{d\theta_i}{dt} \tag{4-10}$$

The Laplace transformation may now be applied to Eq. (4-10) provided that the initial-condition terms which appear can be evaluated (see example in Chap. 2, page 21, where initial conditions were arbitrarily inserted).   Thus, if the expected initial operating conditions are known and can be expressed mathematically, system performance may be determined.   Frequently the required information is not available or not usable, and an arbitrary set of initial conditions are chosen.

While actual operating conditions are obviously the ultimate test for servomechanism performance, certain arbitrary initial conditions have become more or less standard both in mathematical analysis and in laboratory analysis.   There are certain advantages to standard initial con-

* An ideal component is one that responds instantaneously,[31] therefore Eq. (4-9) assumes that the output quantity and the error are measured instantaneously and that the torque applied by the powering device instantaneously follows the error signal ε.

ditions; they provide a ready basis for comparison between numerous specific systems and thus build up a fund of information and experience which eliminates some of the trial and error often required in design; also the standard conditions may be made more severe than actual conditions, and thus the predicted performance tends to be pessimistic, providing a margin of safety. The initial conditions (which are usually chosen depending on the application of the servo system) are:

1. Stationary input with initial output error.
2. Suddenly applied input displacement or step-displacement function.
3. Suddenly applied load torque.
4. Suddenly applied input velocity—also called a step-velocity function or a ramp function.
5. Sinusoidal input function.

Stationary Input with Initial Output Error. It is obviously possible to have an inoperative servomechanism (power turned off) with the input set at the desired value but the output not in correspondence. When power is applied, the output must return to correspondence and the performance of the system during this transient period is sometimes of importance. Since the input is properly located and stationary,

$$\theta_i = 0$$
$$\frac{d\theta_i}{dt} = 0 \qquad (4\text{-}11)$$

The output is out of correspondence by some amount ϕ and cannot instantaneously achieve a velocity because of system inertia; therefore, at $t = 0+$

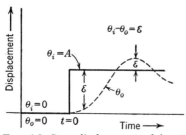

FIG. 4-3. Step displacement of input; $\theta_i = A$.

$$\theta_o = \phi$$
$$\frac{d\theta_o}{dt} = 0 \qquad (4\text{-}12)$$

and because $\mathcal{E} = \theta_i - \theta_o$, it immediately follows that, at $t = 0+$,

$$\mathcal{E} = \phi$$
$$\frac{d\mathcal{E}}{dt} = 0 \qquad (4\text{-}13)$$

Suddenly Applied Input Displacement, or Step-displacement Function. Some servomechanism systems, particularly positioning systems in which the input command is merely a change in position of the input dial, are conveniently studied by assuming a step input displacement as illustrated in Fig. 4-3. This is of course a limiting case which can be approached but never reached in a physical system. Mathematically the initial conditions are:

At $t = 0-$: $\theta_i = 0$ and $\dfrac{d\theta_i}{dt} = 0$

$$(4\text{-}14)$$

At $t = 0+$: $\theta_i = A$ and $\dfrac{d\theta_i}{dt} = 0$

At $t = 0-$: $\theta_o = 0$ and $\dfrac{d\theta_o}{dt} = 0$

$$(4\text{-}15)$$

At $t = 0+$: $\theta_o = 0$ and $\dfrac{d\theta_o}{dt} = 0$

At $t = 0-$: $\mathcal{E} = 0$ and $\dfrac{d\mathcal{E}}{dt} = 0$

$$(4\text{-}16)$$

At $t = 0+$: $\mathcal{E} = A$ and $\dfrac{d\mathcal{E}}{dt} = 0$

Suddenly Applied Load Torque. In many applications the output is subjected to load torques, and frequently these are not constant. For example in a servo-controlled radar antenna the output is loaded by any wind which may arise. If the wind velocity is not constant, the load also varies. As another example consider a profile milling machine with automatic control; this is loaded by the depth of cut, which may vary on successive passes, and since the work is seldom homogeneous, the load also varies during a pass. Such operating conditions are difficult to treat mathematically, and it is customary to assume that the system is operating at steady state, unloaded, when a finite load, T_L, is applied and maintained. Under such conditions the differential equation of the system is changed, *i.e.*, Eq. (4-9) becomes

$$K\mathcal{E} = J\frac{d^2\theta_o}{dt^2} + f\frac{d\theta_o}{dt} + T \tag{4-17}$$

Because the system is assumed initially at steady state, at $t = 0+$,

$$\theta_i = \theta_o = \mathcal{E} = 0 \tag{4-18}$$

and because of inertia

$$\frac{d\theta_i}{dt} = \frac{d\theta_o}{dt} = \frac{d\mathcal{E}}{dt} = 0 \tag{4-19}$$

but

$$T = T_L \tag{4-20}$$

Actually a statement of initial conditions is not necessary since the differential equation may be solved by applying superposition. It might be noted that in many applications involving load torques the performance of a proportional-error servomechanism is not satisfactory and a more complex controller must be used.

Suddenly Applied Input Velocity (Step-velocity Function, or Ramp Function). For many servomechanisms, used as speed controllers, the command signal may be a finite change in speed. Also in many position-control servos, such as gun directors, the input signal may be changed at a nearly constant rate, and the output not only must duplicate the velocity but must maintain position correspondence. A suitable standard initial condition is a suddenly applied velocity, which may be thought of as a step-velocity function (see Fig. 4-4a) or as a ramp function (see Fig. 4-4b). Mathematically, these conditions may be expressed as follows:

At $t > 0$: $\qquad \theta_i = \omega_i t \qquad$ and $\qquad \dfrac{d\theta_i}{dt} = \omega_i$

At $t = 0+$: $\qquad \theta_i = 0 \qquad$ and $\qquad \dfrac{d\theta_i}{dt} = \omega_i$ $\qquad$ (4-21)

Also at $t = 0+$: $\qquad \theta_o = 0 \qquad$ and $\qquad \dfrac{d\theta_o}{dt} = 0$ $\qquad$ (4-22)

Also at $t = 0+$: $\qquad \varepsilon = 0 \qquad$ and $\qquad \dfrac{d\varepsilon}{dt} = \omega_i$ $\qquad$ (4-23)

Sinusoidal Input Function. When the input to a servomechanism is periodic or includes numerous rapid variations a convenient standard test condition is a pure sinusoidal signal.* Ordinarily such tests, whether mathematical or experimental, would be repeated for a number of frequencies and the principle of superposition applied. The frequency range tested would depend on the specific system. In such studies only the steady-state response is of importance.

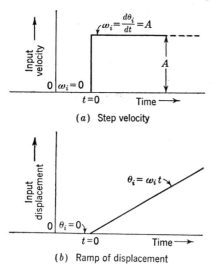

(a) Step velocity

(b) Ramp of displacement

FIG. 4-4. Step-velocity input function.

Equation (4-10), the basic equation of a proportional-error servomechanism, will now be solved for each of the first four sets of initial conditions. The Laplace transformation is used to obtain the solutions. Discussion of these solutions in terms of system performance is delayed until complete tabulation and graphical representation of results is made.

* Actual periodic input to servomechanisms is not considered in this text, but in later chapters much use is made of an assumed variable-frequency input as a tool for analysis.

4-4. Proportional-error Servomechanism with Specific Input Conditions. *Initial Output Error.* The fundamental equation is

$$J \frac{d^2\mathcal{E}}{dt^2} + f \frac{d\mathcal{E}}{dt} + K\mathcal{E} = J \frac{d^2\theta_i}{dt^2} + f \frac{d\theta_i}{dt^2} \qquad (4\text{-}10)$$

Applying the Laplace transformation results in

$$J \left[s^2 E(s) - s\mathcal{E}(0+) - \frac{d\mathcal{E}}{dt}(0+) \right] + f[sE(s) - \mathcal{E}(0+)] + KE(s)$$

$$= J \left[s^2 \Theta_i(s) - s\theta_i(0+) - \frac{d\theta_i}{dt}(0+) \right] + f[s\Theta_i(s) - \theta_i(0+)] \quad (4\text{-}24)$$

where $E(s) = \mathcal{L}[\mathcal{E}(t)]$ and $\Theta_i(s) = \mathcal{L}[\theta_i(t)]$. For the remainder of this text a shortened notation, $E(s) \triangleq E$ and $\Theta_i(s) \triangleq \Theta_i$, will be used. The initial conditions at $t = 0+$ are

$$\theta_i = 0 \qquad \frac{d\theta_i}{dt} = 0 \qquad \mathcal{E} = \phi \qquad \frac{d\mathcal{E}}{dt} = 0$$

and

$$\mathcal{L}(\theta_i) = \Theta_i = 0$$

Then Eq. (4-24) becomes

$$J(s^2 E - s\phi) + f(sE - \phi) + KE = 0 \qquad (4\text{-}25)$$

which reduces to

$$s^2 JE + sfE + KE = sJ\phi + f\phi \qquad (4\text{-}26)$$

and finally

$$E = \frac{sJ + f}{s^2 J + sf + K} \phi \qquad (4\text{-}27)$$

The solution for the error as a function of time is made according to the principles outlined in Chap. 2. Using partial fractions, Eq. (4-27) becomes

$$E = \left[\frac{\frac{1}{2} + \dfrac{jf}{4J\sqrt{K/J - f^2/4J^2}}}{s + f/2J + j\sqrt{K/J - f^2/4J^2}} + \frac{\frac{1}{2} - \dfrac{jf}{4J\sqrt{K/J - f^2/4J^2}}}{s + f/2J - j\sqrt{K/J - f^2/4J^2}} \right] \phi \qquad (4\text{-}28)$$

and by applying the inverse Laplace transform the time solution is

$$\mathcal{E} = \left[\left(\frac{1}{2} + \frac{jf}{4J\sqrt{K/J - f^2/4J^2}} \right) e^{(-f/2J - j\sqrt{K/J - f^2/4J^2})t} \right.$$

$$\left. + \left(\frac{1}{2} - \frac{jf}{4J\sqrt{K/J - f^2/4J^2}} \right) e^{(-f/2J + j\sqrt{K/J - f^2/4J^2})t} \right] \phi \qquad (4\text{-}29)$$

In Eq. (4-29) the coefficients and exponents are complex, but the actual performance of the system depends on the relative value of K/J and $f^2/4J^2$. The solutions obtained will differ depending on three possibilities:

1. $K/J = f^2/4J^2$, referred to as the critically damped case
2. $K/J < f^2/4J^2$, the overdamped case
3. $K/J > f^2/4J^2$, the underdamped, or oscillatory, case

If condition 1 exists, then the solution becomes

$$\varepsilon = \left(1 + \sqrt{\frac{K}{J}}\, t\right) e^{-\sqrt{K/J}\, t}\, \phi \tag{4-30}$$

For condition 2

$$\varepsilon = \left[\left(\frac{1}{2} + \frac{f}{4J\,\sqrt{f^2/4J^2 - K/J}}\right) e^{(-f/2J + \sqrt{f^2/4J^2 - K/J})t} \right.$$
$$\left. + \left(\frac{1}{2} - \frac{f}{4J\,\sqrt{f^2/4J^2 - K/J}}\right) e^{(-f/2J - \sqrt{f^2/4J^2 - K/J})t}\right] \phi \tag{4-31}$$

For condition 3

$$\varepsilon = e^{-ft/2J}\left[\cos\left(\sqrt{\frac{K}{J} - \frac{f^2}{4J^2}}\right) t + \frac{f/2J}{\sqrt{K/J - f^2/4J^2}}\, \sin\left(\sqrt{\frac{K}{J} - \frac{f^2}{4J^2}}\right) t\right] \phi \tag{4-32}$$

Curves illustrating the above equation are shown in Fig. 4-5.

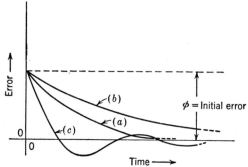

Fig. 4-5. Response of proportional-error servomechanism to initial error. (a) Critically damped system, (b) overdamped system, (c) underdamped system.

Step-displacement Input. Starting with Eq. (4-10), which is the fundamental equation of a proportional-error servomechanism, the Laplace transformation yields Eq. (4-24). The initial conditions for a step-displacement input at $t = 0+$ are

$$\theta_i = A \qquad \frac{d\theta_i}{dt} = 0 \qquad \mathcal{L}(\theta_i) = \Theta_i = \frac{A}{s}$$

$$\varepsilon = A \qquad \frac{d\varepsilon}{dt} = 0$$

Therefore Eq. (4-24) reduces to

$$J(s^2E - sA) + f(sE - A) + KE = J\left(s^2\frac{A}{s} - sA\right) + f\left(s\frac{A}{s} - A\right)$$

(4-33)

which reduces to

$$Js^2E - JsA + fsE - fA + KE = 0 \qquad (4\text{-}34)$$

And solving for the error gives

$$E = \frac{sJ + f}{s^2J + sf + K} A \qquad (4\text{-}35)$$

If desired, this may be rewritten in terms of the transform of the generalized input function,

$$E = \frac{s^2J + sf}{s^2J + sf + K}\frac{A}{s} = \frac{s^2J + sf}{s^2J + sf + K}\Theta_i \qquad (4\text{-}36)$$

Note that if the amplitude of the step input is $A = 1$, then

$$E = \frac{s^2J + sf}{s^2J + sf + K}\frac{1}{s} = \frac{sJ + f}{s^2J + sf + K} \qquad (4\text{-}37)$$

Expanding Eq. (4-35) by partial fractions gives

$$E = A\left[\frac{\frac{1}{2} + \dfrac{jf}{4J\sqrt{K/J - f^2/4J^2}}}{s + f/2J + j\sqrt{K/J - f^2/4J^2}} \right. $$
$$\left. + \frac{\frac{1}{2} - \dfrac{jf}{4J\sqrt{K/J - f^2/4J^2}}}{s + f/2J - j\sqrt{K/J - f^2/4J^2}}\right] \qquad (4\text{-}38)$$

Applying the inverse Laplace transform yields the time solution

$$\varepsilon = A\left[\left(\frac{1}{2} + \frac{jf}{4J\sqrt{K/J - f^2/4J^2}}\right)e^{(-f/2J - j\sqrt{K/J - f^2/4J^2})t} \right.$$
$$\left. + \left(\frac{1}{2} - \frac{jf}{4J\sqrt{K/J - f^2/4J^2}}\right)e^{(-f/2J + j\sqrt{K/J - f^2/4J^2})t}\right] \qquad (4\text{-}39)$$

It should be noted that Eq. (4-29) is identical with (4-39) except that the multiplying factor in (4-29) is ϕ instead of A. Therefore investigation of damping conditions for Eq. (4-39) would result in solutions identical with Eqs. (4-30) to (4-32) except for the multiplying factor. Also curves of error vs. time for a step-displacement input would be identical with the curves of Fig. 4-5, except that the initial error would be A instead of ϕ.

Proportional-error Servomechanism with Load Torque. If there is no input signal to a servomechanism ($\theta_i = 0$) but a sudden load torque is applied to the output shaft, the torque equilibrium is given by

$$J \frac{d^2\theta_o}{dt^2} + f \frac{d\theta_o}{dt} + T_L = K \tag{4-17}$$

Inserting $\theta_o = \theta_i - \varepsilon$ yields

$$J \frac{d^2\theta_i}{dt^2} + f \frac{d\theta_i}{dt} + T_L = J \frac{d^2\varepsilon}{dt^2} + f \frac{d\varepsilon}{dt} + K\varepsilon \tag{4-40}$$

Rearranging and transforming,

$$J \left[s^2 E - s\varepsilon(0+) - \frac{d\varepsilon}{dt}(0+) \right] + f[sE - \varepsilon(0+)] + KE$$

$$= J \left[s^2\Theta_i - s\theta_i(0+) - \frac{d\theta_i}{dt}(0+) \right] + f[s\Theta_i - \theta_i(0+)] + \frac{T_L}{s} \tag{4-41}$$

Since θ_i is kept constant at zero and, at $t = 0+$, θ_i, $\dfrac{d\theta_i}{dt}$, ε, and $d\varepsilon/dt$ are zero, Eq. (4-41) reduces to

$$s^2 JE + sfE + KE = \frac{T_L}{s} \tag{4-42}$$

from which

$$E = \frac{T_L}{s(s^2 J + sf + K)} \tag{4-43}$$

Applying partial fractions to Eq. (4-43),

$$E = \frac{T_L/K}{s} + \frac{\dfrac{T_L f/2JK - j(T_L/K) \sqrt{K/J - f^2/4J^2}}{j2 \sqrt{K/J - f^2/4J^2}}}{s + f/2J + j \sqrt{K/J - f^2/4J^2}}$$

$$+ \frac{\dfrac{-T_L f/2JK - j(T_L/K) \sqrt{K/J - f^2/4J^2}}{j2 \sqrt{K/J - f^2/4J^2}}}{s + f/2J - j \sqrt{K/J - f^2/4J^2}} \tag{4-44}$$

From the inverse Laplace transformation the time solution is

$$\varepsilon = \frac{T_L}{K} \left[1 + \left(\frac{f/2J - j \sqrt{K/J - f^2/4J^2}}{j2 \sqrt{K/J - f^2/4J^2}} \right) e^{(-f/2J + j\sqrt{K/J - f^2/4J^2})t} \right.$$

$$\left. + \left(\frac{-f/2J - j \sqrt{K/J - f^2/4J^2}}{j2 \sqrt{K/J - f^2/4J^2}} \right) e^{(-f/2J - j\sqrt{K/J - f^2/4J^2})t} \right] \tag{4-45}$$

Equation (4-45) will reduce to one of three possible forms depending on the value of the radical $\sqrt{K/J - f^2/4J^2}$. This manipulation is left to the student.   Typical plots of $\mathcal{E}(t)$ for a suddenly applied load torque are shown in Fig. 4-6.

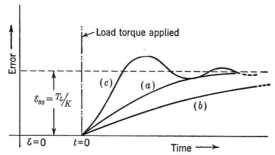

FIG. 4-6. Response of proportional-error servomechanism to impact-load torque. (a) Critically damped system, (b) overdamped system, (c) underdamped system.

Proportional-error Servomechanism with Step Velocity Input. **The** initial conditions at $t = 0+$ are

$$\theta_i = 0 \qquad \frac{d\theta_i}{dt} = \omega_i \qquad \mathcal{E} = 0 \qquad \frac{d\mathcal{E}}{dt} = \omega_i$$

Furthermore, since for $t > 0$,

$$\theta_i = \omega_i t$$

then

$$\mathcal{L}(\theta_i) = \Theta_i = \frac{\omega_i}{s^2}$$

Inserting in (4-24),

$$J(s^2 E - \omega_i) + f(sE) + KE = J\left(s^2 \frac{\omega_i}{s^2} - \omega_i\right) + f\left(s \frac{\omega_i}{s^2}\right) \quad (4\text{-}46)$$

which reduces to

$$Js^2 E + fsE + KE = J\omega_i + \frac{f\omega_i}{s} \quad (4\text{-}47)$$

from which

$$E = \frac{f/s + J}{s^2 J + fs + K} \omega_i = \frac{sJ + f}{s(s^2 J + sf + K)} \omega_i \quad (4\text{-}48)$$

Applying partial fractions results in

$$E = \omega_i \left[\frac{f/K}{s} + \frac{\dfrac{-(1 - f^2/2JK) - j(f/K)\sqrt{K/J - f^2/4J^2}}{j2\sqrt{K/J - f^2/4J^2}}}{s + f/2J + j\sqrt{K/J - f^2/4J^2}} \right.$$
$$\left. + \frac{\dfrac{+(1 - f^2/2JK) - j(f/K)\sqrt{K/J - f^2/4J^2}}{j2\sqrt{K/J - f^2/4J^2}}}{s + f/2J - j\sqrt{K/J - f^2/4J^2}} \right] \quad (4\text{-}49)$$

And using the inverse Laplace transformation gives

$$\varepsilon = \omega_i \left[\frac{K}{f} \right.$$

$$+ \left(\frac{-(1 - f^2/2JK) - j(f/K)\sqrt{K/J - f^2/4J^2}}{j2\sqrt{K/J - f^2/4J^2}} \right) e^{-(f/2J + j\sqrt{K/J - f^2/4J^2})t}$$

$$+ \left. \left(\frac{(1 - f^2/2JK) - j(f/K)\sqrt{K/J - f^2/4J^2}}{j2\sqrt{K/J - f^2/4J^2}} \right) e^{-(f/2J - j\sqrt{K/J - f^2/4J^2})t} \right] \quad (4\text{-}50)$$

Equation (4-50) may be manipulated into three possible forms depending on the value of the radical $\sqrt{K/J - f^2/4J^2}$. This manipulation is left to the student, but representative plots of the solutions are indicated in Fig. 4-7.

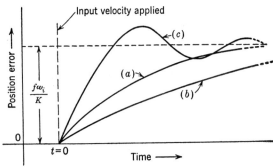

Fig. 4-7. Response of proportional-error servomechanism to step-velocity input. (a) Critically damped system, (b) overdamped system, (c) underdamped system.

4-5. Simplification of Equations.[28] Equations (4-9) to (4-50) are expressed in terms of the actual system parameters, K, J, and f. Before discussing the equations in detail it is convenient to introduce a few simplifications. A dimensionless damping ratio is defined as the ratio of the actual system damping to that required for the system to be critically damped. Mathematically,

$$\zeta = \frac{f}{f_c} \quad (4\text{-}51)$$

The critical damping is obtained when

$$\sqrt{\frac{K}{J} - \frac{f^2}{4J^2}} = 0$$

i.e.,

$$\frac{f^2}{4J^2} = \frac{K}{J}$$

or

$$f = 2\sqrt{KJ} \triangleq f_c \quad (4\text{-}52)$$

Therefore

$$\zeta = \frac{f}{2\sqrt{KJ}} \tag{4-53}$$

It is also convenient to introduce the undamped natural angular velocity,

$$\omega_n = \sqrt{\frac{K}{J}} \tag{4-54}$$

The ratios ω_n and ζ may be substituted into Eqs. (4-9) to (4-50) by proper algebraic manipulation, but it is generally more satisfactory to make the substitution in the original differential equation.   For example, Eq. (4-9), which is

$$K\varepsilon = J\frac{d^2\theta_o}{dt^2} + f\frac{d\theta_o}{dt} \tag{4-9}$$

can be arranged to allow introduction of the ratios by dividing through by J, which gives

$$\frac{K}{J}\varepsilon = \frac{d^2\theta_o}{dt^2} + \frac{f}{J}\frac{d\theta_o}{dt} \tag{4-55}$$

and then multiplying the last term by $2\sqrt{K}/2\sqrt{K}$, yielding

$$\frac{K}{J}\varepsilon = \frac{d^2\theta_o}{dt^2} + \frac{2f}{2\sqrt{KJ}}\sqrt{\frac{K}{J}}\frac{d\theta_o}{dt} \tag{4-56}$$

Then substituting

$$\zeta = \frac{f}{2\sqrt{KJ}} \quad \text{and} \quad \omega_n = \sqrt{\frac{K}{J}}$$

this becomes

$$\omega_n^2\varepsilon = \frac{d^2\theta_o}{dt^2} + 2\zeta\omega_n\frac{d\theta_o}{dt} \tag{4-57}$$

The number of system constants is thus reduced from three to two, which is an obvious simplification.   In much the same fashion the solutions developed thus far can be rewritten as functions of ζ and ω_n.   Compilation of resultant equations is shown in Table 4-1.

Another advantage in the use of simplified parameters becomes apparent when performance characteristics are plotted.   Instead of using a separate set of curves for each type of input disturbance, it is possible to combine essentially all of the information in two families of nondimensionalized curves, as shown in Figs. 4-8a and 4-8b.   These curves may be plotted from the equations in Table 4-1 after a slight rearrangement. Note that the time scale $\omega_n t$ and the error scales ε/θ_i, ε/ϕ, $\varepsilon/\varepsilon_{ss}$ are all dimensionless.   Thus the curves are universal, in that they apply to any proportional-error servomechanism regardless of size or physical nature.

TABLE 4-1
EQUATIONS FOR PROPORTIONAL-ERROR SERVOMECHANISM

Type of disturbance	$\zeta < 1$	$\zeta = 1$	$\zeta > 1$
Initial error ϕ or step input displacement $t < 0,\ \theta_i = 0$ $t > 0,\ \theta_i = \phi$	$\varepsilon = \phi\left(\dfrac{e^{-\zeta\omega_n t}}{\sqrt{1-\zeta^2}}\right)\sin\left(\sqrt{1-\zeta^2}\,\omega_n t + \psi\right)$ where Initial error $= \varepsilon_0 = \phi$ Steady-state error $= \varepsilon_{ss} = 0$ $\psi = \tan^{-1}\sqrt{1-\zeta^2}/\zeta$	$\varepsilon = \phi(1 + \omega_n t)e^{-\omega_n t}$	$\varepsilon = \phi\left[\dfrac{\zeta+\sqrt{\zeta^2-1}}{2\sqrt{\zeta^2-1}}e^{(-\zeta+\sqrt{\zeta^2-1})\omega_n t} - \dfrac{\zeta-\sqrt{\zeta^2-1}}{2\sqrt{\zeta^2-1}}e^{(-\zeta-\sqrt{\zeta^2-1})\omega_n t}\right]$
Load torque T_L	$\varepsilon = \dfrac{T_L}{J\omega_n^2}\left(1 - \dfrac{e^{-\zeta\omega_n t}}{\sqrt{1-\zeta^2}}\right)\sin\left(\sqrt{1-\zeta^2}\,\omega_n t + \psi\right)$ where Initial error $= \varepsilon_0 = 0$ Steady-state error $= \varepsilon_{ss} = \dfrac{T_L}{J\omega_n^2}$ $\psi = \tan^{-1}\sqrt{1-\zeta^2}/\zeta$	$\varepsilon = \dfrac{T_L}{J\omega_n^2}[1 - (1 + \omega_n t)e^{-\omega_n t}]$	$\varepsilon = \dfrac{T_L}{J\omega_n^2}\left[1 - \dfrac{\zeta+\sqrt{\zeta^2-1}}{2\sqrt{\zeta^2-1}}e^{(-\zeta+\sqrt{\zeta^2-1})\omega_n t} - \dfrac{\zeta-\sqrt{\zeta^2-1}}{2\sqrt{\zeta^2-1}}e^{(-\zeta-\sqrt{\zeta^2-1})\omega_n t}\right]$
Step input velocity $t < 0,\ \theta_i = 0$ $t > 0,\ \theta_i = \omega_i t$	$\varepsilon = \dfrac{2\zeta\omega_i}{\omega_n}\left[1 - \dfrac{e^{-\zeta\omega_n t}}{2\zeta\sqrt{1-\zeta^2}}\sin\left(\sqrt{1-\zeta^2}\,\omega_n t + \psi\right)\right]$ where Initial error $= \varepsilon_0 = 0$ Steady-state error $= \varepsilon_{ss} = \dfrac{2\zeta\omega_i}{\omega_n}$ $\psi = \tan^{-1} 2\zeta\sqrt{1-\zeta^2}/(2\zeta^2-1)$	$\varepsilon = \dfrac{2\omega_i}{\omega_n}\left[1 - e^{-\omega_n t}\left(1 + \dfrac{\omega_n t}{2}\right)\right]$	$\varepsilon = \dfrac{2\zeta\omega_i}{\omega_n}\left[1 - \dfrac{2\zeta^2 - 1 + \zeta\sqrt{\zeta^2-1}}{2\zeta\sqrt{\zeta^2-1}}e^{(-\zeta+\sqrt{\zeta^2-1})\omega_n t} + \dfrac{-(2\zeta^2-1) + \zeta\sqrt{\zeta^2-1}}{2\zeta\sqrt{\zeta^2-1}}e^{(-\zeta-\sqrt{\zeta^2-1}\,\omega_n t)}\right]$

The following general remarks may be made from an inspection of these dimensionless curves:

1. Regardless of the value of ζ, the system eventually reaches steady state.

2. If $\zeta \geqq 1$ there is no overshoot, *i.e.*, the steady-state value is approached but never exceeded.

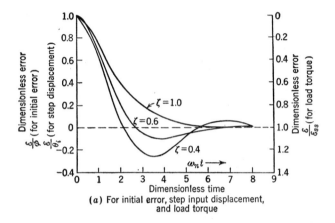

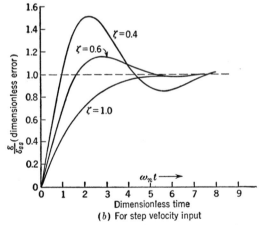

FIG. 4-8. Dimensionless performance curves (sketched) of an ideal proportional-error servomechanism for standard disturbances.

3. If $\zeta < 1$, the system overshoots the steady-state value and oscillates about it. The overshoot is small and the oscillations die out quickly if $\zeta \cong 1$, but the overshoot increases and oscillations are prolonged for a longer period if $\zeta \ll 1$.

4. The system is sluggish, *i.e.*, it responds very slowly, if $\zeta \gg 1$ but responds quickly if $\zeta \ll 1$.

5. When ζ has been evaluated numerically, the amount of overshoot and the duration of oscillation (in dimensionless time) may be determined from the curves without further calculation. If ω_n is also calculated, the actual time duration of oscillation is calculable and its frequency may be estimated.

6. The numerical value of ω_n is seen to be an index of the speed of response for a given ζ. For example, if $\zeta = 1$, the transient is essentially over for $\omega_n t = 6$, and if ω_n is large, then the actual time, t, is small. Thus a large value of ω_n characterizes a system with quick response.

Quantitative information concerning the performance of proportional-error servomechanisms may be obtained from the universal curves with a minimum of labor. The inertia, J, viscous-damping coefficient, f, and system gain, K, must be known, as well as the type of disturbance expected, but all of this information is also necessary for solution of the differential equation. For example, the maximum overshoot caused by a step input displacement is readily calculated, as well as the length of time elapsing between the disturbance and this overshoot.

Example :

$$\theta_i = 25°$$

Let $J = 3$ slug $-$ ft^2
$\quad f = 21.2$ lb-ft/radian/sec
$\quad K = 104$ lb-ft/radian

Then

$$\zeta = \frac{f}{2\sqrt{KJ}} = \frac{21.2}{2\sqrt{104.3}} = 0.6$$

$$\omega_n = \sqrt{\frac{K}{J}} = \sqrt{\frac{104}{3}} = 5.9 \text{ radians/sec}$$

From Fig. 4-8a for $\zeta = 0.6$, $\mathcal{E}/\theta_i$ at maximum overshoot equals -0.087.

$$\therefore \ \mathcal{E}_{\text{max}} = -(0.087)(25°) = -2.18°$$

Also from Fig. 4-8a, maximum overshoot for $\zeta = 0.6$ occurs at $\omega_n t = 3.8$. Therefore

$$t = \frac{\omega_n t}{\omega_n} = \frac{3.8}{5.9} = 0.645 \text{ sec}$$

4-6. General Discussion of Proportional-error Servomechanism. It should be emphasized that all of the mathematical equations derived in this chapter refer to a single system, a proportional-error servomechanism. The difference in the equations is due to the fact that such a system may be subjected to different operating conditions, and therefore a series of tests are required to determine performance under these different conditions. It is to be expected that certain of the performance characteristics depend solely on the system itself, while others may be affected by the type of disturbance. As will be shown later, the speed of response and the oscillating frequency of the system depend solely on the system characteristics, while the maximum overshoot and steady-state error depend somewhat on the type of operation. In any case, if performance is not satisfactory, some change must be made in the system and any such change will probably affect more than one of the performance characteristics.

In the following paragraphs each of the performance characteristics is discussed separately, and suggestions are made as to the possible methods of improving the performance. It is therefore necessary to preface this discussion with a few remarks on the practical availability of system adjustments. The physical parameters of any system are basically f, K, and J, and any adjustment involves changing at least one of these parameters. In brief, the gain K is a convenient parameter to vary; f may occasionally be adjusted, but the inertia J is seldom, if ever, a useful variable. The gain of a system is ordinarily easily adjusted, since amplification of some sort is a necessary part of any servomechanism; and in addition changes in K usually do not affect f or J. There is, however a practical upper limit to the value of gain for any specific system. The friction coefficient f, may often be increased without difficulty, but in general it is not readily decreased without considerable change in the system. However, increasing f has several disadvantages.[28,160] It frequently cannot be accomplished without changing system inertia, it dissipates power in the form of heat, and it requires that the power supply furnish not only the power required to drive the system but also the power for the friction losses. In general, the power demand of a friction damper precludes its use in systems of more than a few hundred watts' capacity, i.e., it is a useful design variable only for instrument-type servomechanisms. The inertia, J, is not a useful parameter to alter since the application in which the system is used ordinarily sets the minimum inertia possible, and most performance deficiencies would require decreased inertia for improvement.

4-7. Speed of Response. As a general rule, a servomechanism is required to reach its steady-state condition in minimum time after a disturbance, with special limitations for specific applications. Some applications cannot tolerate any overshoot, while other applications permit more or less overshoot if the speed of response is thereby improved. Since a system with critical damping has no overshoot and responds more rapidly than an overdamped system there is no practical advantage to overdamping and the equations in Table 4-1 for $\zeta > 1$ are only of academic interest. For all underdamped and critically damped systems the speed of response depends on the factor $e^{-\omega_n t}$, since this factor is a multiplier in all of the equations. From simple transient theory the time constant of the system is then

$$\tau = \frac{1}{\zeta \omega_n} \tag{4-58}$$

and approximately 63 per cent of the system change is accomplished when $t = \tau$, or 98 per cent of the change is accomplished when $t = 4\tau$.

The servomechanism therefore has high speed response if the product $\zeta \omega_n$ is large but is slow in responding if $\zeta \omega_n$ is small. It would therefore seem that the product $\zeta \omega_n$ should be made as large as possible to provide rapid response. While this is largely true, certain practical limits must be set before means of adjustment can be discussed and it is also necessary to expand the physical interpretation of "speed of response" as opposed to the purely mathematical concept. Though there is no reason for limiting the value of ω_n (except the possibility of getting an unwanted resonance at some particular frequency due to the nature of the application; or to limit the effect of noise), ζ must be limited within the range of $0.4 < \zeta < 1.0$ because values of $\zeta < 0.4$ give excessive overshoot and values of $\zeta > 1$ are over-damped systems and inherently sluggish. In a particular application the value of ζ may be limited to a still smaller range due to specifications on the maximum overshoot. Considering only the mathematical concept of speed of response, the value of $\zeta \omega_n$ in terms of actual system parameters is then

$$\zeta \omega_n = \frac{f}{2 \sqrt{KJ}} \sqrt{\frac{K}{J}} = \frac{f}{2J} \tag{4-59}$$

Thus, on a purely mathematical basis, changing the gain K has no effect on the speed of response; some improvement can be obtained by increasing f, but this is limited by the restriction on ζ; and the inertia of the system must be decreased if the system is to respond more quickly, which is frequently impossible.

A more physical approach to the concept of speed of response, however, indicates that the gain, K, may be used as an adjustment. This results from the fact that the mathematical concept uses *absolute correspondence* as a reference, and in brief it states that the critically damped system approaches perfect correspondence more rapidly than a system with any other degree of damping. Practically there are always tolerances on the correspondence during transient conditions; for example, specifications may require that a proportional-error servomechanism regain correspondence within ± 5 deg after a step-displacement input of 30 deg and should accomplish this within 0.7 sec. Without performing any calculations it may be seen from Fig. 4-9 that a slightly underdamped system can reduce the error to less than ∓ 5 deg much more rapidly than a critically damped system. The response time for the critically damped system is $\omega_n t_1$, and for the underdamped system is $\omega_n t_2$, since for each system the error is always less than 5 deg for any later time. It is obvious that the underdamped system is faster for such an application.

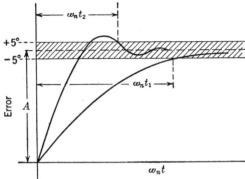

Fig. 4-9. Practical interpretation of response time for proportional-error servomechanism.

For practical attainment of increased speed of response, then, the gain K may be increased, since this increases ω_n and decreases ζ. The system therefore becomes more oscillatory but in general responds more quickly. The practical limitations on this procedure are the allowable overshoot and the specified tolerance on correspondence. In many cases only a slight increase in K is permissible, and there may be little difference between the performance of a critically damped and an underdamped system. It is not possible to set any general rule for the value of ζ which gives fastest response because this is set in any particular case by the tolerance on correspondence. In conclusion, it should be noted that the only factors which affect the speed of response (for a given set of specifications) are ζ and ω_n, so that speed of response is entirely a system characteristic.

4-8. Maximum Overshoot.[37-39] From the universal curves of Figs. 4-8a and b it may be seen that the maximum overshoot depends on the values of ζ and that the overshoot increases as ζ decreases. Basically then the overshoot depends on the system. However, the overshoot variation caused by a step-velocity input is different from that of a step displacement, initial error, or load torque and therefore depends somewhat on the disturbance.

In order to control the amount of overshoot, the gain K or the viscous-damping coefficient f may be adjusted (the inertia is not a desirable variable). Overshoot may be decreased by decreasing K or increasing f, both of which increase ζ. Such procedures inherently make the system more sluggish. The limit on the maximum permissible overshoot depends partly on the process or system which is being controlled and partly on the physical nature of equipment. If there is no limit to the output variation during the transient period, then the maximum over-shoot is determined on the basis of the allowable stresses in the system.

4-9. Resonant Frequency. Servomechanisms, even of the small-instrument type, usually have considerable inertia and are not extremely high-gain systems. Therefore their natural frequencies (ω_n) are normally well below the audio range, usually below 15 cps and frequently below 1 cps. The resonant frequency, for $\zeta < 1$, is given by

$$\omega_r = \omega_n \sqrt{1 - \zeta^2} \qquad (4\text{-}60)$$

and therefore is entirely a system characteristic. In design it is some-times important to set ω_r at such a value that the nature of the expected disturbances will not set up sustained vibrations in the system. In general it is desirable to make ω_n (and therefore ω_r) as high as possible in order to get a high speed response.

4-10. Steady-state Error. From the equations of Table 4-1 it may be seen that a proportional-error servomechanism has no steady-state error when the disturbance is an initial error or a step-displacement input but does have a steady-state error when there is a load torque or when the system is operated at constant velocity. Furthermore, the magnitude of these errors

$$\varepsilon_{ss} = \frac{T_L}{J\omega_n^2} = \frac{T_L}{K}$$

$$\varepsilon_{ss} = \frac{2\zeta\omega_i}{\omega_n} = \frac{f\omega_i}{K}$$

depends on the magnitude of the disturbance T_L or the input velocity ω_i. Thus steady-state error is not wholly a system characteristic, but depends on the application. If some steady-state error is permitted by the appli-cation, the steady-state error can be decreased by increasing the gain K. The error cannot be reduced to zero because it is not possible to obtain infinite gain. Practically, the increase in gain is limited by the fact that increasing K decreases ζ and thus increases overshoot.

4-11. Field of Application of Proportional-error Servomechanisms. The proportional-error servomechanism is the simplest type of servo-mechanism and therefore is usually the cheapest servomechanism. Since it inherently has zero position error when operated with stationary input, it is normally ideal for controlling position. In such applications the transient performance usually can be adjusted to meet specifications. In applications where load torques are encountered, and in applications where the system must operate at constant velocity, a proportional-error system has a displacement between input and output, or a steady-state error. If some steady-state error is permissible, or may be tolerated to obtain a cheaper control system, then the proportional-error system may be used if the transient performance can be brought within acceptable limits.   If the transient performance cannot be made acceptable for a given steady-state error, or if no steady-state error is permissible, then a proportional-error system cannot be used and a more complex controller must be designed.   This subject is treated in the following paragraphs.

4-12. Derivative and Integral Controls.[28,30,34,43-45]   Attention is now turned to the improvement of servomechanism performance through the use of derivative- and integral-control components.   Such system-correction units are more frequently known as compensating devices because of the purpose they serve.   The transient analysis of compensated systems is more difficult than for the simple proportional-error systems because of the increased complexity, and consequently the transient analysis of such systems has little actual design value.   However, the physical picture presented (since it is in familiar mathematical terms)

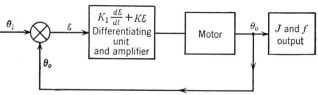

Fig. 4-10. Block diagram of servomechanism with series differentiating device.

illustrates in a straightforward manner the effects of these compensating networks on over-all system performance.

The introduction of derivative- and integral-control components into a proportional-error servomechanism affects both the transient and the steady-state performance.   In the present chapter emphasis is placed on the change in steady-state error due to the addition of a compensating device, and the effect on the transient performance is not discussed in detail.   In a later chapter a thorough study is made of such compensating devices (including basic design principles), using the transfer-function method, which is better suited to a detailed presentation.

4-13. First-derivative Error Control.   Corrective devices may be inserted at any point in the servomechanism loop or may be placed in parallel with a portion of the loop.   In general, however, it is necessary to maintain the actual error signal, and the corrective device may not be added in such a way as to eliminate the error signal.   Probably the simplest and commonest compensating device is a network (or other unit) which is added in series with the main power loop of the system and which takes the first derivative of the error signal.   The derivative network must also permit the error signal itself to appear in the output. The location of such a component is shown schematically in Fig. 4-10.

The signals ε and $d\varepsilon/dt$ may be added directly and amplified by a common gain channel, or each may have a separate gain channel before addition; therefore gain constants K and K_1 are used.

With the first-derivative error component included in the system the driving torque becomes

$$T = K\varepsilon + K_1 \frac{d\varepsilon}{dt} \tag{4-61}$$

and the equilibrium equation is then

$$J \frac{d^2\theta_o}{dt^2} + f \frac{d\theta_o}{dt} = T = K\varepsilon + K_1 \frac{d\varepsilon}{dt} \tag{4-62}$$

The error equation is still

$$\varepsilon = \theta_i - \theta_o \tag{4-63}$$

and to this must be added the condition

$$\frac{d\varepsilon}{dt} = \frac{d\theta_i}{dt} - \frac{d\theta_o}{dt} \tag{4-64}$$

Substituting Eq. (4-64) in Eq. (4-62) gives

$$J \frac{d^2\theta_i}{dt^2} + f \frac{d\theta_i}{dt} = J \frac{d^2\varepsilon}{dt^2} + (f + K_1) \frac{d\varepsilon}{dt} + K\varepsilon \tag{4-65}$$

If Eq. (4-65) is transformed and standard initial conditions inserted, the following results are obtained:

1. For initial error, ϕ,

$$E = \frac{s + \dfrac{f + K_1}{J}}{s^2 + \dfrac{f + K_1}{J} s + \dfrac{K}{J}} \phi = \frac{s + 2\zeta_1\omega_n}{s^2 + 2\zeta_1\omega_n s + \omega_n^2} \phi \tag{4-66}$$

2. For a step-displacement input

$$E = \frac{s + f/J}{s^2 + \dfrac{f + K_1}{J} s + \dfrac{K}{J}} = \frac{s + \gamma\omega_n}{s^2 + 2\zeta_1\omega_n s + \omega_n^2} \tag{4-67}$$

3. For a suddenly applied load torque

$$E = \frac{-T_L/J}{s\left(s^2 + \dfrac{f + K_1}{J} s + \dfrac{K}{J}\right)} = \frac{-T_L/J}{s(s^2 + 2\zeta_1\omega_n s + \omega_n^2)} \tag{4-68}$$

4. For a step-velocity input

$$E = \frac{(s + f/J)\omega_i}{s\left(s^2 + \dfrac{f + K_1}{J} s + \dfrac{K}{J}\right)} = \frac{(s + 2\gamma\omega_n)\omega_i}{s(s^2 + 2\zeta_1\omega_n s + \omega_n^2)} \tag{4-69}$$

where ζ_1 = ratio of total damping to critical damping

$$= \zeta_1 = \frac{(f + K_1)/J}{2\sqrt{K/J}}$$

γ = ratio of viscous component of damping to critical damping

$$= \frac{f/J}{2\sqrt{K/J}}$$

ω_n = natural frequency

$$= \sqrt{K/J}$$

The effects of adding a first-derivative control to a proportional-error servomechanism may be seen by comparing Eqs. (4-66) to (4-69) with the corresponding equations for the proportional-error system.   For an initial error or a suddenly applied load torque there is no essential difference between the systems, either in transient performance or in steady-state error.   The equation for the proportional-error system,

$$E = \frac{sJ + f}{s^2J + sf + K} \tag{4-27}$$

is seen to be identical with Eq. (4-66) provided only that

f (for proportional error) $= f + K_1$ (for proportional plus derivative error)

which is normally true since the over-all damping is usually kept constant.   Likewise, for a suddenly applied load torque,

$$E = \frac{T_L}{s(s^2J + sf + K)} \tag{4-43}$$

may be compared with Eq. (4-68), and again the only condition for identical performance is the same as for an initial error.   It should also be noted that first-derivative error control does not affect the steady-state error due to load torque and therefore some other type of compensating unit is needed if steady-state error is objectionable.

For a step-displacement input,

$$E = \frac{sJ + f}{s^2J + sf + K} \tag{4-37}$$

may be compared with Eq. (4-67).   It is seen that the denominators are different, and so the time solutions must be different.   The solution to Eq. (4-67) is:

For $\zeta_1 < 1$:

$$\varepsilon = \frac{e^{-\zeta_1\omega_n t}}{\sqrt{1 - \zeta_1^2}} \sin\left(\sqrt{1 - \zeta_1^2}\,\omega_n t + \psi_1\right) \tag{4-70}$$

where $\psi_1 = \tan^{-1}\dfrac{\sqrt{1 - \zeta_2^2}}{2\gamma - \zeta_1}$

For $\zeta_1 = 1$:

$$\varepsilon = [1 + (2\gamma - 1)\omega_n t]e^{-\omega_n t} \tag{4-71}$$

For $\zeta_1 > 1$:

$$\varepsilon = \frac{\zeta_1 + \sqrt{\zeta_1^2 - 1} - 2\gamma}{2\sqrt{\zeta_1^2 - 1}} e^{-(\zeta_1 + \sqrt{\zeta_1^2 - 1})\omega_n t}$$

$$- \frac{\zeta_1 - \sqrt{\zeta_1^2 - 1} - 2\gamma}{2\sqrt{\zeta_1^2 - 1}} e^{-(\zeta_1 - \sqrt{\zeta_1^2 - 1})\omega_n t} \tag{4-72}$$

These solutions may be compared with the corresponding equations for the proportional-error servomechanism in Table 4-1. The steady-state error is obviously not affected by the derivative control, but the transient response is seen to be faster, i.e., with ζ_1 (for the derivative controller) equal to ζ (for the proportional) the parameter γ is seen to decrease ε for any value of $\zeta_1 = \zeta$ and for all values of t.

For a step-velocity input,

$$E = \frac{sJ + f}{s(s^2 J + sf + K)} \omega_i \tag{4-48}$$

may be compared with Eq. (4-69). Again the denominators are different. The time solution for Eq. (4-69) is:

For $\zeta_1 < 1$:

$$\varepsilon = \frac{2\gamma\omega_i}{\omega_n}\left[1 - \frac{e^{-\zeta_1\omega_n t}}{2\gamma\sqrt{1 - \zeta_1^2}} \sin\left(\sqrt{1 - \zeta_1^2}\,\omega_n t + \psi\right)\right] \tag{4-73}$$

where $\psi = \tan^{-1}\dfrac{2\gamma\sqrt{1 - \zeta_1^2}}{1 - 2\gamma}$

For $\zeta_1 = 1$:

$$\varepsilon = \frac{2\gamma\omega_i}{\omega_n}\left\{1 + \left[\left(\frac{1}{2\gamma} - 1\right)\omega_n t - 1\right]e^{-\omega_n t}\right\} \tag{4-74}$$

For $\zeta_1 > 1$:

$$\varepsilon = \frac{2\gamma\omega_i}{\omega_n}\left[1 + \frac{2\gamma - \zeta_1 + \sqrt{\zeta_1^2 - 1}}{2\gamma(-\zeta_1 + \sqrt{\zeta_1^2 - 1})(2\sqrt{\zeta_1^2 - 1})} e^{-(\zeta_1 - \sqrt{\zeta_1^2 - 1})\omega_n t}\right.$$

$$\left. + \frac{2\gamma - \zeta_1 - \sqrt{\zeta_1^2 - 1}}{2\gamma(\zeta_1 + \sqrt{\zeta_1^2 - 1})(2\sqrt{\zeta_1^2 - 1})} e^{-(\zeta_1 + \sqrt{\zeta_1^2 - 1})\omega_n t}\right] \tag{4-75}$$

and in all of the above cases the steady-state error is

$$\varepsilon_{ss} = \frac{2\gamma\omega_i}{\omega_n} \tag{4-76}$$

When these solutions are compared with the response of a proportional-error system to the same type of disturbance (see Table 4-1), a difference is noted in both transient and steady-state performances.

In general $\gamma < \zeta_1$; and normal adjustment requires that ζ_1 should be approximately equivalent to ζ for the proportional-error system.   Thus the addition of a derivative control reduces the steady-state error (velocity-lag error) by permitting additional gain increases.   During the

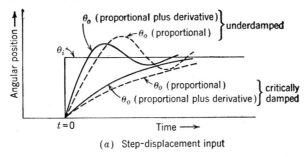

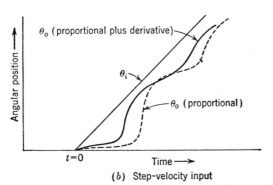

FIG. 4-11. Comparison of responses of proportional-error and proportional-error plus first-derivative-error servomechanisms.

transient period the peak overshoot is also limited by the damping effect of the derivative control.   This can be seen from the relationship

$$\frac{d\varepsilon}{dt} = \frac{d\theta_i}{dt} - \frac{d\theta_o}{dt} \tag{4-77}$$

When $t = 0$, $\varepsilon = 0$ for a step-velocity input and so the proportional-error system produces no torque.   However, at $t = 0$,

$$\frac{d\theta_i}{dt} = \omega_i \quad \text{and} \quad \frac{d\theta_o}{dt} = 0$$

and so

$$\frac{d\varepsilon}{dt} = \frac{d\theta_i}{dt} = \omega_i$$

and the derivative controller does produce a torque $T = K_1\,d\theta_i/dt = K_1\omega_i$ which in a sense anticipates the error and begins to correct it before it occurs.   Figures 4-11a and b compare the responses of a proportional-error servomechanism and a proportional-error plus first-derivative control servomechanism.

4-14. First-derivative Input Control.[30]   A second type of derivative control which may be used is shown in the block diagram of Fig. 4-12.

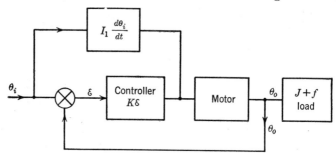

FIG. 4-12. Proportional-error servomechanism with first-derivative input control.

The driving torque for a proportional-error plus first-derivative input control is

$$T = K\varepsilon + I_1 \frac{d\theta_i}{dt} \tag{4-78}$$

where I_1 is the gain constant of the channel carrying the input signal. The equilibrium equation of the system is then

$$J \frac{d^2\theta_o}{dt^2} + f \frac{d\theta_o}{dt} = K\varepsilon + I_1 \frac{d\theta_i}{dt} \tag{4-79}$$

and substituting $\theta_o = \theta_i - \varepsilon$ gives

$$J \frac{d^2\theta_i}{dt^2} + (f - I_1) \frac{d\theta_i}{dt} = J \frac{d^2\varepsilon}{dt^2} + f \frac{d\varepsilon}{dt} + K\varepsilon \tag{4-80}$$

When transformed for a step-velocity input and solved for the error, Eq. (4-80) becomes

$$E = \frac{s^2 J + s(f - I_1)}{s^2 J + sf + K} \frac{\omega_i}{s^2} \tag{4-81}$$

Only the step-velocity input is used in this case, and in the subsequent discussion of derivative controls, because the other standard initial conditions are of no interest.   It has been indicated in the discussion of the first-derivative control that such control is of no value for systems subjected to initial errors or load torques.   For a step-displacement input some improvement in transient response is obtained which is often important.   For velocity operation, however, both the transient and steady-state performance are improved appreciably, and it is this fact which warrants the investigation of other types of derivative controls.   Since only the step-velocity input is to be considered, discussion may be carried out in most cases with the transformed equation and the time solution is obtained only when necessary.

Inspection of Eq. (4-81) shows that the first-derivative input control affects only the numerator. Therefore the only effect produced in the time solution is a change in the coefficients. Physically the nature of the transient performance is unchanged, but the amplitude of any oscillations is affected. For a system operated at nearly constant velocity, it may be shown that the steady-state error is easily controlled. The equation for the steady-state velocity-lag error is

$$\mathcal{E}_{ss} = \frac{f}{k}\left(1 - \frac{I_1}{f}\right)\omega_i = \frac{2\zeta}{\omega_n}\left(1 - \frac{I_1}{f}\right)\omega_i \qquad (4\text{-}82)$$

Thus proper adjustment of I_1 can reduce the steady-state error to zero or even make it reverse direction (lead instead of lag).

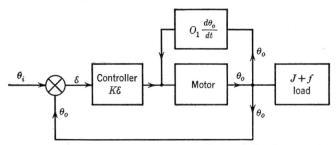

FIG. 4-13. Proportional-error servomechanism with first-derivative output control.

4-15. First-derivative Output Control.[30]   If a subsidiary feedback loop containing the proper components is connected as shown in Fig. 4-13, first-derivative output control is added to a proportional-error servomechanism. For this case the driving torque is

$$T = K\mathcal{E} - 0_1\frac{d\theta_o}{dt} \qquad (4\text{-}83)$$

where 0_1 = gain constant of feedback loop

The equilibrium equation is

$$J\frac{d^2\theta_o}{dt^2} + f\frac{d\theta_o}{dt} = K\mathcal{E} - 0_1\frac{d\theta_o}{dt} \qquad (4\text{-}84)$$

and substituting $\theta_o = \theta_i - \mathcal{E}$ gives

$$J\frac{d^2\theta_i}{dt^2} + (f + 0_1)\frac{d\theta_i}{dt} = J\frac{d^2\mathcal{E}}{dt^2} + (f + 0_1)\frac{d\mathcal{E}}{dt} + K\mathcal{E} \qquad (4\text{-}85)$$

which may be transformed for a step-velocity input to give

$$E = \frac{s^2J + s(f + 0_1)}{s^2J + s(f + 0_1) + K}\frac{\omega_i}{s^2} \qquad (4\text{-}86)$$

It may be seen from Eq. (4-86) that output control affects both the numerator and denominator of the error equation, thus affecting the roots of the time equation as well as the coefficients, which of course changes the nature of the transient response. In the denominator the coefficient 0_1 appears in the first-derivative term, which controls the damping, and thus the speed of response and the amplitude of any oscillations are changed. The steady-state error for this system is

$$\mathcal{E}_{ss} = \frac{f}{K}\left(1 - \frac{0_1}{f}\right)\omega_i = \frac{2\varsigma}{\omega_n}\left(1 - \frac{0_1}{f}\right)\omega_i \qquad (4\text{-}87)$$

so that adjustment of the gain constant 0_1 can reduce the steady-state error to zero or make it negative. In practice, however, the magnitude and duration of the oscillations are affected, and so proper precautions are necessary in adjusting 0_1.

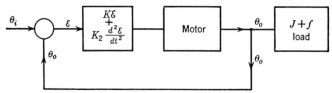

FIG. 4-14. Proportional-error servomechanism with second-derivative error control.

4-16. Second-derivative Error Control.[28,30] It is possible to combine second-derivative controllers with proportional-error servomechanisms and adjust the steady-state error due to velocity operation. The second-derivative controls change $\mathcal{E}_{ss}$ by altering the apparent inertia, whereas first-derivative controls were seen to affect the viscous damping. Figure 4-14 shows the block diagram of a proportional-error servomechanism plus the simplest second-derivative controller. The applied torque for this system is

$$T = K\mathcal{E} + K_2\frac{d^2\mathcal{E}}{dt^2} \qquad (4\text{-}88)$$

and the equilibrium equation is

$$J\frac{d^2\theta_o}{dt^2} + f\frac{d\theta_o}{dt} = K_2\frac{d^2\mathcal{E}}{dt} + K\mathcal{E} \qquad (4\text{-}89)$$

Substituting $\theta_o = \theta_i - \mathcal{E}$ gives

$$J\frac{d^2\theta_i}{dt^2} + f\frac{d\theta_i}{dt} = (J + K_2)\frac{d^2\mathcal{E}}{dt^2} + f\frac{d\mathcal{E}}{dt} + K\mathcal{E} \qquad (4\text{-}90)$$

which may be transformed for a step-velocity input to give

$$E = \frac{s^2J + sf}{s^2(J + K_2) + sf + K}\frac{\omega_i}{s^2} \qquad (4\text{-}91)$$

Equation (4-91) shows that the effective inertia of the system is now $J + K_2$, and the new natural frequency may be defined as

$$\omega_n = \sqrt{K/(J + K_2)}$$

The design of the second-derivation portion may be varied to make K_2 either positive or negative as desired, so that the effective inertia may be increased or decreased.   Adjustments in K_2 ordinarily affect the transient performance of the system as well as the steady state performance; for this reason second-derivative error control is not used for the reduction of steady-state error but is occasionally used for adjustment of the transient response.   Discussion of these factors is beyond the scope of this text but may be found in the literature.[10,12]

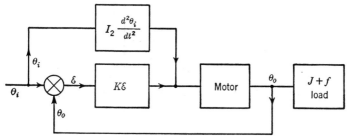

FIG. 4-15. Proportional-error servomechanism with second-derivative input control.

4-17. Second-derivative Input Control.[30]   Figure 4-15 shows a block diagram of a system with proportional-error plus second-derivative input control.   The equation for the drive torque is

$$T = K\varepsilon + I_2 \frac{d^2\theta_i}{dt^2} \tag{4-92}$$

and the equilibrium equation is

$$J \frac{d^2\theta_o}{dt^2} + f \frac{d\theta_o}{dt} = I_2 \frac{d^2\theta_i}{dt^2} + K\varepsilon \tag{4-93}$$

Substituting $\theta_o = \theta_i - \varepsilon$ in (4-93) gives

$$(J - I_2) \frac{d^2\theta_i}{dt^2} + f \frac{d\theta_i}{dt} = J \frac{d^2\varepsilon}{dt^2} + f \frac{d\varepsilon}{dt} + K\varepsilon \tag{4-94}$$

which may be transformed for a step-velocity input to give

$$E = \frac{s^2(J - I_2) + sf}{s^2 J + sf + K} \frac{\omega_i}{s^2} \tag{4-95}$$

From Eq. (4-95) it may be seen that second-derivative input control affects only the magnitude of the errors, but not the natural frequency or damping. It is suggested that the student verify this by solving Eq. (4-94) for several input conditions.

4-18. Second-derivative Output Control.[30]   Second-derivative output control may be obtained by adding a feedback loop as shown in Fig. 4-16. For this case the drive torque is

$$T = K\varepsilon + 0_2 \frac{d^2\theta_o}{dt^2} \tag{4-96}$$

and the equilibrium equation is

$$J \frac{d^2\theta_o}{dt^2} + f \frac{d\theta_o}{dt} = 0_2 \frac{d^2\theta_o}{dt^2} + K\varepsilon \tag{4-97}$$

Substituting $\theta_o = \theta_i - \varepsilon$ gives

$$(J - 0_2) \frac{d^2\theta_i}{dt^2} + f \frac{d\theta_i}{dt} = (J - 0_2) \frac{d^2\varepsilon}{dt^2} + f \frac{d\varepsilon}{dt} + K\varepsilon \tag{4-98}$$

and transforming for a step-velocity input results in

$$E = \frac{s^2(J - 0_2) + sf}{s^2(J - 0_2) + sf + K} \frac{\omega_i}{s^2} \tag{4-99}$$

From Eq. (4-99) it is seen that the transient performance is changed while the steady-state error of the system is not affected by the output control.

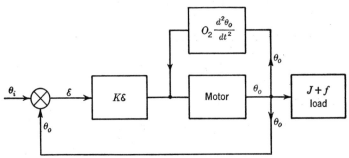

Fig. 4-16. Proportional-error servomechanism with second-derivative output control.

4-19. Summary and Extension of Derivative-control Theory.   First-derivative controls in general affect the damping terms, while second-derivative controls affect the inertia terms.   Error and output derivative controls affect both the numerator and denominator of the characteristic equation.   Thus they affect the amplitude of any error (transient or steady state) and also the roots of the stability equation (denominator), which control the magnitude and duration of oscillations.   Input derivatives affect only the numerator and therefore control the magnitude of the errors without affecting stability.   This is to be expected because the input loop is not a feedback loop, and in general only feedback affects stability.

The use of an error signal is always required to obtain the initial synchronization between input and output and also to compensate for the fact that practical derivative controls are seldom ideal.   Several derivative controls may be used simultaneously if desired.   First-derivative controls are more likely to be useful than second derivatives, not only because it is more difficult to design equipment for measuring accelerations than it is to design velocity-measuring equipment, but in general because many systems operate at nearly constant velocities, while rapid accelerations are relatively rare.

While the use of derivative controls to improve transient performance is not too difficult to visualize, a few remarks are in order concerning their effects on steady-state performance.   Derivative error controls can reduce steady-state velocity lag but cannot eliminate it.   Input and output derivatives can theoretically reduce velocity lag error to zero, or even make the output lead the input.   However, the gain constants of the input and output loops have to be set to compensate for a given condition.   Thus they cannot keep the error at zero if the load inertia, friction, or load torque is variable.   In addition, if the system is used for static positioning, so that θ_i, θ_o, $d\theta_i/dt$, $d\theta_o/dt$, $d\varepsilon/dt$, etc., are all zero, then the derivative controls have no effect on such steady-state position error as may result from a load torque.

4-20. Integral Control.[28,30,45]   Since derivative controls are not capable of eliminating steady-state errors under all conditions, and because certain systems require zero steady-state error under those conditions for which derivative controllers are useless, it is necessary to devise some other means of eliminating steady-state error.   One method for reducing steady-state error to zero is to use a controller which produces a torque

$$T = K\varepsilon + K_3 \int_{t=0}^{t=\infty} \varepsilon \, dt \tag{4-100}$$

where K_3 = gain constant of integrating device

It is obvious that the drive torque produced by such a controller can never be zero unless ε is identically zero and the integral of $\varepsilon \, dt$ is also zero.   Thus such a device increases the torque produced as long as an error persists and maintains a torque even after the error is reduced to zero because of the integral effect.   In this way it is able to compensate for load torques.   The gain constant K_3 determines the magnitude of the torque produced for a given error integral and thus controls the time required to reduce the error to zero.   It should also be obvious that any derivative controls used in addition to integral control would be included because of their effect on the transient period, since the integral control is sufficient for the correction of steady-state error.

The addition of an integral-control component is shown in Fig. 4-17, and the mathematical relationships involved are pointed out in the following equation. The torque applied to the output shaft is

$$T = K\varepsilon + K_3 \int_0^t \varepsilon\, dt \mp T_L \tag{4-101}$$

and the equilibrium equation becomes

$$J\frac{d^2\theta_o}{dt^2} + f\frac{d\theta_o}{dt} = K\varepsilon + K_3 \int_0^t \varepsilon\, dt \mp T_L \tag{4-102}$$

Inserting $\theta_o = \theta_i - \varepsilon$ gives

$$J\frac{d^2\theta_i}{dt^2} + f\frac{d\theta_i}{dt} = J\frac{d^2\varepsilon}{dt^2} + f\frac{d\varepsilon}{dt} + K\varepsilon + K_3 \int_0^t \varepsilon\, dt \mp T_L \tag{4-103}$$

If this equation is transformed for a stationary input with suddenly applied load torque, the solution for the error is

$$E = \frac{\pm T_L/J}{s^3 + 2\zeta\omega_n s^2 + \omega_n^2 s + P\omega_n^3} \tag{4-104}$$

where $\omega_n = \sqrt{K/J}$
$\zeta = f/2\sqrt{KJ}$
$P = \dfrac{K_3/J}{\omega_n^3}$

The transformed error equation given by (4-104) is not suitable for detailed discussion of integral control. While the actual time solution is

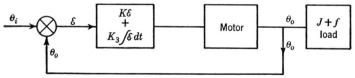

Fig. 4-17. Proportional-error servomechanism with integral error control.

desirable for complete discussion, the labor involved is too great for inclusion in this text, and the student is referred to the literature.[9] The following discussion indicates the procedures involved in obtaining the time solution, as well as the form of the solution, which is sufficient for the purposes of this text.

Equation (4-104) has a cubic denominator, and in order to apply the partial fraction theorem, the roots of this cubic must be found. Algebraic methods are available,[9] and a number of authors[9,10,14] have prepared graphs which are very helpful in numerical work, as is also the differential analyzer. In general, a cubic equation has three roots, and in servomechanism work these roots normally consist of one real root and two complex conjugate roots (the reasons for this to be given later). The partial fraction expansion of Eq. (4-104) is therefore of the form

$$E = \frac{A}{s + X} + \frac{B}{s + (Y + jZ)} + \frac{C}{s + (Y - jZ)} \qquad (4\text{-}105)$$

where A, B, and C are determined in the usual manner. It should be noted that Eq. (4-104) is for the special case of stationary input and sudden load torque, and so the numerator of this equation is not representative of all initial conditions.

The solution of Eq. (4-105) has the general form

$$\varepsilon = Ae^{-Xt} + Be^{-(Y+jZ)t} + Ce^{-(Y-jZ)t} \qquad (4\text{-}106)$$

and this reduces to the form

$$\varepsilon = Ae^{-Xt} + De^{-Yt} \sin [f(t) + \psi] \qquad (4\text{-}107)$$

The error is seen to have two exponentially decaying components, one of which is a damped harmonic function. Both components are affected to some extent by the integral coefficient K_3, and therefore the quantitative effect of integral control in the transient period is not apparent. If dimensionless curves[9,10] are prepared to study the effect of the magnitude of the integral-control signal, the following observations can be made:

1. The steady-state error ultimately becomes zero.

2. If integral control is added to a given servomechanism, the system responds more rapidly but becomes more oscillatory.

Thus the use of integral control tends to improve steady-state performance and impair transient performance, so that the use of integral control frequently requires the addition of some type of derivative control to counterbalance the effects during the transient period.

4-21. Systems with Response Delays. Before concluding the discussion of transient analysis of servomechanisms, it is desirable to include a brief study of systems in which the components are not ideal.[30,202] Assuming ideal components implies that error is measured instantaneously, that torque is applied to the output at the instant a signal is transmitted to the motor, and that all derivatives are taken instantaneously. In any practical system not all of these assumptions are fulfilled, for some of the components have inherent time-delay characteristics. While these response delays may be quite small, it is possible to have several such delays in the system and the additive effect may be appreciable.

Any energy-storage device may introduce a time delay in the transfer of energy. The time-lag effects of these components can be handled mathematically in much the same fashion regardless of the physical nature of the components (mechanical, electrical, thermal, etc.). The general expression which must be used to modify the system equations is the same for all single-delay units. Therefore the characteristic equation of a single-time-delay unit will be derived and generalized for use in further discussion.

A typical single-delay unit is a shunt-wound d-c motor operating with constant-field excitation. The signal voltage is applied to the armature, and the response is a torque at the motor shaft. In general the torque is directly proportional to the instantaneous armature current,

$$T = K_t ia \tag{4-108}$$

but the armature current lags the signal voltage because of the inductance of the armature. The output torque is therefore delayed in time with respect to the signal voltage. Mathematically,

$$V = L\frac{di}{dt} + iR \rightarrow i(LS + R) \tag{4-109}$$

where L = self-inductance of entire armature circuit including any interpole or compensating windings

R = resistance of entire armature circuit (brush drop neglected)

From Eq. (4-109) the transformed current equation is

$$i = \frac{V}{Ls + R} \tag{4-110}$$

and

$$T = \frac{K_t V/R}{(L/R)s + 1} = \frac{A}{Bs + 1} \tag{4-111}$$

which may be used as the general equation of a single time delay, where A and B are constants depending on the specific component.

The effect of such a component on the mathematical equation of a system may be illustrated by considering a proportional-error plus first-derivative error controller. For such a controller the applied torque has been described as

$$T = K\varepsilon + K_1\frac{d\varepsilon}{dt} \rightarrow (K + K_1 s)E(s) \tag{4-112}$$

when it was assumed that there were no time delays. If the only time delay in the system is in the motor, then the above expression does not give the torque, but only the signal applied to the motor, and would therefore correspond* to the quantity V of Eq. (4-104). With a time

* In Eq. (4-112) as applied to a system without time delay, the constants K and K_1 contain the torque constant of the motor and therefore do not correspond exactly to the term V in (4-109). Likewise the constants K_a and K_b of Eq. (4-113) do not correspond to any easily defined quantity. In actually setting up the equations of a system, however, no particular difficulty is encountered.

delay in the motor the expression for torque is more correctly

$$T = \frac{(K_a + K_b s)E(s)}{Bs + 1} \tag{4-113}$$

If Eq. (4-113) is used in setting up the torque-equilibrium equation of the system, the result is

$$s^2 J \Theta_o(s) + sf\Theta_o(s) = \frac{(K_a + sK_b)E(s)}{Bs + 1} \tag{4-114}$$

which may be nondimensionalized to give

$$s^2\Theta_o + 2s\gamma\omega_n\Theta_o = \frac{2\delta\omega_n s + \omega_n{}^2}{(\alpha/\omega_n)s + 1} E \tag{4-115}$$

where $\omega_n = \sqrt{K_a/J}$
$2\delta\omega_n = K_b/J$
$2\gamma\omega_n = f/J$
$\dfrac{\alpha}{\omega_n} = B$

When the substitution $\Theta_o(s) = \Theta_i(s) - E(s)$ is made in Eq. (4-115) and the result is solved for E, the error equation becomes

$$E = \frac{[s^3\alpha + s^2(\omega_n + 2\gamma\alpha\omega_n) + s2\gamma\omega_n{}^2]\Theta_i}{s^3\alpha + s^2(\omega_n + 2\gamma\alpha\omega_n) + s(2\gamma\omega_n + 2\delta\omega_n) + \omega_n{}^3} \tag{4-116}$$

The presence of a single time delay therefore changes the denominator of the error equation from a quadratic to a cubic expression. Thus the over-all transient performance is affected, and in general the system becomes more oscillatory.

If two time delays are in series in the system, for example a time delay in the controller and one in the motor, the algebraic form of the ideal torque expression must be multiplied by a time-delay factor.

$$\text{Time-delay factor} = \frac{A}{(Bs + 1)(Cs + 1)} = \frac{A}{BCs^2 + (B + C)s + 1} \tag{4-117}$$

This factor would then raise the characteristic equation of the system to the fourth power, making solution and analysis more laborious and the system even more unstable. Some discussion of single and double time delays is available in the literature[30,33,40–42,204] and is worth reading. Further discussion is beyond the scope of this text.

PROBLEMS

4-1. In the system of Fig. 4P-1 the following are known as determined experimentally for a d-c shunt motor with inertia and friction loading. Assume motor armature inductance is negligible and that the shunt field is excited from constant voltage source.

K_T = motor torque constant = 0.554×10^{-4} ft-lb/amp
K_M = back-emf constant = 0.200 volt-sec/revolution
K_1 = isolation amplifier gain = 0.185 volt/volt
J_M = motor armature inertia = 1.05×10^{-6} slug-ft^2
J_L = load inertia = 400×10^{-6} slug-ft^2
f_L = load friction coefficient = 5.68×10^{-4} ft-lb/radian/sec
n = motor-load gear ratio = $20:1$
R_a = motor armature resistance = 0.2 ohm.

a. Write the differential equation of the system relating θ_o to the input voltage, and solve for θ_o and ω_o if a unit step function is applied to the input.

b. Assume a step input of 150 volts is applied, and determine the equations for the dynamic variation of θ_o, θ_m, $\omega_o = d\theta_o/dt$, and $\omega_m = d\theta_m/dt$.

c. Plot the curves of part b on the same coordinate axis.

d. Calculate the power dissipated in the friction damper for part b.

4-2. Repeat parts b and c of Prob. 4-1 for each of the following conditions:

a. All data are the same as in Prob. 4-1 except that R_a is increased to 0.4 ohm.

b. All data are the same as in Prob. 4-1 except that the friction coefficient is zero.

c. All data are the same as in Prob. 4-1 except that the armature inductance is no longer negligible and is 0.02 henry.

Compare response curves for the various conditions.

4-3. In the system of Fig. 4P-2, $R_f = 1000$ ohms; $L_f = 4$ henrys; $K_g = 440$ volts/ amp; $K_m = 0.292$ volt/radian/sec; $R_g = 0.2$ ohm; $R_m = 0.3$ ohm; $K_t = 0.182$ ft-lb/amp; $K_1 = 3.92$ volts/volt; $J = 2.51$ slug-ft^2; $f = 1.93$ ft-lb/radian/sec; and $n = 10:1$. Write the differential equation of motion of the system, and solve for the dynamic variation of θ_o and ω_o for a unit step function of voltage applied to the input. Neglect the inductance of the motor and generator armatures as well as the inertia of the motor armature.

4-4. If the open-loop system of Fig. 4P-1 is closed by inserting a potentiometer-type error detector as shown in Fig. 4P-3, write and solve the system equation for the variation in θ_o caused by a step input of $\theta_i = 10$ deg. Assume each potentiometer has an effective 360 deg of mechanical travel and the motor constants are as stated originally in Prob. 4-1 except for $K_1 = 0.194$.

4-5. If a synchro control transformer (geared directly to the load) and a synchro generator (serving as an input member) are employed to close the open-loop system of Fig. 4P-2,

a. Draw a schematic diagram of the closed-loop system.

b. Use the same system constants as given in Prob. 4-3 except that K_1 is changed to 1.37 and the synchro sensitivity is 28.7 volts/radian; write and solve the system differential equation of motion for a step input of 10 deg.

c. Plot θ_i, θ_o, and ε as functions of time for part b.

d. Assume as an input to the system a step-velocity disturbance of 1.0 radian/sec. Determine and plot θ_i, θ_o, ω_i, and ω_o for this condition of operation.

4-6. Repeat Prob. 4-5, parts b and c, for each of the following variations of system parameters:

a. Assume that the motor inertia is no longer negligible and is equal to 0.0251 slug-ft^2. All other constants remain the same.

b. All constants are the same as originally stated except that the friction coefficient is reduced 50 per cent.

c. All constants are as originally stated except that the friction coefficient is reduced to zero.

4-7. For the system of Prob. 4-5 attempt to obtain (by altering the friction coefficient, f, and/or K_1)

a. Maximum overshoot of 50 per cent

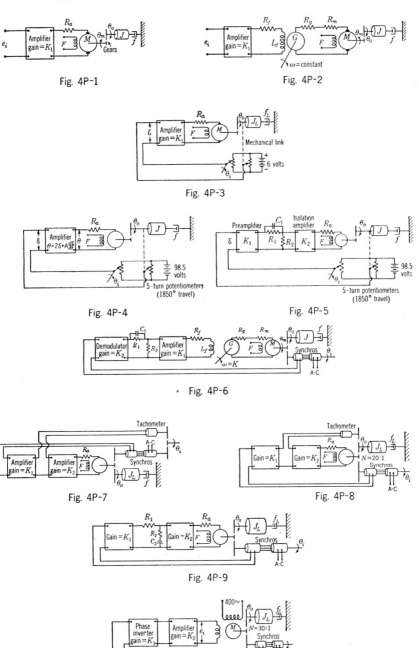

Fig. 4P-1

Fig. 4P-2

Fig. 4P-3

Fig. 4P-4

Fig. 4P-5

Fig. 4P-6

Fig. 4P-7

Fig. 4P-8

Fig. 4P-9

Fig. 4P-10

    b. A critically damped response

4-8. The basic differential equation of a proportional-error servomechanism is

$$\frac{d^2\theta_o}{dt^2} + 2\zeta\omega_n \frac{d\theta_o}{dt} + \omega_n{}^2\theta_o = \omega_n{}^2\theta_i$$

where $\theta_i - \theta_o = \varepsilon$

    a. Solve this equation for θ_o (as a function of time) if the input, θ_i, is given a step displacement and $\zeta < 1$.

    b. Repeat (a) if the input is a step velocity.

    c. Repeat (a) if the output is initially in error by an angle of ϕ.

    d. Repeat (a) if the output is suddenly subjected to a constant load torque.

4-9. Repeat Prob. 4-8, solving for the error, ε; determine the steady-state error in each case.

4-10. From the equations of Prob. 4-9a prepare dimensionless curves of ε/θ_i vs. $\omega_n t$ for various values of ζ between $\zeta = 0.3$ and $\zeta = 1.0$. Adjust the ordinate scales so that these curves may also be used to predict ε/ϕ for an initial error and $\varepsilon/\varepsilon_{ss}$ for a load torque.

4-11. From the equations of Prob. 4-9b prepare dimensionless curves of $\varepsilon/\varepsilon_{ss}$ vs. $\omega_n t$ for values of $0.3 < \zeta < 1.0$.

4-12. From the curves of Probs. 4-10 and 4-11 prepare curves of per cent maximum overshoot vs. ζ.

4-13. From the curves of Probs. 4-10 and 4-11 prepare curves of $\omega_n t$ vs. ζ for the following percentage tolerances on correspondence: 2, 5, 10, 15 per cent.

4-14. In the system of Fig. 4P-4, essentially the same motor and load constants may be used as orginally stated in Prob. 4-1, the only change being a reduction in motor inertia to 0.025×10^{-6} slug ft². Write the differential equation of the system, and solve when

    a. There is a step displacement input of 30 deg and for $A = 0, 0.02, 0.04$, and 0.1. Plot curves of θ_o vs. time.

    b. There is a step-velocity input of 10 deg/sec and values of A are as in part a. Plot curves of ω_o vs. time.

    c. What happens if A is negative?

4-15. The system shown in Fig. 4P-5 uses the same motor and load constants as employed in Prob. 4-14, and $K_2 = 10$ while $K_1 = 2$. The constants of the derivative-type network are $R_1 = 0.5 \times 10^6$ ohms, $R_2 = 4.5 \times 10^6$ ohms, and $C_1 = 0.0126$ μf.

    a. Write and solve the system equations, determining θ_o for a step-displacement input of 30 deg and for an input velocity of 10 deg/sec.

    b. What would be the trend of the system error for higher input velocities?

    c. Plot θ_i, θ_o for the step-displacement input, and also plot θ_i, θ_o, ω_i, and ω_o for the step-velocity input.

4-16. Insert an RC derivative-type network and an isolation amplifier in the closed-loop system of Prob. 4-5 as shown in Fig. 4P-6, and

    a. Set up the dynamic-equilibrium equations, and solve for θ_o, assuming a step input of 10 deg. The constants of the network are $R_2 = 1$ megohm, $R_1 = 4$ megohms, and $C_1 = 0.112$ μf. The isolation amplifier gain is $K_2 = 5$ volts/volt. ($K_1 = 1.37$ volts/volt.)

    b. Assume an input velocity of 1 radian/sec, and determine the steady-state position error.

    c. Plot θ_i, θ_o, and ε as functions of time for part a.

    d. Plot θ_i, θ_o, ω_o, and ω_i vs. time for part b.

4-17. Repeat Prob. 4-16 (parts a and b only) for the system modification noted as follows: $R_2 = 1$ megohm; $R_1 = 1.5$ megohm; $C_1 = 0.209$ μf; $K_2 = 2.5$ volts/volt.

4-18. Figure 4P-7 shows the addition of an input velocity signal to a closed-loop system. The input synchro is geared down to give a sensitivity of 0.1 volt/radian. Tachometer rating is 6 volts output at 2,000 rpm shaft speed. The tachometer is geared down 3:1. Motor and load are the same as in Prob. 4-1; $K_1 = 1$ volt/volt, and $K_2 = 1.82$ volts/volt.

a. With the constants as stated above, write and solve the system equations for θ_o and ω_o for a step-velocity input of 1 radian/sec.

b. Determine the steady-state position error.

c. Plot θ_i, θ_o, ω_o, and ω_i from the above calculations.

d. Repeat parts a, b, and c, with the tachometer reduction gearing changed to $1\frac{1}{2}$:1.

e. Repeat parts a, b, and c, with the tachometer disconnected from the input and amplifiers K_1 and K_2 cascaded directly together.

f. What effect would reversal of the tachometer output leads have on the results of part a?

4-19. Figure 4P-8 shows the addition of an output velocity signal to a closed-loop system. The tachometer constant, 0_1, is 12 volts/radian/sec; $K_2 = 0.87$; $K_T = 0.2$ ft-lb/amp; K_s (synchro sensitivity) = 1.0 volt/deg; $f_L = 1.0$ ft-lb/radian/sec; $R_a = 0.5$ ohm; $K_M = 0.475$ volt/radian/sec; $J_L = 10$ slug-ft^2; load-motor gear ratio is 10:1; $K_1 = 2.5$. Neglect the inertia and friction of the motor drive.

a. Write and solve the system equations for a step-displacement input of 1 radian and for a step-velocity input of 1 radian/sec.

b. Plot the dynamic variation of θ_i, θ_o, ω_i, and ω_o from the results of part a on a common time base.

c. Repeat parts a and b, assuming that the tachometer gearing is changed to give $0_1 = 18$ volts/radian/sec.

d. What effect would reversal of the output of the tachometer have on the system operation?

4-20. In the system of Fig. 4P-9, $R_2 = 1$ megohm; $R_1 = 4$ megohms; $C_2 = 0.5\mu f$; $K_2 = 1$; $K_1 = 1.44$; and the synchro sensitivity is 0.01 volt/deg. Use the motor and load constants of Prob. 4-1, and

a. Write and solve the system equation for θ_o and ω_o for a step-velocity input of 18 rpm.

b. Plot θ_i, θ_o, ω_i, and ω_o on the same coordinate axes, and determine the steady-state error.

c. Remove the integrating-type network, and repeat parts a and b.

d. Compare system solutions for the two cases considered.

4-21. For the computer-type servo shown in Fig. 4P-10, the following constants are known or determined experimentally:

K_1 = phase-inverter gain = 0.2 volt/volt

K_2 = power-amplifier gain = 1.2 volts/volt

f_{load} = output-member friction coefficient = 41×10^{-4} ft-lb/radian/sec

J_{load} = output-member inertia = 9.25×10^{-4} slug-ft^2

$J + f_{motor}$ = negligible

K_e = mean motor torque-voltage constant = 39.1×10^{-6} ft-lb/volt

K_n = mean motor torque-speed constant = 8.1×10^{-6} ft-lb/radian/sec

K_s = synchro sensitivity = 27 volts/radian

n = gear ratio = 30:1

a. Write the system equation, and solve for θ_o for a step input displacement of 10 deg and for a step velocity displacement of 10 rpm.

b. Plot θ_o, θ_i, ω_o, and ω_i for part a.

c. Assume that the gain K_2 is increased to 3, and repeat part a.

CHAPTER 5

TRANSFER FUNCTIONS

5-1. Introduction. The difficulties previously encountered in analyzing complex servomechanisms and designing satisfactory systems are minimized in transfer-function analysis. The transfer-function approach provides essentially the same information regarding the performance characteristics of servomechanisms as does the transient analysis, but it does so with decidedly less labor. The information, however, is not given directly (which is sometimes a disadvantage) but must be obtained from appropriate graphical plots of transfer-function data. The construction of these plots, as well as the technique of interpretation, is reserved for subsequent chapters.

The advantages of transfer-function methods over transient methods are most apparent when preliminary tests indicate that system performance must be improved. If only transient methods have been used, it is usually difficult to predict the effect of any chosen variation in system parameters. In direct contrast to this, the transfer-function method establishes for each component a unique mathematical expression which specifies the contribution of the individual component to the over-all system performance. The "transfer functions" for each component are easily identified in the over-all system equation, and so the effect of changing a component or adding components is readily seen. The present chapter is devoted to the standard procedures for setting up the transfer functions of system components. Consideration is also given to the manner of correctly combining these transfer functions to get the over-all system transfer function, which is necessary to predict servomechanism performance.

5-2. Definition of Transfer Function.[31,45,*] The transfer function of any device may be defined as the complex ratio of the output of the device to its input. The use of such expressions in communication systems is reasonably common, and their use in servomechanism analysis is due to the similarity between transmission networks and servomechanisms. The function of a communication-transmission network is to transfer information from a command station (transmitter) to an output

---

* Superior numbers, when they appear in the text proper, are the numbers of references given in the Bibliography.

station (receiver). To accomplish this, an energy transfer is required, and usually power amplification is involved. Whether or not the information is faithfully reproduced at the output depends on the characteristics of the connecting networks. Thus the ratio of output to input describes the characteristics of the networks. Similarly, the general function of a servomechanism is to transfer a signal from a command station to an output station, usually with considerable increase in power level, and the correspondence of output and input signals is also a function of the characteristics of the components of the system. It is this similarity that permits the use of much of the highly developed network theory[48–50] in servomechanism analysis and design.

Transfer functions may be calculated either by employing ordinary circuit theory or by means of the Laplace transform. In a few of the following examples both methods are used to show their equivalence.

5-3. Derivation of Transfer Functions. In the following paragraphs the transfer functions of a selected group of servo components are derived. Some are then combined into a complete servomechanism to illustrate the methods used in obtaining the transfer function of a system.

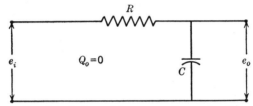

FIG. 5-1. Series resistance-capacitance circuit.

RC Network.[46] For the network shown the equilibrium equations are

$$e_i = iR + \frac{1}{C} \int i \, dt = R \frac{dq}{dt} + \frac{q}{C} \tag{5-1}$$

$$e_o = \frac{q}{C} \tag{5-2}$$

These transform to

$$E_i(s) = \left(sR + \frac{1}{C} \right) Q(s) \tag{5-3}$$

$$E_o(s) = \left(\frac{1}{C} \right) Q(s) \tag{5-4}$$

Dividing,

$$\frac{E_o(s)}{E_i(s)} = \frac{(1/C)Q(s)}{(sR + 1/C)Q(s)} = \frac{1}{sRC + 1} = \frac{1}{s\tau + 1} \tag{5-5}$$

where $\tau = RC$ = time constant of the network

Equation (5-5) is the transfer function of the RC network, since it expresses the complex ratio of output to input for any type of input wave. Note that the transfer function is obtained from the direct Laplace transform of the differential equations and is not retransformed into the time variable.   This usually means a considerable saving in labor.   If a sinusoidal input is assumed,* the variable s is changed to $j\omega$.   This may be justified from complex-variable theory, but no attempt will be made to explain it at this point.   The reasons may be seen from the treatment of the Nyquist stability criterion in a later chapter.   However, if the substitution is made in Eq. (5-5), the result is

$$\frac{E_o}{E_i}(j\omega) = \frac{1}{j\omega\tau + 1} \tag{5-6}$$

and this equation for the transfer function may be checked by normal circuit theory.   Assuming a sinusoidal input, then

$$E_i \text{ (effective)} \triangleq E \tag{5-8}$$

$$I = \frac{E}{R - j/\omega C} \tag{5-9}$$

$$E_o = I\left(\frac{-j}{\omega C}\right) = \frac{E(-j/\omega C)}{R - j/\omega C} \tag{5-10}$$

$$\frac{E_o}{E_i} = \frac{\dfrac{E(-j/\omega C)}{R - j/\omega C}}{E} = \frac{-j/\omega C}{R - j/\omega C} = \frac{-j}{\omega CR - j} = \frac{1}{j\omega CR + 1} \tag{5-11}$$

Obviously, then, the transfer function may be obtained either from the Laplace transformation or from circuit theory.

RL Network.   The   equilibrium equations are

$$e_i = R_i + L\frac{di}{dt} \tag{5-12}$$

$$e_o = L\frac{di}{dt} \tag{5-13}$$

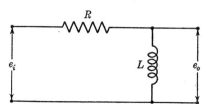

FIG. 5-2. Series resistance-inductance circuit.

These transform to

$$E_i(s) = RI(s) + sLI(s) \tag{5-14}$$
$$E_o(s) = sLI(s) \tag{5-15}$$

from which

$$\frac{E_o}{E_i}(s) = \frac{sLI(s)}{(R + sL)I(s)} = \frac{sL}{R + sL} = \frac{s\tau}{1 + s\tau} \tag{5-16}$$

where $\tau = L/R$ = circuit time constant

* In determining the transfer function of system components, ordinarily the standard test signal (see Chap. 4) employed is the sinusoidal input.   Often transfer-function analysis is referred to as sinusoidal-transfer analysis.

For a sinusoidal input, s is replaced by $j\omega$, resulting in

$$\frac{E_o}{E_i}(j\omega) = \frac{j\omega\tau}{1 + j\omega\tau} \qquad (5\text{-}17)$$

Using circuit theory to derive the transfer function for an assumed sinusoidal input, the equations are

$$e_i = Em \sin \omega t \qquad (5\text{-}18)$$
$$E_i(\text{effective}) = E \qquad (5\text{-}19)$$
$$I = \frac{E}{R + j\omega L} \qquad (5\text{-}20)$$
$$E_o = Ij\omega L = \frac{Ej\omega L}{R + j\omega L} \qquad (5\text{-}21)$$
$$\frac{E_o}{E_i} = \frac{Ej\omega L/(R + j\omega L)}{E} = \frac{j\omega L}{R + j\omega L} = \frac{j\omega L/R}{1 + j\omega L/R} = \frac{j\omega\tau}{1 + j\omega\tau} \qquad (5\text{-}22)$$

Once the transfer function of a system or component has been derived, the physical nature of the component is of no importance in the mathematical analysis. Hence several simplifications can be made in handling components and their transfer functions. Instead of complicated schematic drawings, or even simplified equivalent circuits, an equivalent block diagram can be introduced. For the RC and RL networks the equivalent blocks are shown in Fig. 5-3, as well as the notation usually employed. Any complicated system can be replaced by series and parallel arrangements of these blocks and shown on a single line diagram.

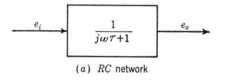

(a) RC network

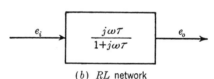

(b) RL network

FIG. 5-3. Block diagrams of transfer functions.

A second simplification is to introduce a shorthand notation for the transfer function. Generally the transfer function is made up of two factors, a constant term and a complex, or frequency-dependent, term. In the preceding cases of the RC and RL networks, the constant factor is unity in each case, and the frequency-dependent factors are

$$\frac{1}{j\omega\tau + 1} \quad \text{and} \quad \frac{j\omega\tau}{j\omega\tau + 1}$$

respectively. The two factors common to a transfer function may be denoted by simple algebraic symbols. A convenient notation is to use K, with suitable subscripts, for the constant factor, and G, again with subscripts, for the complex factor. Then in general:

$$\text{Any transfer function} = KG \qquad (5\text{-}23)$$

It is frequently convenient to denote the variable used in the calculation; thus $KG(s)$ means that the transfer function is to be expressed in the complex variable, s, while $KG(j\omega)$ means that the transfer function is to be expressed in terms of the frequency variable, $j\omega$. Thus for the RC network

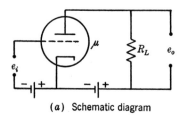

(a) Schematic diagram

$$KG(s) = \frac{1}{s\tau + 1}$$
$$KG(j\omega) = \frac{1}{j\omega\tau + 1} \qquad (5\text{-}24)$$

and for the RL network

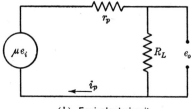

(b) Equivalent circuit

$$KG(s) = \frac{s\tau}{s\tau + 1}$$
$$KG(j\omega) = \frac{j\omega\tau}{j\omega\tau + 1} \qquad (5\text{-}25)$$

Usually algebraic manipulations are more readily accomplished using the KG notation, and the actual transfer functions are substituted when the equation is in approximately final form.

Electronic Amplifier. A simple electronic amplifier, as in Fig. 5-4a, may be represented by the equivalent circuit of Fig. 5-4b at low frequencies, and the dynamic plate resistance, r_p, may be considered constant. Then from the equivalent circuit

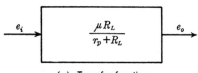

(c) Transfer function

Fig. 5-4. Transfer function of an electronic amplifier.

$$\mu e_i = i_p(r_p + R_L) \qquad (5\text{-}26)$$
$$e_o = i_p R_L \qquad (5\text{-}27)$$

Applying the Laplace transform,

$$\mu E_i(s) = I_p(s)(r_p + R_L) \qquad (5\text{-}28)$$
$$E_o(s) = I_p(s)(R_L) \qquad (5\text{-}29)$$
$$\frac{E_o}{E_i}(s) = \frac{I_p(s)R_L\mu}{I_p(s)(r_p + R_L)}$$
$$= \frac{\mu R_L}{R_L + r_p} = KG(s) \qquad (5\text{-}30)$$

In this case the transfer function is simply a constant, but the KG notation is kept intact to avoid confusion in manipulation.

Ideal D-C Generator. Figure 5-5 shows schematically a d-c shunt-wound generator rotating at constant speed with a signal voltage applied to its field circuit. If the generator is open-circuited, or if its loading is

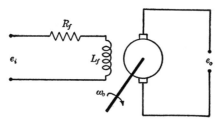

FIG. 5-5. Direct-current generator.

known to produce little internal drop, then the following equations may be written:

From the magnetization curve

$$K_g = \frac{e_o}{i_f} \tag{5-31}$$

and from the schematic circuit diagram

$$e_i = i_f R_f + \frac{di_f}{dt} L_f \tag{5-32}$$

where K_g = generator constant, volts per field ampere
R_f = generator field resistance
L_f = generator field inductance (assume constant)
Transforming,

$$K_g = \frac{E_o(s)}{I_f(s)} \tag{5-33}$$

$$E_i(s) = I_f(s)R_f + sL_f I_f(s) \tag{5-34}$$

from which

$$\frac{E_o}{E_i}(s) = \frac{K_g I_f(s)}{(R_f + sL_f)I_f(s)} = \frac{K_g/R_f}{1 + sL_f/R_f}$$

$$= \frac{K_g}{R_f}\left(\frac{1}{1 + s\tau_f}\right) = KG(s) \tag{5-35}$$

where $\tau_f = L_f/R_f$
$K = K_g/R_f$
$G(s) = 1/(1 + s\tau_f)$

Example 1.   A shunt-wound generator has a field resistance of $R_f = 40$ ohms and a field inductance of $L_f = 0.5$ henry.   The magnetization curve of the machine is shown in Fig. 5-6.   Find its transfer function.

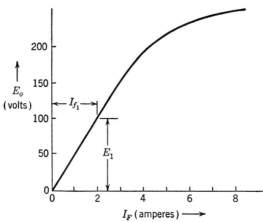

FIG. 5-6. Magnetization curve of a d-c shunt generator.

Solution.   Assuming that the operation of the generator will be limited to the linear portion of the magnetization curve, and neglecting hysteresis effects, the generator constant is

$$K_g = \frac{E_1}{I_{f_1}} = \frac{100}{2} = 50 \text{ volts/amp}$$

$$\tau_f = \frac{L_f}{R_f} = \frac{0.5}{40} = 0.0125 \text{ sec}$$

$$KG(s) = \frac{K_g}{R_f}\left(\frac{1}{1 + \tau_f s}\right) = \frac{50}{40}\left(\frac{1}{1 + 0.0125s}\right) = 1.25\left(\frac{1}{1 + 0.0125s}\right)$$

$$K = 1.25$$

$$G(s) = \frac{1}{1 + 0.0125s}$$

Ideal D-C Motor with Constant Field.[55–57]   Figure 5-7 shows a shunt-wound d-c motor with constant-field excitation.   The input voltage is applied to the armature, and the output is the shaft rotation $d\theta_o/dt$.   The transfer function of the motor relates the position of the output shaft, θ_o, to the input voltage, e_i.   Assuming that the inductance of the armature is negligible, the equations of the motor are

$$e_i = i_a R_a + E_b \tag{5-36}$$

where

$$E_b = K_v \frac{d\theta_o}{dt} \tag{5-37}$$

and K_v is the motor back-emf constant. Then

$$e_i = i_a R_a + K_v \frac{d\theta_o}{dt} \tag{5-38}$$

The torque developed by an ideal d-c motor is proportional to the armature current, that is, $T = K_1 \Phi i_a$ (neglecting armature reaction); so here

$$T = K_t i_a \tag{5-39}$$

where T = shaft torque

K_t = torque constant, lb-ft/amp, for a given excitation

The torque itself is a function of operating conditions, and therefore Eq. (5-39) cannot be used directly. In an ideal motor, however, there is

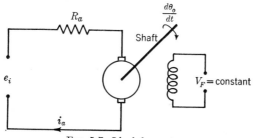

Fig. 5-7. Ideal d-c motor.

negligible friction, and so the motor need only supply torque to balance inertia effects; thus the torque equilibrium can be written as

$$T = J \frac{d^2\theta_o}{dt^2} \tag{5-40}$$

where J is the inertia of the motor plus any load inertia. Then

$$i_a = \frac{J}{K_t} \frac{d^2\theta_o}{dt^2} \tag{5-41}$$

and

$$e_i = \frac{J R_a}{K_t} \frac{d^2\theta_o}{dt^2} + K_v \frac{d\theta_o}{dt} \tag{5-42}$$

Transforming gives

$$E_i(s) = \left(s^2 \frac{J R_a}{K_t} + s K_v \right) \Theta_o(s) \tag{5-43}$$

from which

$$\frac{\Theta_o}{E_i}(s) = \frac{1}{s\left(\dfrac{J R_a}{K_t} s + K_v \right)} = KG(s) \tag{5-44}$$

$$\frac{\Theta_o}{E_i}(j\omega) = \frac{1}{j\omega\left(\dfrac{J R_a}{K_t} j\omega + K_v \right)} = KG(j\omega) \tag{5-45}$$

By algebraic manipulation

$$KG(j\omega) = \cfrac{1}{j\omega K_v \left(j\omega \dfrac{JR_a}{K_t K_v} + 1 \right)} = \frac{1}{K_v} \frac{1}{j\omega(j\omega\tau_m + 1)} \qquad (5\text{-}46)$$

where $\tau_m = JR_a/K_t K_v$ = motor time constant

τ_m has the dimensions of time (seconds) and is the time required for the motor to speed up to 63.2 per cent of its final velocity, when supplied from a constant-voltage source. It therefore has some practical use in the design of d-c motors for automatic-control systems,[158] in addition to simplifying the equation.

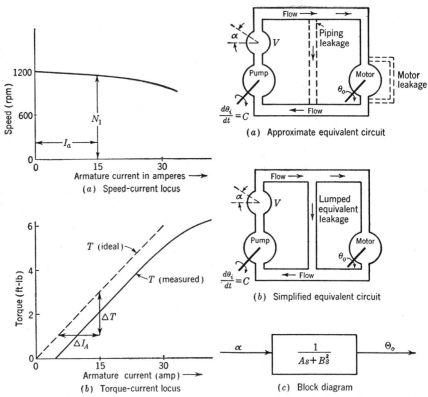

(a) Speed-current locus

(b) Torque-current locus

Fig. 5-8. Characteristic curves of a d-c shunt motor.

(a) Approximate equivalent circuit

(b) Simplified equivalent circuit

(c) Block diagram

Fig. 5-9. Hydraulic transmission and its transfer function.

Example 2. The speed-current and current-torque curves of a d-c shunt motor are shown in Fig. 5-8. Determine the transfer function of the motor if it is connected as in Fig. 5-7 and if operation is limited to the linear portions of the curve.

Given $R_a = 0.5$ ohm, $V = 115$ volts, $J = 5$ slug-ft^2. Then

$$K_t = \frac{T}{i_a} = \frac{\Delta T}{\Delta I_a} = \frac{2}{8} = 0.25 \text{ ft-lb/amp}$$

$$K_v = \frac{E_b}{d\theta_o/dt} = \frac{E_b}{N} = \frac{V - I_a R_a}{\text{radians/sec}}$$

$$= \frac{115 - 15 \times 0.5}{1,175/60} = \frac{107.5}{2\pi \times 1,175/60} = 0.876 \text{ volt/radian/sec}$$

$$KG(s) = \frac{1}{K_v} \frac{1}{s(s\tau_m + 1)}$$

$$\tau_m = \frac{JR_a}{K_t K_v} = \frac{5 \times 0.5}{0.25 \times 0.876} = 11.4 \text{ sec}$$

$$KG(s) = \frac{1}{0.876} \frac{1}{s(11.4s + 1)}$$

$$KG(j\omega) = \frac{1}{0.876} \frac{1}{j\omega(11.4j\omega + 1)}$$

Hydraulic Transmission.[143] In Fig. 5-9a is shown the approximate equivalent circuit of a hydraulic-pump and motor combination, often used as the final power amplifier and servomotor drive in applications with high torque and rapid speed-of-response requirements. Various types of hydraulic members may be combined to form a satisfactory system, but here it is assumed that a variable-displacement pump is connected to a constant-displacement motor.

In a typical hydraulic pump, a multiple array of pistons, driven by external means, provide the fluid flow. The angular displacement, or tilt, of these pistons from a neutral, or no-fluid-flow, position determines both the quantity of fluid delivered by the pump and the direction of the flow. The fluid-flow control action is represented by the valve, V, in the figure shown. The hydraulic motor, a unit similar to the pump, has speed-torque characteristics which are a function of the pump output. The speed and direction of rotation of the hydraulic servomotor are functions of the quantity of fluid flow and the direction of fluid flow provided by the pump. In normal operation, control of the fluid flow is accomplished by mechanically adjusting the stroke of the piston arrangement to control the quantity and porting of the outflow to give the desired directional response.

In the simplified equivalent circuit the pump outflow is controlled by the action of the butterfly valve, and it should be kept in mind that the angular displacement, α, of this valve corresponds directly to the actual tilt of the pistons in normal operation. Because of the relatively high pressures at which such systems operate, there usually is leakage past the pump and motor pistons and leakage in the piping and past the valves.   These leakage paths are symbolically shown in Fig. 5-9a.   The difficulty in determining actual leakage, which is distributed about the entire system, necessitates assuming an equivalent lumped leakage as shown in Fig. 5-9b.   The assumptions which are made in drawing the simplified equivalent circuit and in calculating the transfer function are

1. Pump displacement (flow) is directly proportional to α.

2. Leakages may be lumped into a single equivalent leakage which varies directly with system pressure.

3. The pump speed is constant, and the motor is ideal.

4. The only loading is inertia and friction.

5. Compression in the fluid is negligible (this leads to large errors at times but is still a desirable simplification here).

6. Line losses are negligible.

On the basis of the above assumptions the following equations may be written to obtain the desired transfer function:

$$Q_p = Q_m + Q_L \tag{5-47}$$

where Q_p = total fluid displaced by the pump
  Q_m = fluid passing through motor
  Q_L = fluid flowing through leakage path

but

$$Q_p = K_p\alpha \tag{5-48}$$

where K_p = pump displacement per unit tilt angle
  α = angle of tilt

and

$$Q_m = K_m \frac{d\theta_o}{dt} \tag{5-49}$$

where K_m = motor displacement per unit angular speed
  θ_o = angular position of motor shaft

Also,

$$Q_L = K_L P \tag{5-50}$$

where K_L = leakage coefficient in unit displacement per unit pressure
  P = effective pressure of the fluid-transmission system

Substituting,

$$K_p\alpha = K_m \frac{d\theta_o}{dt} + K_L P \tag{5-51}$$

The pressure, P, depends on the delivered torque and is thus a function of the output.   As such it must be expressed in terms of the output quantities before the transfer function can be found.   The developed torque is

$$T_D = K_m P \tag{5-52}$$

but with only inertia and friction loading

$$T_D = J \frac{d^2\theta_o}{dt^2} + f \frac{d\theta_o}{dt} \tag{5-53}$$

where J = effective inertia of motor and load referred to output shaft
f = viscous-damping coefficient of output
Then

$$P = \frac{1}{K_m} \left(J \frac{d^2\theta_o}{dt^2} + f \frac{d\theta_o}{dt} \right) \tag{5-54}$$

and this is substituted in Eq. (5-51) to give

$$K_p \alpha = K_m \frac{d\theta_o}{dt} + \frac{K_L}{K_m} \left(J \frac{d^2\theta_o}{dt^2} + f \frac{d\theta_o}{dt} \right) \tag{5-55}$$

Then

$$\alpha = \left(\frac{K_m}{K_p} + \frac{K_L f}{K_m K_p} \right) \frac{d\theta_o}{dt} + \frac{K_L J}{K_p K_m} \frac{d^2\theta_o}{dt^2} \tag{5-56}$$

$$= A \frac{d\theta_o}{dt} + B \frac{d^2\theta_o}{dt^2} \tag{5-57}$$

where $A = K_m/K_p + K_L f/K_p K_m$
$B = K_L J/K_p K_m$
Transforming with initial conditions assumed zero,

$$\alpha = As\Theta_o + Bs^2\Theta_o = \Theta_o(As + Bs^2) \tag{5-58}$$

$$\frac{\Theta_o(s)}{\alpha} = KG(s) = \frac{1}{As + Bs^2} \tag{5-59}$$

Additional transfer functions will not be derived in the text except where needed for specific illustrations. It should be noted that the preceding methods are applicable to all types of components (electrical, mechanical, hydraulic, etc.) provided that proper care is taken when interactions are encountered. For example, the amplifier of Fig. 5-4 has the transfer function of Eq. (5-30) only if the output voltage, e_o, is fed into a very high impedance. If the network, into which e_o is fed, is a low impedance, it effectively interacts with the amplifier, i.e., it acts as a path in parallel with R_2 and absorbs a portion of the plate current, so that the net impedance of R_2 plus the load in parallel with it determines the transfer function of the amplifier.

5-4. Over-all Transfer Function of a Simple Positioning Servomechanism. The transfer functions developed for an amplifier, generator, and motor are now to be combined to illustrate the procedures involved in determining the transfer function of a system. Figure 5-10 is a schematic diagram of a simple positioning servomechanism which incorporates the desired equipment. The over-all, or composite, transfer function of a servomechanism is needed in order to determine system performance, though actual interpretation is obtained most readily from graphical plots of the transfer-function equation rather than from the equation itself.

The operation of the automatic positioning controller may be seen from Fig. 5-10a. Under quiescent conditions the input and output potentiometers are in correspondence, and so no error voltage is developed across the potentiometer take-off. If the input, connected to potentiometer 1,

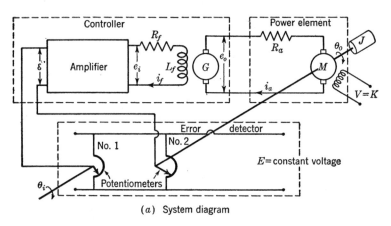

(a) System diagram

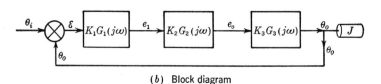

(b) Block diagram

Fig. 5-10. Elementary positioning servomechanism.

is moved to a new position, an error voltage, ε, will be set up and fed into the controller. This signal voltage is amplified and applied to the generator field. The voltage, e_1, must be of the proper polarity to drive the motor, load, and potentiometer 2 into correspondence with the input dial. Thus the rotation of the motor reduces the error, and ultimately the system comes to steady state with the load in a new position.

It should be noted that the amplifier used in Fig. 5-10a must differ somewhat from that given in Fig. 5-4, as the amplifier needed here must be phase-sensitive, i.e., must reverse the polarity of its output voltage, e_1, when the input voltage reverses. Also, the field impedance of a generator is usually low; so the transfer function of the amplifier should be derived in such a way as to include the effect of the generator field. For brevity in completing the illustration it is assumed that the proper type of amplifier is available and that

$$e_1 = \mu_a \mathcal{E} \tag{5-60}$$

when the generator field is connected to the amplifier.

Figure 5-10a may be replaced by a series of block diagrams as shown in Fig. 5-10b. The transfer functions of the blocks are then

$$K_1 G_1(j\omega) = \mu_a \tag{5-61}$$

$$K_2 G_2(j\omega) = \frac{K_g}{R_f} \frac{1}{j\omega\tau_f + 1} \tag{5-62}$$

$$K_3 G_3(j\omega) = \frac{1}{K_v} \frac{1}{j\omega(j\omega\tau_m + 1)} \tag{5-63}$$

The over-all transfer function of the system may be derived either by writing differential equations relating the physical parameters of each component and properly manipulating them or by using the mathematics of block diagrams and the known transfer functions of the components. Both methods will be used here to illustrate the advantage of the latter method. The equations which may be written for the differential equation approach are

$$\mu_a \mathcal{E} = e_i = i_f R_f + L \frac{di_f}{dt} \tag{5-64}$$

$$i_f = \frac{e_o}{K_g} \tag{5-65}$$

$$e_o = i_a R_a + K_v \frac{d\theta_o}{dt} \tag{5-66}$$

$$i_a = \frac{J}{K_T} \frac{d^2\theta_o}{dt^2} \tag{5-67}$$

Substituting (5-65) in (5-64),

$$\mu_a \mathcal{E} = \frac{e_o}{K_g} R_f + \frac{L}{K_g} \frac{de_o}{dt} \tag{5-68}$$

Substituting (5-67) in (5-66),

$$e_o = \frac{JR_a}{K_T} \frac{d^2\theta_o}{dt^2} + K_v \frac{d\theta_o}{dt} \tag{5-69}$$

Substituting (5-69) in (5-68)

$$\mu_a \mathcal{E} = \frac{JR_a R_f}{K_T K_g} \frac{d^2\theta_o}{dt^2} + \frac{K_v R_f}{K_g} \frac{d\theta_o}{dt} + \frac{LJR_a}{K_T K_g} \frac{d^3\theta_o}{dt^3} + \frac{LK_v}{K_g} \frac{d^2\theta_o}{dt^2} \tag{5-70}$$

Transforming (5-70) gives

$$\mu_a E(s) = \left[s^3 \frac{LJR_a}{K_T K_g} + s^2 \left(\frac{JR_a R_f}{K_T K_g} + \frac{LK_v}{K_g} \right) + s \frac{K_v R_f}{K_g} \right] \Theta_o(s) \tag{5-71}$$

from which

$$KG(s) = \frac{\Theta_o}{E}(s) = \cfrac{\mu_a}{s\left[s^2 \dfrac{LJR_a}{K_T K_g} + s\left(\dfrac{JR_a R_f}{K_T K_g} + \dfrac{LK_v}{K_g}\right) + \dfrac{K_v R_f}{K_g}\right]} \quad (5\text{-}72)$$

By proper manipulation, Eq. (5-72) reduces to

$$KG(s) = \frac{\mu_a K_g}{R_f K_v} \frac{1}{s(\tau_m s + 1)(\tau_f s + 1)}$$

$$KG(j\omega) = \frac{\mu_a K_g}{R_f K_v} \frac{1}{j\omega(j\omega\tau_m + 1)(j\omega\tau_f + 1)} \quad (5\text{-}73)$$

where τ_m and τ_f are as previously defined.

The derivation of the transfer function from the block diagram is relatively simple.   It is easily seen that

$$\begin{aligned}
\frac{\theta_o}{\mathcal{E}} &= \frac{\theta_o}{e_o}\frac{e_o}{e_1}\frac{e_1}{\mathcal{E}} = K_3 G_3 K_2 G_2 K_1 G_1 \\
&= \frac{1}{K_v}\frac{1}{j\omega(j\omega\tau_m + 1)}\frac{K_g}{R_f}\frac{1}{(j\omega\tau_f + 1)}\mu_a \\
&= \frac{\mu_a K_g}{R_f K_v}\frac{1}{j\omega(j\omega\tau_m + 1)(j\omega\tau_f + 1)} \quad (5\text{-}74)
\end{aligned}$$

Thus the advantage of using the block-diagram method is apparent.

It should be mentioned at this point that a solution of the system equations for the ratio of the output quantity to the error is not always the most desirable.   Those quantities which are of importance in servomechanism analysis are

1. $\dfrac{\theta_o}{\mathcal{E}} \triangleq KG$, the direct transfer function

2. $\dfrac{\theta_o}{\theta_i} \triangleq$, the frequency-response function

3. $\dfrac{\mathcal{E}}{\theta_o} \triangleq KG^{-1}$, the inverse transfer function

4. $\dfrac{\theta_i}{\theta_o} \triangleq$, the inverse frequency-response function

The information usually desired about servomechanisms is contained implicitly in the frequency-response function θ_o/θ_i, since this directly relates the input and output quantities.   However, none of the equations can be interpreted without plotting curves, and under these conditions interpretation of the direct transfer-function curves is simplest, and so the majority of this chapter is still concerned with $\theta_o/\mathcal{E}$.   When it is desired to get θ_o/θ_i, simple algebraic operations may be performed on the direct transfer function to get the desired result.   The inverse functions are often convenient to use, particularly when parallel circuits are encountered.

5-5. Algebra of Block Diagrams and Transfer Functions. Since block diagrams and transfer functions facilitate quick and accurate servo-circuit analysis and design, a few rules for algebraic manipulation of these can be set down. These rules are most easily derived by considering a few examples.

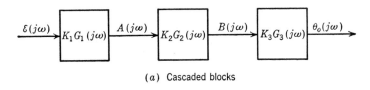

(*a*) Cascaded blocks

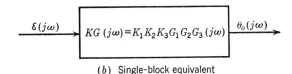

(*b*) Single-block equivalent

Fig. 5-11. Servo components in series.

Over-all Transfer Function of Series Components. A number of components, having transfer functions as indicated, are shown in series in Fig. 5-11*a*. The over-all transfer of the series combination is determined by noting that

$$KG(j\omega) = \frac{\theta_o}{\mathcal{E}}(j\omega) = \frac{A}{\mathcal{E}}(j\omega)\frac{B}{A}(j\omega)\frac{\theta_o}{B}(j\omega) \qquad (5\text{-}75)$$

and it is readily seen that

$$\frac{A}{\mathcal{E}}(j\omega) = K_1G_1(j\omega)$$

$$\frac{B}{A}(j\omega) = K_2G_2(j\omega)$$

$$\frac{\theta_o}{B}(j\omega) = K_3G_3(j\omega)$$

so that

$$KG(j\omega) = K_1G_1(j\omega)K_2G_2(j\omega)K_3G_3(j\omega)$$
$$= K_1K_2K_3G_1G_2G_3(j\omega) \qquad (5\text{-}76)$$

Thus the over-all transfer function of any number of noninteracting components in series is simply the product of the individual transfer functions. In order to simplify the block diagram, it is usually convenient to group such combinations in an equivalent single block as shown in Fig. 5-11b.   The inverse transfer function,

$$\mathcal{E}/\theta_o(j\omega) = KG^{-1}(j\omega) = 1/KG(j\omega)$$

is simply the reciprocal of the above function.

Determination of $\theta_o/\theta_i(j\omega)$ from the Transfer-function Solution.   When the frequency-response function is desired, it is necessary to consider the

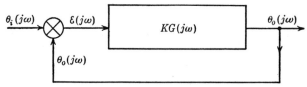

FIG. 5-12. Closed servomechanism loop.

fact that the loop is closed through a feedback path as shown in Fig. 5-12. The error equation $\mathcal{E} = \theta_i - \theta_o$ must be used as follows:

$$\frac{\theta_o}{\mathcal{E}}(j\omega) = KG(j\omega) \tag{5-77}$$

$$\mathcal{E}(j\omega) = \frac{\theta_o}{KG}(j\omega) = \theta_i(j\omega) - \theta_o(j\omega) \tag{5-78}$$

from which

$$\theta_i(j\omega) = \frac{\theta_o}{KG}(j\omega) + \theta_o(j\omega) \tag{5-79}$$

$$\frac{\theta_o}{\theta_i}(j\omega) = \frac{KG(j\omega)}{1 + KG(j\omega)} \tag{5-80}$$

which is the frequency-response function in terms of the transfer function.

Determination of $\theta_o/\theta_i(j\omega)$ When the Feedback Is Not Equal to 1.   If the feedback is not unity, *i.e.*, if the output-measuring device or the error-measuring device is not ideal, or if there is an additional component in

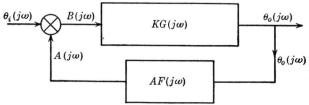

FIG. 5-13. Servomechanism with feedback $\neq$ unity.

the feedback path, then an additional transfer function must be considered.   Since it is the feedback which is affected, a block representing the transfer function is placed in the feedback loop and the symbol $AF(j\omega)$ is used to denote its transfer function.   A different symbol (instead of a subscript) is used in order to make its effect on the resulting equations more apparent.   Such a system is shown in Fig. 5-13.

Under the conditions of Fig. 5-13 the error $\varepsilon(j\omega)$ is not actually present in the system as a physical signal since the true output signal is not fed into the error detector. For the system shown the following equations may be written:

$$\frac{\theta_o}{B}(j\omega) = KG(j\omega) \tag{5-81}$$

$$\frac{A}{\theta_o}(j\omega) = AF(j\omega) \tag{5-82}$$

$$B(j\omega) = \theta_i(j\omega) - A(j\omega) \tag{5-83}$$

Substituting (5-83) in (5-81) gives

$$\theta_o(j\omega) = [\theta_i(j\omega) - A(j\omega)]KG(j\omega) \tag{5-84}$$

and substituting (5-82) in (5-84) gives

$$\begin{aligned} \theta_o(j\omega) &= [\theta_i(j\omega) - \theta_o(j\omega)AF(j\omega)]KG(j\omega) \\ &= \theta_i(j\omega)KG(j\omega) - \theta_o(j\omega)AF(j\omega)KG(j\omega) \end{aligned} \tag{5-85}$$

From this

$$\theta_o(j\omega)[1 + AF(j\omega)KG(j\omega)] = \theta_i(j\omega)KG(j\omega) \tag{5-86}$$

and

$$\frac{\theta_o}{\theta_i}(j\omega) = \frac{KG(j\omega)}{1 + AF(j\omega)KG(j\omega)} \tag{5-87}$$

If Eq. (5-87) is compared with Eq. (5-80), it is seen that the feedback component affects only one term in the denominator of the frequency-response function.

It is readily seen that the form of the frequency-response function is mathematically the same as that of a feedback amplifier. The transfer-function analysis takes advantage of this fact by making use of the mathematical methods already developed for feedback amplifiers, particularly the stability criteria. Also, in servomechanism design, it is possible to alter the characteristics of a component or group of components and make their frequency response depend only on the component in the feedback path. If $AF(j\omega)KG(j\omega) \gg 1$,

$$\frac{\theta_o}{\theta_i}(j\omega) = \frac{KG(j\omega)}{1 + AF(j\omega)KG(j\omega)} \cong \frac{KG(j\omega)}{AF(j\omega)KG(j\omega)} \cong \frac{1}{AF(j\omega)} \tag{5-88}$$

Determination of Transfer Functions in Parallel Component Combinations. In a large number of complicated systems, auxiliary feedback paths are provided in order to improve performance. Sometimes provision must be made for control from several remotely located input stations. In the schematic block diagram of Fig. 5-14a two possible input stations are shown, as well as two auxiliary feedback paths. Because the additional feedback loops appear to be in parallel with the main system components, the term "parallel" is used to describe such combinations. The system chosen is sufficiently complex to illustrate the more important aspects of the algebra of such cases. In addition some of the advantages of inverse transfer and frequency-response functions are shown.

The transfer functions of the components in Fig. 5-14a are indicated. The parenthetical ($j\omega$) is omitted for simplicity. In analyzing such a

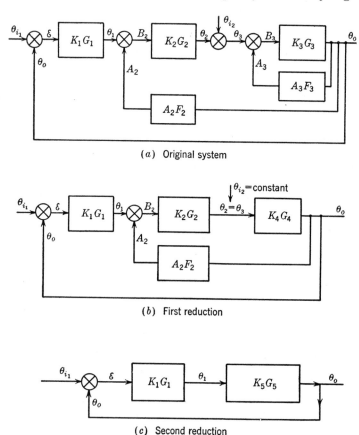

(*a*) Original system

(*b*) First reduction

(*c*) Second reduction

Fig. 5-14. Servomechanism with parallel loops.

system it is usually best to combine subsidiary loops with the main path components to form an equivalent block and a single transfer function. When this procedure is exhausted, the remaining equations must be solved simultaneously. The transfer function of the system shown in Fig. 5-14a would depend on which of the two inputs is used. Two transfer functions are thus required. It is convenient to assume that one input is stationary when the other is used. Assuming θ_{i2} is held fixed, derivation of the transfer function is as follows:

1. Replace the combination K_3G_3 and A_3F_3 with a single block,

$$\frac{\theta_o}{\theta_3} = \frac{K_3G_3}{1 + A_3F_3K_3G_3} = K_4G_4 \qquad (5\text{-}89)$$

The block diagram thus becomes Fig. 5-14b.

2. Figure 5-14b may now be treated in similar fashion and a single block used to replace K_2G_2, K_4G_4, and A_2F_2,

$$\frac{\theta_o}{\theta_1} = \frac{K_2G_2K_4G_4}{1 + A_2F_2K_2G_2K_4G_4} = K_5G_5 \qquad (5\text{-}90)$$

which reduces the diagram to Fig. 5-14c. It then follows immediately that the transfer function is

$$KG = \frac{\theta_o}{\mathcal{E}} = K_1G_1K_5G_5 \qquad (5\text{-}91)$$

and the frequency-response function is

$$\frac{\theta_o}{\theta_i} = \frac{K_1G_1K_5G_5}{1 + K_1G_1K_5G_5} \qquad (5\text{-}92)$$

Expanding Eqs. (5-91) and (5-92) gives

$$\frac{\theta_o}{\mathcal{E}} = \frac{K_1G_1K_2G_2K_3G_3}{1 + K_3G_3(A_3F_3 + K_2G_2A_2F_2)} \qquad (5\text{-}93)$$

$$\frac{\theta_o}{\theta_i} = \frac{K_1G_1K_2G_2K_3G_3}{1 + K_3G_3(A_3F_3 + K_2G_2A_2F_2) + K_1G_1K_2G_2K_3G_3} \qquad (5\text{-}94)$$

Note that the effects of all components are expressed in the solutions.

At times it is more convenient to work with the inverse transfer and frequency-response functions. These can be obtained by manipulation of Eqs. (5-93) and (5-94), but a more symmetrical equation results if the inverse functions are built up from the system equations. Thus

1. For the parallel combinations of K_3G_3 and A_3F_3,

$$\frac{\theta_3}{\theta_o} = \frac{1}{K_3G_3} + A_3F_3 = K_4G_4^{-1} \qquad (5\text{-}95)$$

2. With θ_{i2} constant, $\theta_o/\theta_2 = \theta_o/\theta_3$; and

$$\frac{\theta_3}{B_2} = K_2G_2 \qquad (5\text{-}96)$$

$$B_2 = \frac{\theta_3}{K_2G_2} = \theta_1 - A_2F_2\theta_o \qquad (5\text{-}97)$$

Therefore

$$\theta_3 = (K_2G_2)B_2 = K_2G_2\theta_1 - K_2G_2A_2F_2\theta_o \qquad (5\text{-}98)$$

and

$$\frac{\theta_3}{\theta_o} = K_2 G_2 \frac{\theta_1}{\theta_o} - K_2 G_2 A_2 F_2 \tag{5-99}$$

Combining Eqs. (5-95) and (5-99),

$$\frac{1}{K_3 G_3} + A_3 F_3 = K_2 G_2 \frac{\theta_1}{\theta_o} - K_2 G_2 A_2 F_2 \tag{5-100}$$

from which

$$\frac{\theta_1}{\theta_o} = \frac{1}{K_2 G_2} \left(\frac{1}{K_3 G_2} + A_3 F_3 \right) + A_2 F_2 \tag{5-101}$$

Then the outer loop is added by considering

$$\frac{\theta_1}{\varepsilon} = K_1 G_1 \tag{5-102}$$

$$\varepsilon = \theta_{i1} - \theta_o \tag{5-103}$$

Therefore

$$\theta_1 = K_1 G_1 \theta_{i1} - K_1 G_1 \theta_o \tag{5-104}$$

and

$$\frac{\theta_1}{\theta_o} = K_1 G_1 \frac{\theta_{i1}}{\theta_o} - K_1 G_1 \tag{5-105}$$

Combining (5-101) and (5-105) and simplifying gives

$$\frac{\theta_{i1}}{\theta_o} = \frac{1}{K_1 G_1} \left[\frac{1}{K_2 G_2} \left(\frac{1}{K_3 G_3} + A_3 F_3 \right) + A_2 F_2 \right] + 1 \tag{5-106}$$

Equation (5-106) is the inverse frequency-response function. The inverse transfer function is obtained by noting that

$$\frac{\theta_i}{\theta_o} = \frac{\theta_o + \varepsilon}{\theta_o} = 1 + \frac{\varepsilon}{\theta_o} \tag{5-107}$$

and if this is substituted in Eq. (5-106), the result is

$$KG^{-1} = \frac{\varepsilon}{\theta_o} = \frac{1}{K_1 G_1} \left[\frac{1}{K_2 G_2} \left(\frac{1}{K_3 G_3} + A_3 F_3 \right) + A_2 F_2 \right] \tag{5-108}$$

which is the inverse transfer function.

The system transfer function will now be derived, assuming that the system is driven from the second independent input, θ_{i2}. The procedures used in reduction to a simpler block diagram are quite similar to the preceding illustration.

1. $K_3 G_3$ and $A_3 F_3$ are again combined to give $K_4 G_4$, and the resulting block diagram is shown in Fig. 5-15a.

2. K_1G_1 and A_2F_2 may be combined from

$$\frac{A_2}{\theta_o} = A_2F_2 \tag{5-109}$$

$$\frac{\theta_1}{\theta_o} = K_1G_1 \tag{5-110}$$

$$B_2 = \theta_1 - A_2 = K_1G_1\theta_o - A_2F_2\theta_o \tag{5-111}$$

$$K_6G_6 = \frac{B_2}{\theta_o} = \frac{1}{K_1G_1} - \frac{1}{A_2F_2} = K_1G_1 - A_2F_2 \tag{5-112}$$

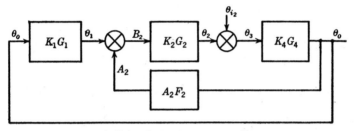

(a) First reduction (assume $\theta_{i_1} = 0$)

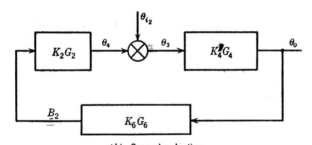

(b) Second reduction

FIG. 5-15. Reduction of system of Fig. 5-14 with θ_{i2} as input.

From Fig. 5-15b it immediately follows that the frequency-response function is

$$\frac{\theta_o}{\theta_{i2}} = \frac{K_4G_4}{1 + K_4G_4K_2G_2K_6G_6} \tag{5-113}$$

which expands to

$$\frac{\theta_o}{\theta_{i2}} = \frac{K_3G_3}{1 + K_3G_3(A_3F_3 + K_1G_1K_2G_2 - K_2G_2A_2F_2)} \tag{5-114}$$

Then the inverse frequency-response function is

$$\frac{\theta_{i2}}{\theta_o} = \frac{1}{K_3G_3} + A_3F_3 + K_1G_1K_2G_2 - K_2G_2A_2F_2 \tag{5-115}$$

Again it should be noted that the effects of all components are explicit in the equations.

5-6. Summary of Procedures in Working with Transfer-function Algebra.

1. Draw schematic diagram of system, including load.

2. Replace with simplified equivalent circuit where practical (mechanical, hydraulic, and other nonelectrical components may be replaced by electrical analogues if desired).

3. Divide equivalent circuit into convenient noninteracting sections.

4. Determine the transfer function of each section, either by applying the Laplace transformation to its equations or by circuit-analysis methods.

5. Redraw circuit in block-diagram form, with transfer functions indicated in each block.

6. Simplify the block diagram as much as possible.

7. Determine over-all transfer function by algebraic manipulation.

The next step in the analysis of a system would be interpretation of the equations. This topic is developed in the following chapters.

PROBLEMS

5-1. Derive transfer functions for the systems shown in Figs. 3P-5 to 3P-14.

5-2. Derive transfer functions for the electrical networks shown in Fig. 5P-1 to 5P-12.

5-3. Derive the transfer function of an amplidyne generator, including the effect of the quadrature field inductance (see Appendix C).

5-4. Derive the transfer function θ_o/E_i of the system of Fig. 4P-1, including numerical values.

5-5. Derive the transfer function θ_o/E_i of the system of Fig. 4P-2, including numerical values.

5-6. Derive the transfer function θ_o/ε and frequency-response function θ_o/θ_i of the system of Fig. 4P-3, including numerical values.

5-7. Derive the transfer function θ_o/ε and frequency-response function θ_o/θ_i of the system of Fig. 4P-4, including numerical values.

5-8. Derive the transfer function and frequency-response function of the system of Fig. 4P-5, including numerical values.

5-9. Derive the transfer function of the system of Fig. 4P-6, including numerical values.

5-10. Derive the transfer function of the system of Fig. 4P-7, including numerical values.

5-11. Derive the direct and inverse transfer functions of the system of Fig. 4P-8.

5-12. Derive the transfer function of the system of Fig. 4P-9.

5-13. *a.* The two-phase induction motor of Fig. 5P-13 has torque-speed curves as in Fig. 5P-14, and the general expression for shaft torque is

$$T = \frac{n\,\partial T}{\partial n} + e_i \frac{\partial T}{\partial e_i} \qquad (n = \text{speed})$$

Derive the transfer function of the motor, assuming inertia loading only.

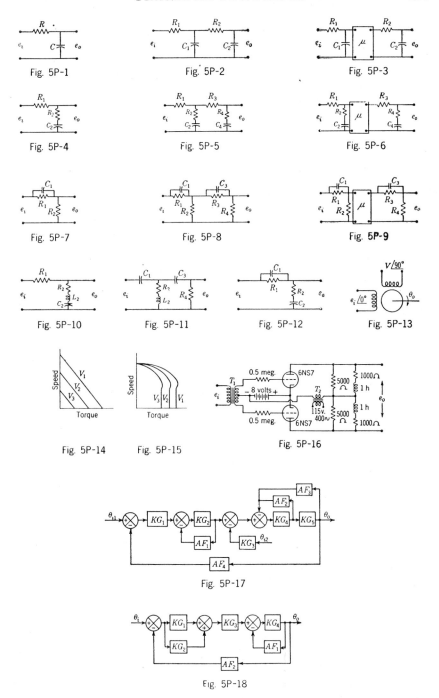

Fig. 5P-1

Fig. 5P-2

Fig. 5P-3

Fig. 5P-4

Fig. 5P-5

Fig. 5P-6

Fig. 5P-7

Fig. 5P-8

Fig. 5P-9

Fig. 5P-10

Fig. 5P-11

Fig. 5P-12

Fig. 5P-13

Fig. 5P-14

Fig. 5P-15

Fig. 5P-16

Fig. 5P-17

Fig. 5P-18

  b. Repeat (*a*) if the motor has the torque-speed curves of Fig. 5P-15, assuming inertia and friction loading.

5-14. Derive the transfer function of the system of Fig. 4P-10.

5-15. Derive the transfer function of the push-pull phase-detector amplifier of Fig. 5P-16. T_1 is a 1:1 unit with secondary center-tapped, and T_2 is a 2:1 step-up transformer. Use graphical computations or approximations if necessary, but specify the step taken, and justify it.

5-16. Determine θ_o/θ_{i1} and θ_o/θ_{i2} for the system of Fig. 5P-17.

5-17. Determine θ_o/θ_i for the system of Fig. 5P-18.

CHAPTER 6

GRAPHICAL REPRESENTATION OF
TRANSFER FUNCTIONS

6-1. Introduction. The derivation of transfer functions for elementary noninteracting physical units has shown that complicated systems may be replaced by simple arrays of equivalent blocks. The algebraic methods developed for combining the transfer functions of these equivalent blocks into a single over-all transfer function greatly reduce the labor in obtaining a solution. The next step in the transfer-function analysis is to obtain from the resultant equations the desired performance characteristics of the servomechanism. This is most easily accomplished by graphing appropriate equations and applying certain criteria which translate the form of the curves and the position of the curves (with respect to reference points and coordinate axes) into the desired steady-state and transient performance information. The graphical methods for representing the various system transfer equations are presented in this chapter, while the analysis of the resulting curves is reserved for later chapters.

In many cases, servomechanism performance can be satisfactorily found by assuming step-position and step-velocity input conditions, though the actual input conditions might be decidedly different. Performance is then predicted by solving the differential equation. (Predicted performance characteristics are then pessimistic, but they provide an often desirable factor of safety.) The transfer function analysis, however, is carried out assuming adjustable-frequency sinusoidal input conditions. Briefly this may be justified by noting that if the response of a system to all frequencies from zero to infinity is known, then theoretically, the response to a step function can be found by completing a Fourier analysis of the servomechanism in question. Fortunately it is not necessary to set up a wave analysis by Fourier methods at all, for direct means of interpreting frequency-response curves in terms of desired performance information have been developed.

6-2. Types of Graphs Used. In general it is far easier to analyze and design servomechanisms when graphical methods are used. Analytical methods may be more accurate but are far too cumbersome and labor-

ious.   Various types of curves are used to present graphically the characteristics of the system.   They are:

1. Frequency-response curves.   These may be plotted as separate
curves of the magnitude of the output-input ratio vs. frequency and the
phase angle between output and input vs. frequency or may be represented as a polar plot with frequency as a parameter.   If separate curves
of magnitude and phase angle are used, they may be plotted on rectangular coordinates or may be represented logarithmically.

2. Curves of the direct transfer function.   Graphical representation
is made by the same methods as in (1) except that rectangular coordinates
are not used.

3. Curves of the inverse transfer function.   Here the graphical representation is exclusively polar.

Discussion of logarithmic representation is presented in Chap. 12, which
is devoted entirely to logarithmic methods.

It should be clearly understood that the work of Fourier relates the
system transient response to the system frequency response.   The
sinusoidal transfer-function response is a useful tool because it is related
to the system frequency response; there is no direct relationship between
the transfer-function response and the system transient response.   Transfer-function equations are useful because they provide an easy method
for obtaining the system frequency-response equation.   Transfer-function curves are useful for a similar reason; they provide an easy method
for obtaining the system frequency-response data and have the additional
advantage of being better adapted to design manipulations.

6-3. Frequency-response Curves.   The over-all frequency response
of a simple servomechanism[51,52,*] is directly expressed by the equation

$$\frac{\theta_o}{\theta_i}(j\omega) = \frac{KG(j\omega)}{1 + KG(j\omega)} \tag{6-1}$$

[where $KG(j\omega)$ is the over-all transfer function].

If numerical values of $\theta_o/\theta_i (j\omega)$ are computed for a specific system
and for a number of sinusoidal input frequencies, the result is a series of
vectors.   The magnitude of each vector is the magnitude of the ratio
θ_o/θ_i, and the phase angle of the vector is the angle between θ_o and θ_i.
The simplest method of graphically representing these data is to plot
two separate curves in rectangular coordinates: a curve of magnitude
ratio vs. frequency as shown in Fig. 6-1a and a phase-angle vs. frequency
curve as in Figure 6-1b.

---

* Superior numbers, when they appear in the text proper, are the numbers of references given in the Bibliography.

The shape of the magnitude response and the phase-angle response depends on the damping of the system, and thus a whole family of curves is possible since the damping is an additional parameter. Therefore, the curves of Fig. 6-1 show only two possible shapes of the frequency-response curves.

A second possible method of representing the same data is to plot the frequency-response curve in polar coordinates with frequency (the independent variable) as a parameter. This amounts to constructing a vector for each frequency and connecting the tips of the vectors by a smooth curve. The polar-plot equivalent of Figs. 6-1a and b is shown in Fig. 6-1c. Again this illustration is for a particular case, and one should expect that a family of curves would be realized for different values of damping. There is some advantage in the use of a polar plot, for it expresses all of the information in a single curve rather than two curves. At times, however, the rectangular-coordinate curves are easier to interpret.

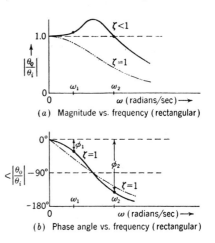

(a) Magnitude vs. frequency (rectangular)

(b) Phase angle vs. frequency (rectangular)

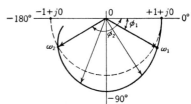

(c) Magnitude and phase angle vs. frequency (polar)

Fig. 6-1. Plots of magnitude and phase angle vs. frequency.

Example. The transfer function of a servomechanism is

$$KG(j\omega) = \frac{5}{j\omega(0.6j\omega + 1)(0.1j\omega + 1)}$$

The frequency-response equation of the system then is

$$\frac{\theta_o}{\theta_i}(j\omega) = \frac{KG}{1 + KG} = \frac{5}{j\omega(0.6j\omega + 1)(0.1j\omega + 1) + 5}$$

Inserting numerical values for ω, this equation becomes, for $\omega = 0$,

$$\frac{\theta_o}{\theta_i}(j0) = \frac{5/0°}{0 + 5/0°} = 1/0°$$

for $\omega = 5$,

$$\frac{\theta_o}{\theta_i}(j5) = \frac{5/0°}{j5(j3 + 1)(j0.5 + 1) + 5/0°}$$

$$= \frac{5/0°}{(5)(3.16)(1.12)/90° + 71.5° + 26.5° + 5/0°}$$

$$= 0.393/-178.8°$$

The results are then tabulated.

ω	$\dfrac{\theta_o}{\theta_i}$	Angle of $\dfrac{\theta_o}{\theta_i}$
0	1	0
1	1.135	-12.1
2	1.87	-34.6
2.5	2.97	-68
3	2.62	-133.9
5	0.393	-178.8

These data are plotted in Fig. 6-2.

Frequency-response curves are often easier to obtain than transfer-function curves in taking experimental measurements on systems. They are also necessary in cases where the servomechanism loop is only one part of a complex system, because under such circumstances the frequency response of the servomechanism is merely its transfer function as far as the rest of the system is concerned. They are also valuable as a check on specifications in many cases.

The principal disadvantage to the use of the frequency-response equation and curves lies in the fact that they are not readily interpreted for use in design. This may be seen from the curves of Fig. 6-2 and the frequency-response equation in the preceding example. The resonance peak is too high for most servomechanism applications, but neither the curves nor equation indicates what should be done to the system to reduce the height of the peak.

6-4. Polar Plot of the Transfer-function Equation. While the frequency-response equation explicitly relates the output to the input, interpretation of the resulting curves is not accomplished with sufficient ease to make use of the frequency-response plots a desirable approach. On the other hand, the transfer function $\theta_o/\mathcal{E}(j\omega)$, though it expresses only an implicit relationship between input and output, is much more satisfactory to work with for the following reasons: first of all, the algebraic expression for the transfer function is simpler than that of the frequency response; second, the frequency response may be obtained from the polar transfer-function plot through relatively simple graphical relationships; and third, the interpretation of system performance is more easily accomplished from the transfer-function plot.

Figure 6-3 shows a sketch of possible polar transfer-function locus. The actual calculation of such a locus requires the same methods as used for the polar frequency-response plot. It should be noted that at $\omega = \infty$ the locus is at the origin. This is always true because there is no known

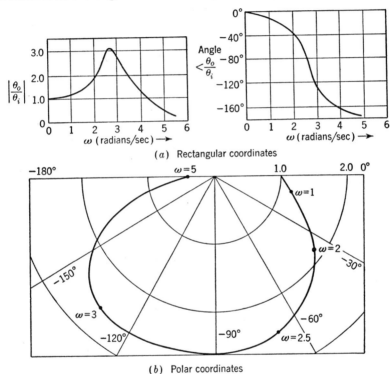

(a) Rectangular coordinates

(b) Polar coordinates

Fig. 6-2. Frequency-response loci for $\dfrac{\theta_o}{\theta_i}(j\omega) = \dfrac{5}{j\omega(0.6j\omega + 1)(0.1j\omega + 1) + 5}$.

system which will transfer infinite frequencies. The other extreme of the locus, at $\omega = 0$, may have a number of possible locations on the plot depending on the nature of the transfer function.

An illustrative vector $\theta_o/\varepsilon(j\omega)$ is shown in Fig. 6-3 and will be used in showing the graphical relationship between the transfer-function and the frequency-response function. For a simple servomechanism,

$$\frac{\theta_o}{\varepsilon}(j\omega) = KG(j\omega) \tag{6-2}$$

$$\frac{\theta_o}{\theta_i}(j\omega) = \frac{KG(j\omega)}{1 + KG(j\omega)} = \frac{\theta_o/\varepsilon(j\omega)}{1 + \theta_o/\varepsilon(j\omega)} \tag{6-3}$$

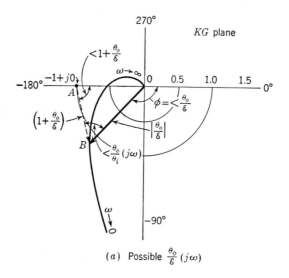

(a) Possible $\frac{\theta_o}{\varepsilon}(j\omega)$

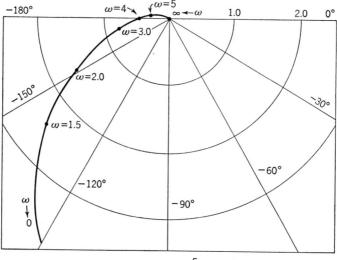

(b) $KG(j\omega) = \dfrac{5}{j\omega(0.6\,j\omega+1)(0.1\,j\omega+1)}$

Fig. 6-3. Polar plot of transfer function, $\dfrac{\theta_o}{\epsilon}(j\omega)$.

Applying these relationships to Fig. 6-3, it is noted that point A is located at $-1 + j0$, so that the vector AO is the vector $+1 + j0$, and

$$\frac{\theta_o}{\varepsilon}(j\omega) = OB$$

Therefore

$$AO + OB = AB \tag{6-4}$$

$$1 + \frac{\theta_o}{\varepsilon}(j\omega) = AB \tag{6-5}$$

Then

$$\frac{OB}{AB} = \frac{\theta_o/\varepsilon(j\omega)}{1 + \theta_o/\varepsilon(j\omega)} = \frac{KG(j\omega)}{1 + KG(j\omega)} = \frac{\theta_o}{\theta_i}(j\omega) \tag{6-6}$$

Thus the magnitude of the frequency-response vector may be determined from the transfer-function plot by the following procedure:

1. Locate point $A = -1 + j0$ on the transfer-function plot, and select any point B on the transfer function curve.

2. Draw vector AB and vector OB, and measure their lengths.

3. $|\theta_o/\theta_i| = |OB/AB|$.

The angle of $\theta_o/\theta_i(j\omega)$ is the angle included between vectors OB and AB. This can be seen from Fig. 6-3 on which the angles of the vectors are marked. From vector algebra, when the division OB/AB is performed, the resultant angle is $\underline{/OB} - \underline{/AB}$, which is equal to $\underline{/\theta_o/\varepsilon(j\omega)} - \underline{/1 + \theta_o/\varepsilon(j\omega)}$ and it is then apparent that this is $\underline{/ABO} = \underline{/\theta_o/\theta_i(j\omega)}$. Therefore the frequency response $\theta_o/\theta_i(j\omega)$ may be obtained from the transfer-function plot $\theta_o/\varepsilon(j\omega)$.

Example.   The transfer function used in the example of Sec. 6.3 is

$$KG(j\omega) = \frac{5}{j\omega(0.6j\omega + 1)(0.1j\omega + 1)}$$

Inserting numerical values for ω, this equation becomes, for $\omega = 0$,

$$KG(j0) = \frac{5\underline{/0°}}{0\underline{/+90°}} = \infty\underline{/-90°}$$

for $\omega = 5$,

$$KG(j5) = \frac{5\underline{/0°}}{(5)(3.16)(1.12)\underline{/90° + 71.5° + 26.5°}}$$

$$= \frac{5\underline{/0°}}{17.7\underline{/188°}} = 0.283\underline{/-188°}$$

The results of the computations would normally be tabulated. The transfer-function curve is plotted in Fig. 6-3b.

It is clear that the computations required to plot the transfer-function curve are less laborious than for the frequency-response curve. It is easily shown that this curve lends itself more readily to studies concerned with design. For example, the numerator of the transfer function (in this case) is just the system gain. Doubling this number doubles the length of each vector. The effect on the resonance peak is seen at once by checking the vector ratio defined by Eq. (6-6). The effects of other changes and adjustments in the system are seen almost as quickly. In later chapters methods are developed which make quantitative adjustments possible.

When the feedback loop has a component in it, then the preceding relationships between transfer function and frequency response do not hold and a plot of the direct transfer function alone is of little value in studying performance. However, if the system output-error equation is still defined to be $\theta_o/\mathcal{E}(j\omega)$, this quantity may be found algebraically even though the error, $\mathcal{E}$, does not appear in the system as a physical signal. The output-error ratio $\theta_o/\mathcal{E}(j\omega)$ may still be called a transfer function though it is not such physically, and its equation may be derived as follows:

$$\frac{\theta_o}{\theta_i}(j\omega) = \frac{KG}{1 + KGAF} = \frac{\theta_o}{\mathcal{E} + \theta_o}(j\omega) \tag{6-7}$$

$$\frac{\mathcal{E} + \theta_o}{\theta_o} = \frac{\mathcal{E}}{\theta_o} + 1 = \frac{1 + KGAF}{KG} \tag{6-8}$$

$$\frac{\mathcal{E}}{\theta_o} = \frac{1 + KGAF}{KG} - 1 = \frac{1 + KG(AF - 1)}{KG} \tag{6-9}$$

$$\frac{\theta_o}{\mathcal{E}}(j\omega) = \frac{KG}{1 + KG(AF - 1)} \tag{6-10}$$

Polar plots may be made of Eq. (6-10), and all of the analysis methods to be applied to true transfer functions are equally applicable to the output-error locus. When design problems are encountered, certain other graphical methods are perhaps more advantageous in the case of parallel loops. Discussion on this point is reserved to a later chapter.

6-5. Polar Plots of Inverse Functions. There are times when the polar plots of inverse functions may be used to best advantage. Mathematically there is sometimes a saving in labor, depending on the equation to be evaluated, and graphically some simplifications are possible in constructing one inverse function from another. Actually any manipulations which can be performed with the direct-transfer-function polar plot may also be performed with the inverse polar plot. The polar plot of the direct transfer function is more commonly used, though there is no good reason for this except familiarity.

A mathematical comparison shows, for a simple system,

$$\frac{\theta_o}{\theta_i}(j\omega) = \frac{KG}{1 + KG}$$

$$\frac{\theta_i}{\theta_o}(j\omega) = \frac{1}{KG} + 1 \tag{6-11}$$

$$\frac{\theta_o}{\varepsilon}(j\omega) = KG$$

$$\frac{\varepsilon}{\theta_o}(j\omega) = \frac{1}{KG} \tag{6-12}$$

and for a system with a parallel transfer function,

$$\frac{\theta_o}{\varepsilon}(j\omega) = \frac{KG}{1 + KG(AF - 1)}$$

$$\frac{\varepsilon}{\theta_o}(j\omega) = \frac{1}{KG} + AF - 1 \tag{6-13}$$

$$\frac{\theta_o}{\theta_i}(j\omega) = \frac{KG}{1 + KGAF}$$

$$\frac{\theta_i}{\theta_o}(j\omega) = \frac{1}{KG} + AF \tag{6-14}$$

The numerical evaluation of any one of these terms is just about as laborious as the evaluation of its reciprocal, though some slight saving in labor might result from use of the inverse functions. When there is a component in the feedback path, the inverse transfer function has definite design advantages. As may be seen from Eqs. (6-13) and (6-14), when the direct form is used the feedback term AF is part of a rather complicated denominator so that its effect on the system is masked. With the inverse form the feedback term is isolated, and the effects of changes are apparent. This is discussed in detail in Chap. 11.

It is important to note that the differences between the inverse transfer function and the inverse frequency-response function is simply ± 1. This means that when the polar plots of inverse transfer functions are made, they are easily changed to inverse-frequency-response plots, and vice versa, by a simple shift in origin. Figure 6-4a shows the inverse-transfer-function plot of the system used to illustrate Secs. 6-3 and 6-4, and Fig. 6-4b shows the shift of the origin to obtain the frequency-response plot.

Once the inverse plot is obtained, it is readily transformed into the direct-function plot, simply by calculating the vector magnitude at each frequency and laying off the reciprocal vector at the negative of the original angle. This is sometimes helpful in experimental work where the frequency response may be readily measured, but the output-error locus

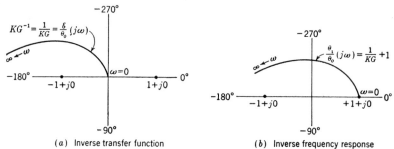

(a) Inverse transfer function   (b) Inverse frequency response

FIG. 6-4. Inverse-function polar plots.

is desired for analysis purposes. In such a case, the experimental frequency response may be plotted in the inverse form, giving a locus possibly as shown in Fig. 6-4b. The origin is then shifted to get the inverse-output-error plot as in Fig. 6-4a and the reciprocal calculations give the direct-output-error locus if desired.

PROBLEMS

6-1. Plot polar curves for the following transfer functions:

a. $1/j\omega$
b. $16/(j\omega)^2$
c. $1/(j\omega)^3$
d. $1/(j\omega + 5)$
e. $1/(j\omega + 5)(j\omega + 10)$
f. $1/[2 + 3j\omega + 4(j\omega)^2]$
g. $1/[j\omega(j\omega + 5)]$
h. $1/[j\omega(j\omega + 5)(j\omega + 10)]$
i. $1/\{j\omega[2 + 3j\omega + 4(j\omega)^2]\}$

6-2. Plot the inverse polar curves for the transfer functions of Prob. 6-1.

6-3. Plot the polar transfer-function and frequency-response curves for a system whose transfer function is

$$\frac{\theta_o}{\varepsilon} = \frac{200}{j\omega(j\omega + 5)(j\omega + 10)}$$

6-4. Plot, on the same axis, the polar transfer-function curves for the networks shown in Figs. 5P-1 to 5P-3 where $R = R_1 = R_2 = 1$ megohm, $C = C_1 = C_2 = 0.2$ μf, and $\mu = 1$.

6-5. Plot, on the same axis, the polar transfer-function curves for the approximate derivative network shown in Fig. 5P-4 for the following sets of circuit constants, and note the maximum phase shift:

a. $\tau_1 = R_1C_1 = 0.2$; $\alpha = \tau_2/\tau_1 = 0.025$, where $\tau_2 = R_2C_1/(R_1 + R_2)$
b. $\tau_1 = 0.2$; $\alpha = 0.1$
c. $\tau_1 = 0.2$; $\alpha = 0.4$
d. $\tau_1 = 0.05$; $\alpha = 0.1$
e. $\tau_1 = 0.05$; $\alpha = 0.4$

6-6. Plot, on the same axis, the polar transfer-function curves for the approximate integral network shown in Fig. 5P-5, for the following set of circuit constants, and note the maximum phase shift produced:

a. $R_2 = 10^6$ ohms; $R_1 = 4 \times 10^6$ ohms; $C_2 = 0.5$ μf where $R_2C_2 = \tau_2$,

$$(R_1 + R_2)C_2 = \tau_1, \quad \text{and} \quad \alpha = \tau_2/\tau_1$$

b. $\alpha = 0.2$; $\tau_2 = 0.1$
c. $\alpha = 0.2$; $\tau_2 = 1.0$
d. $\alpha = 0.05$; $\tau_2 = 0.1$
e. $\alpha = 0.5$; $\tau_2 = 0.1$
f. $\alpha = 0.5$; $\tau_2 = 1.0$

6-7. Plot the polar transfer-function curves for the networks in Figs. 5P-6 to 5P-9. Suggested sets of circuit constants are, for Figs. 5P-6 and 5P-7, $R_1 = R_3 = 0.5$ megohms, $R_2 = R_4 = 4.5$ megohms, and $C_1 = C_3 = 0.0126$ μf.

6-8. Plot, on separate axes, the polar transfer-function curves for the networks of Figs. 5P-10 to 5P-12. Specify the values used for the circuit elements.

6-9. *a.* Plot the transfer-function curve for the system of Fig. 4P-1.

b. Repeat, plotting only the $G(j\omega)$ factor.

6-10. Repeat Prob. 6-9 for the open-loop system of Fig. 4P-2.

6-11. Repeat Prob. 6-9 for the system of Prob. 4-4. From this locus determine the frequency-response curve (θ_o/θ_i), and plot on rectangular coordinates.

6-12. Repeat Prob. 6-9 for the system of Prob. 4-5.

6-13. Repeat Prob. 6-9 for the system of Prob. 4-14, determine the frequency response from the transfer-function locus, and plot on rectangular coordinates.

6-14. *a.* Plot the transfer-function locus for the system of Prob. 4-15.

b. Repeat, plotting only the $G(j\omega)$ factor.

6-15. Repeat Prob. 6-14 for the system of Prob. 4-16.

6-16. Repeat Prob. 6-14 for the system of Prob. 4-17.

6-17. Repeat Prob. 6-14 for the system of Prob. 4-18.

6-18. Repeat Prob. 6-14 for the system of Prob. 4-19.

6-19. Repeat Prob. 6-14 for the system of Prob. 4-20.

6-20. Repeat Prob. 6-14 for the system of Prob. 4-21.

6-21. Plot the polar locus of the inverse transfer function of the system of Prob. 4-15.

6-22. Repeat Prob. 6-21 for the system of Prob. 4-19.

6-23. Repeat Prob. 6-21 for the system of Prob. 4-20.

CHAPTER 7

ANALYSIS OF SERVOMECHANISM PERFORMANCE FROM EQUATIONS AND TRANSFER FUNCTION PLOTS

7-1. Introduction. While the preceding chapter does not contain all of the manipulations possible with plots of the transfer function and frequency-response function, it seems desirable to discuss the analysis of servomechanism systems in terms of these plots before proceeding to more complicated possibilities. The analysis of servomechanisms may be subdivided into three general topics:

1. Absolute stability
2. Relative stability, or transient performance
3. Steady-state performance

Each of these items may be studied in terms of the polar transfer function (or output-error) plot as well as by other means. This chapter is devoted to a detailed, though not necessarily complete, discussion of these three topics.

7-2. Absolute Stability—General Discussion. A system is termed absolutely stable if any oscillations set up in the system are eventually damped out. Conversely, a system is absolutely unstable if oscillations are self-sustaining and tend to last indefinitely. There is a possibility of absolute instability in any servomechanism loop because there is a feedback path and it is always possible that this feedback may become regenerative under certain conditions of adjustment. In practice it is necessary to adjust servomechanisms (both while designing and after a model has been built); so it is necessary to know whether or not the system is stable and what adjustments are possible without causing instability. There are several methods for determining whether a system is absolutely stable or not. The most useful is probably the Nyquist criterion[31,49,51,]* as applied to the polar plot of the transfer function. Some preliminary discussion is required before this method can be presented, and in the preliminary discussion several other tests for stability are included.

* Superior numbers, when they appear in the text proper, are the numbers of references given in the Bibliography.

It has been previously stated that the differential equation of a servo-mechanism contains all of the necessary information concerning system performance. The differential equations of a number of systems together with their solutions have been presented in Chap. 4. It may be noted that each of these solutions contains an exponential factor in which the exponent is a real number, and is either a root or the real part of a root of the differential equation. As long as the exponent of the exponential factor is a negative real number, the factor eventually approaches zero, the error, ε, approaches either zero or a constant number (see Table 4-1), and the system is therefore stable. On the other hand, if the exponent is a positive real number, then the error, ε, approaches infinity and the system is said to be unstable. The true test of system stability, there-fore, is to check the existence of positive real roots to the differential equation (or complex roots with positive real parts). If any such roots exist, the system is unstable; if they do not exist, the system is stable. All of the tests of servomechanism stability, including the Nyquist cri-terion, are simply tests for the existence of positive real roots of the differential equation.

7-3. Instability from Inspection of the Differential Equation. Certain simple tests are available which may be applied directly to the differential equation. Some of these are presented here, not only because they have some practical use, but because the tests are based on certain impor-tant characteristics of the system. The first test is one of simple inspec-tion. The differential equation of a servomechanism is a linear differ-ential equation of the first degree but of second order or greater. The existence of all derivatives and the algebraic sign of all coefficients are determined by inspection. If any derivative is missing, the system is unstable, i.e., if the third derivative $d^3\theta/dt^3$ is present and the first deriva-tive $d\theta/dt$ is also present but the second derivative $d^2\theta/dt^2$ is not present, then the system is unstable. Likewise all terms must be positive or all terms must be negative for stability. If one term is negative while the rest are positive, the system is unstable. It should be carefully noted that this test is not conclusive; i.e., if this test shows the system to be unstable, then there certainly is a positive real root, but it is possible for a positive real root to exist without affecting the differential equation sufficiently to indicate instability by inspection. This will be explained later.

The presence of positive real roots in the solution of a differential equa-tion is sometimes shown by inspection of the differential equation for the following reasons: The differential equation of a servomechanism is the mathematical representation of a physical system. The coefficients of the equation are physical quantities in the sense that they represent inertia, friction, elasticity, etc. Since these coefficients represent physical quantities, they must be real numbers and may not be complex numbers because there is no such thing as a physical quantity which is mathematically complex.   Thus the coefficients of the terms of the differential equation of a servomechanism must be real numbers, and for this condition to exist, any complex roots of the differential equation must occur in conjugate pairs.   This is illustrated by the following algebraic treatment.

Let it be assumed that there is a cubic differential equation of the form

$$A\,\frac{d^3x}{dt^3} + B\,\frac{d^2x}{dt} + C\,\frac{dx}{dt} + D = 0 \tag{7-1}$$

or

$$As^3 + Bs^2 + Cs + D = 0 \tag{7-2}$$

This is a cubic equation and therefore has three roots.   If it is further assumed that this equation represents a servomechanism, that its solution does contain complex roots, and that the complex roots occur in conjugate pairs, then the three roots of the equation may be written as

$$\begin{array}{l} m_1 = a \\ m_2 = b + jc \\ m_3 = b - jc \end{array} \tag{7-3}$$

The factors of the differential equation are then

$$(s - m_1)(s - m_2)(s - m_3) = 0$$

or

$$(s - a)[s - (b + jc)][s - (b - jc)] = 0 \tag{7-4}$$

Expanding gives

$$s^3 - (a + 2b)s^2 + (2ab + b^2 + c^2)s - a(b^2 + c^2) = 0 \tag{7-5}$$

and it may be seen that the coefficients $(2ab + b^2 + c^2)$ and $a(b^2 + c^2)$ would be complex for any other combination of roots, i.e., three complex roots, one complex root, or two nonconjugate complex roots.

It may also be seen from (7-5) that the coefficients will all have the same sign if the real parts of all roots (a and b) are negative numbers. Conversely, then, if the numerical form of the equation has one term with an algebraic sign different from that of the other terms, there must be a positive real root!   By inspection, if the root a is a positive number, then the term $-a(b^2 + c^2)$ must be negative although all other terms may be positive.   On the other hand, if the real root b is positive, then it is possible for all terms to have the same sign though it is also possible for the coefficients $-(a + 2b)$ and $+(2ab + b^2)$ to be negative depending on the relative magnitudes of a and b.   Thus it is clearly shown that the inspection test for positive real roots to a differential equation may work if the positive real root has no complex component or if the magnitude of the positive real root lies within a certain range of values relative to the other roots. It is also shown that it is possible for positive real roots to exist even though not shown by the inspection test.

If all signs in the differential equation are the same, there is still one possible case in which the inspection test will work. That possible case exists when the positive real root is of just the proper magnitude to reduce one coefficient to zero without affecting the sign of any other term. In this case one of the terms of the equation would be missing. For example, if a is negative and b is positive and $a = 2b$, then $(a + 2b) = 0$ and the equation would have no s^2 term; or if $2ab = b^2 + c^2$, then

$$(2ab + b^2 + c^2) = 0$$

and the equation would have no s term.

Unfortunately, the inspection test is seldom applicable in servomechanism equations since positive roots, if they exist, are usually small and do not affect the sign of any term, nor do they usually reduce a coefficient to zero. Therefore some method is needed to determine the presence of real roots in the more normal form of equation. Several methods are available for doing this. They consist primarily in manipulations with the numerical coefficients of the differential equation. The method most commonly referred to in servomechanism literature is Routh's criterion. This method will now be outlined without proof, for which the student is referred to the literature.

7-4. Routh's Criterion. In general, a linear differential equation has the form

$$A_0 s^n + A_1 s^{n-1} + \cdots + A_{n-1} s + A_n = 0 \qquad (7\text{-}6)$$

The coefficients may be arranged in a triangular array as follows:

$$
\begin{array}{llll}
A_0 & A_2 & A_4 & A_6 \quad \cdots \\
A_1 & A_3 & A_5 & A_7 \quad \cdots \\
b_1 & b_3 & b_5 \quad \cdots \\
c_1 & c_3 \quad \cdots \\
d_1 \quad \cdots
\end{array}
\qquad (7\text{-}7)
$$

where

$$b_1 = \frac{A_1 A_2 - A_0 A_3}{A_1} \qquad (7\text{-}8)$$

$$b_3 = \frac{A_1 A_4 - A_0 A_5}{A_1} \qquad (7\text{-}9)$$

etc.

$$c_1 = \frac{b_1 A_3 - A_1 b_3}{b_1} \qquad (7\text{-}10)$$

$$c_3 = \frac{b_1 A_5 - A_1 b_5}{b_1} \tag{7-11}$$

etc.

$$d_1 = \frac{c_1 b_3 - b_1 c_3}{c_1} \tag{7-12}$$

etc.

In general each succeeding horizontal row will have fewer terms than the preceding row, and thus the array is triangular. The procedure of forming additional horizontal rows must be carried out until no more rows can be formed by the indicated procedure. Once the array is complete, it is necessary only to inspect the *signs* in front of the left hand column. If all terms have the same sign, then there are no positive roots and the system is stable. If there is a change in sign in the column, then a positive root exists and the system is unstable. If there are several changes in sign, the number of positive real roots corresponds to the number of changes in sign.

If the coefficients of the terms are large, then the calculations are quite laborious. Some of the labor can be eliminated by proper manipulation of the coefficients. A suggested manipulation is as follows:

1. Divide through by some constant g, choosing $g = A_n$.
2. Transform the variable by letting $s = VX$, where V is an arbitrary constant, and choose V such that $A_0 V^n / g = 1$.

A useful relationship derived from Routh's criterion is the relationship which must exist between the coefficients of a cubic equation if the system represented by the equation is to be stable. If the equation is of the form

$$As^3 + Bs^2 + Cs + D = 0 \tag{7-12a}$$

application of Routh's criterion shows that if no positive roots are to exist $AD > BC$.

7-5. Absolute Stability from the Transfer Function. When a servomechanism analysis or design is being carried out by the transfer function method, the differential equation frequently is not available. It is therefore desirable to have a test for absolute stability which can be applied to the transfer function equations. Such a test was originally worked out by Nyquist[49] for use in feedback-amplifier theory and has since been adapted to work on servomechanisms. The mathematical approach to the Nyquist criterion proves by means of complex-variable theory that the existence of positive real roots for the differential equation affects the polar plot of the loop transfer function. The following discussion outlines the important features of the proof and is rather lengthy because physical and graphical representations are used whenever possible. Also, since the mathematical results lead to conclusions which are not readily applicable, a simplified version, based on normal servo-mechanism construction, is included at the end of the discussion.

Figure 7-1 shows block diagrams for two possible servomechanism loops, one without and one with a transfer function in the feedback path. Normally an individual component such as KG cannot oscillate because there is no path for energy feedback inside the unit itself. When a feedback path is provided, however, as shown in Fig. 7-1, oscillation is possible because the feedback may be regenerative. The tendency to oscillate thus depends on the nature of the energy which travels round the closed loop. Therefore, if the feedback path is opened at the error detector (point A) and an input signal is applied, a study of the relationships between the input signal and the signal obtained at A when the loop is open should tell whether or not the system will oscillate, i.e., be absolutely unstable.

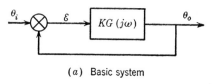

(a) Basic system

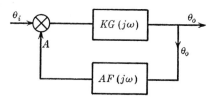

(b) With element in feedback path

FIG. 7-1. Block diagram of a single-loop system.

From this it appears that the important stability consideration is the *loop transfer function*, which for the system of Fig. 7-1a is simply $KG(j\omega)$ and for the system of Fig. 7-1b is $KG(j\omega)\,AF(j\omega)$. That this is a correct interpretation may be shown from the frequency-response equations.

For Fig. 7-1a,

$$\frac{\theta_o}{\theta_i}(j\omega) = \frac{KG(j\omega)}{1 + KG(j\omega)} \tag{7-13}$$

For Fig. 7-1b,

$$\frac{\theta_o}{\theta_i}(j\omega) = \frac{KG(j\omega)}{1 + KG(j\omega)AF(j\omega)} \tag{7-14}$$

If the system is absolutely unstable and is linear, then $\theta_o/\theta_i(j\omega) \to \infty$ at some value of $j\omega$. This can happen only if the denominator of the equation becomes zero, and for this to be true, $KG(j\omega)$ or $KG(j\omega)AF(j\omega)$ must become -1.

The mathematical conditions for instability are then

$$1 + KG(j\omega) = 0$$

or

$$1 + KG(j\omega)AF(j\omega) = 0 \tag{7-15}$$

[From this point on only the equation $1 + KG(j\omega) = 0$ is used in order to simplify the discussion. All remarks are equally applicable to the case when there is a transfer function in the feedback path.]   Equation (7-15) is actually the differential equation of the system and in addition may be represented by the ratio of two polynomials as will now be shown. Equation (5-73) gives the transfer function of a specific system:

$$KG(s) = \frac{\Theta_o}{E}(s) = \frac{\mu_a K_g / R_f K_v}{s(\tau_m s + 1)(\tau_f s + 1)} \qquad (5\text{-}73)$$

and

$$E(s) = \Theta_i(s) - \Theta_o(s)$$

Substituting,

$$\frac{\Theta_o(s)}{\Theta_i(s) - \Theta_o(s)} = \frac{\mu_a K_g / R_f K_v}{s(\tau_m s + 1)(\tau_f s + 1)} \qquad (7\text{-}16)$$

This may be solved for

$$\frac{\Theta_o}{\Theta_i}(s) = \frac{\dfrac{\mu_a K_g / R_f K_v}{s(\tau_m s + 1)(\tau_f s + 1)}}{1 + \dfrac{\mu_a K_g / R_f K_v}{s(\tau_m s + 1)(\tau_f s + 1)}} \qquad (7\text{-}17)$$

The denominator of Eq. (7-17) is obviously the differential equation of the system and, if it is expanded, yields

$$1 + \frac{\mu_a K_g / R_f K_v}{s(\tau_m s + 1)(\tau_f s + 1)} = \frac{s(\tau_m s + 1)(\tau_f s + 1) + \mu_a K_g / R_f K_v}{s(\tau_m s + 1)(\tau_f s + 1)} \qquad (7\text{-}18)$$

and Eq. (7-18) shows that the denominator of the frequency-response equation may be considered as the ratio of two polynomials.   Thus Eq. (7-15) may be generalized and written in the form

$$1 + KG(s) = \frac{(s - s_1)(s - s_2)(s - s_3) \cdots}{(s - s_a)(s - s_b)(s - s_c) \cdots} = 0 \qquad (7\text{-}19)$$

where s_1, s_2, s_3, etc., are the roots of the numerator, i.e., the values of s for which the numerator becomes zero; s_a, s_b, s_c, etc., are the roots of the denominator; and s in general is a complex variable, $s = \Delta + j\omega$.   In mathematical terminology s_1, s_2, etc., are "zeros" of the equation, and s_a, s_b, etc., are "poles" of the equation.[52,54]

If it is noted that Eq. (7-19) actually is the differential equation of the system, then it is easily seen that the only significant values are the zeros, since only these can make the frequency response go to infinity. Furthermore, only those zeros which have positive real parts are of interest since only the roots which have positive real parts can cause instability in the system.   Therefore, further treatment of Eq. (7-14) must be aimed at determining the existence of any zeros with positive real parts.   Of course in any specific case it is theoretically possible to factor the numerator and evaluate the roots, but the following discussion leads to a graphical method which minimizes the labor:

Equation (7-19) relates the transfer function, KG, which normally is represented by a polar plot, with the ratio of two complex polynomials which would have graphical representation on a complex or s plane. It will now be shown that a relationship exists between the number and location of the poles and zeros on the s plane and the shape of the $1 + KG$ locus on the polar plane. Figure 7-2 shows a sketch of a complex s plane. On this plane are shown a number of points which represent the poles and zeros of Eq. (7-19). These may be determined in any particular case by factoring as previously indicated.

In Fig. 7-2, several zeros (s_1, s_2) and several poles (s_a, s_c) are shown on the right-hand half of the plane. These roots would therefore have positive real parts. The poles cannot make the servomechanism unstable but must be considered because they may affect the graphical relationships. Since only zeros with positive real parts are important, it is logical to confine the investigation to the right-hand half of the s plane,

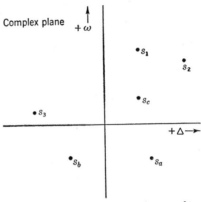

FIG. 7-2. Poles and zeros on the complex s plane.

where the ω axis is included in this half since $\Delta = 0$ is considered positive.

It is obviously impossible to consider every point in the right-hand half of the s plane, and some shorter method must be devised. Since Eq. (7-19) relates the s plane to the polar plot, any line may be chosen in the s plane, and if values of s selected from points on this line are substituted in Eq. (7-19), a series of points are evaluated which permit plotting a curve on the polar plane. If the line on the s plane is chosen to be a closed curve which encloses one zero, the effect on Eq. (7-19) and the polar plot may be seen with the help of Fig. 7-3.

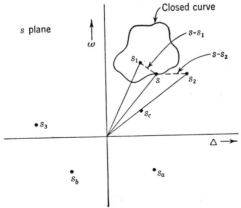

FIG. 7-3. Construction of closed curve on the s plane.

Each point in the s plane is the tip of a vector; thus the points s_1 and s_2 are tips of the vectors s_1 and s_2 as shown in Fig. 7-3. Likewise a variable point, s, on the arbitrary curve enclosing s_1 is the tip of the variable vector s. By vector subtraction the difference vectors $s - s_1$ and $s - s_2$ are therefore as shown in Fig. 7-3. Now these difference vectors are factors of Eq. (7-19),

$$1 + KG = \frac{(s - s_1)(s - s_2)(s - s_3) \cdot \cdot \cdot}{(s - s_a)(s - s_b)(s - s_c) \cdot \cdot \cdot} = 0 \qquad (7\text{-}19)$$

and all other difference vectors may be formed by performing the proper vector subtraction. Let the variable point s move in a clockwise direction one full revolution about the closed path. Then the difference vector $(s - s_1)$ makes one complete clockwise revolution because the zero (s_1) is enclosed by the path. All other difference vectors make no

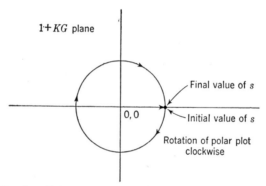

Fig. 7-4. Polar plot of the closed curve on the s plane.

net angular displacement because all other zeros and poles are external to the closed path.

Thus in Eq. (7-19) the factor $(s - s_1)$ incurs a phase change of 360 deg, while all other factors undergo no net phase change. But the polynominal ratio of Eq. (7-19) is equal to $1 + KG$; so on the polar plot the locus of $1 + KG$ must go through a net clockwise rotation of 360 deg, enclosing the origin as illustrated in Fig. 7-4.

Now the $1 + KG$ plane is readily changed into the KG, or loop-transfer-function, plane by a simple shift in origin. The polar plot of Fig. 7-4 changed into the KG, or loop-transfer-function, plane might look as in Fig. 7-5.

The origin of the $1 + KG$ plot becomes the $-1 + j0$ point on the transfer-function plot, and therefore the presence of a zero inside the closed loop of Fig. 7-3 is shown by the clockwise encirclement of the $-1 + j0$ point in Fig. 7-5.

If the closed loop on the s plane is enlarged so that it encloses two zeros, s_1 and s_2, then both of the difference vectors $(s - s_1)$ and $(s - s_2)$ will go through a 360-deg clockwise rotation.   Since both factors are in the numerator of Eq. (7-19), the product of the two factors causes a net 720-deg (or 2-revolution) phase shift in the net value of $1 + KG$.   Thus on the transfer-function plane the polar plot must encircle the $-1 + j0$ point twice.

If the loop on the s plane is still further enlarged so that it also encloses a pole s_c, then the difference vectors $(s - s_1)$, $(s - s_2)$, and $(s - s_c)$ go through one clockwise revolution each.   However the factor $(s - s_c)$ is in the denominator of Eq. (7-19), so that in evaluating the equation the angle of this factor subtracts from the net phase change.   Therefore, when the loop encloses two zeros and one pole, the net phase charge of $1 + KG$ is only one revolution.   Thus the locus on the transfer-function plane encloses the $-1 + j0$ point only once in a clockwise direction.

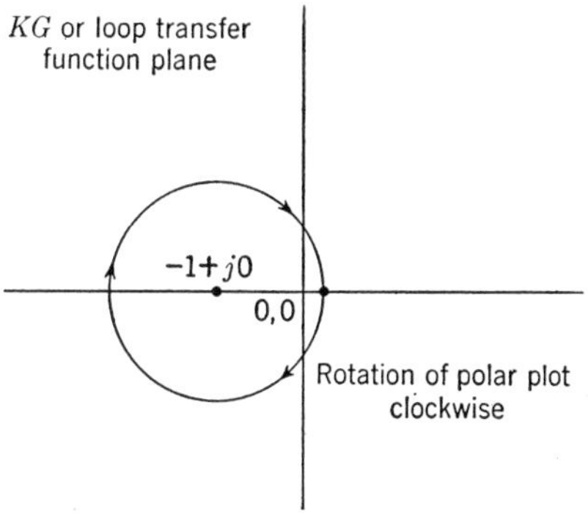

Fig. 7-5. Polar plot of Fig. 7-4 with the origin shifted.

The loop on the s plane may be enlarged until it encloses the entire right-hand half of the plane including the ω axis.   Then it must enclose all zeros and poles with positive real parts.   From the preceding discussion it may be seen that the number of zeros and poles enclosed will determine the number of enclosures of the $-1 + j0$ point on the KG plane!

For practical plotting of the transfer-function locus it is obviously impossible to evaluate the right-hand half of Eq. (7-19).   However, if the transfer function itself, $KG(s)$, is known, values of s may be substituted in it to obtain the plot.   The values of s to be used are in general $s = j\omega$, since the path to be traced on the KG plane corresponds to a complex plane path which lies along the ω axis, that is, Δ (the real part of s) = 0, and closes along an infinite semicircle.   It is not necessary to consider points on the infinite semicircle, since for all such points $s = \infty$, and in Eq. (7-19) (if all the zeros and poles are finite) when $s = \infty$, the polynomial $= 1$ and $KG = 0$.   Thus to evaluate the polar curve for $KG(s)$, let $0 < (s = j\omega) < +\infty$, substitute $j\omega$ for s, and let $j\omega$ vary from 0 to $+\infty$.   It may be noted that this is the reason for substituting $j\omega$ for s in the transfer function derived by the Laplace transformation.   Actually to close the loop on the s plane, it is necessary that $j\omega$ also vary from

$-\infty$ to 0, but this gives a polar plot which is the mirror image about the horizontal axis of the 0 to $+\infty$ plot.

The resulting polar transfer-function plot, or Nyquist diagram as it is sometimes called, may have three possible general forms, depending on the actual system investigated:

1. There may be clockwise encirclements.
2. There may be no encirclements.
3. There may be counterclockwise encirclements.

In case 1 the system is definitely unstable because the locus shows that there are excess zeros with positive real parts. In case 2 there may be no zeros and no poles, in which case the system is stable, or there may be equal numbers of zeros and poles, in which case the system is unstable because positive real roots are present. Thus in case 2 further tests are necessary definitely to determine stability. In case 3 there are at least excess poles, but there may also be zeros, so that again additional tests are necessary.

If case 2 or 3 arises, then Eq. (7-19) must be expanded to the normal differential equation form and Routh's criterion applied. Now Routh's criterion does not predict stability from this equation because some of the positive roots shown may be poles. However, if the plot shows case 2, *i.e.*, no encirclements, then Routh's criterion must show *no positive roots* if the system is to be stable, for if any positive roots occur, there will be equal numbers of zeros and poles, which means that zeros exist and the system is unstable.

If case 3 occurs, then Routh's criterion must show exactly the same number of positive roots as there are counterclockwise encirclements for the system to be stable. This is true because the system is known to have a definite number of poles equal to the number of encirclements, and if Routh's method shows exactly that number of positive roots, then all the positive roots are poles and there are no zeros. If Routh's method shows additional positive roots, then half of them are poles and half are zeros, which would mean that zeros with positive real parts exist and the system would be unstable.

The preceding discussion outlines the physical interpretation of the Nyquist criterion in all its ramifications. As presented, it is of little practical value since it cannot be used conclusively without Routh's criterion. Fortunately a physical study of practical servomechanisms permits simplification of the criterion to the point where it is extremely valuable practically. This is discussed in the following paragraphs.

7-6. Simplified Nyquist Criterion. From a general survey of servomechanism systems and feedback amplifiers it may be said that there are two physical causes of encirclements in the Nyquist diagram. One is instability in a component part or in a group of component parts which form one portion of the system. This instability could be either a pole or a zero depending on the function of the component. In other words, a servomechanism may be stable even though one of its parts is unstable, depending on the location of that part in the system.

The second possible cause for an encirclement corresponds to an interaction between two or more components due to coupling. This is essentially positive feedback. Such an encirclement would therefore correspond to a zero and would make the system or portion of the system unstable.

In practical design the components of a system are normally stable, *i.e.*, a designer would hardly choose an unstable component. Furthermore most components or groups of components which form subsidiary portions of a system are stabilized before the system is completed. Thus it is seldom that a pole exists in a practical servomechanism, unless it is deliberately inserted by the designer. In general, then, only two forms of the Nyquist diagram are to be expected:

1. Net clockwise encirclements—unstable system
2. No encirclements—no poles and no zeros—stable

7-7. Interpretation of the Nyquist Diagram for Stability. There is occasionally some difficulty in determining whether a Nyquist diagram encircles the $-1 + j0$ point. To clarify this, the following illustrations and discussion are given. Figure 7-6*a*, *b*, and *c* shows examples of "closed plots," which normally are easily interpreted. In these plots the solid lines represent positive values of $j\omega$ and the broken lines negative values. The complete plot from $j\omega = -\infty$ to $j\omega = +\infty$ forms a closed loop of itself and therefore is called a closed plot. The illustrations all represent stable units since the point $-1 + j0$ is not enclosed.

Generally the Nyquist plot is an "open plot" as shown in Fig. 7-6*d*. The term "open plot" simply means that the zero-frequency ends of the $+j\omega$ and $-j\omega$ branches go to infinity and thus the plot does not close on itself to make a continuous curve. In order to interpret the diagram, the locus must be closed by an infinite semicircle, and it must be determined whether this semicircle should go to the left or the right. It is therefore desirable to know:

1. Why the plot is open.
2. A mathematical method for closing it.
3. A practical method for closing it by inspection.

A typical system giving an open plot is the simple positioning system of Eq. (5-73),

$$\frac{\theta_o}{\varepsilon}(j\omega) = KG(j\omega) = \frac{\mu_a K_g}{R_f K_v} \frac{1}{(j\omega)(j\omega\tau_m + 1)(j\omega\tau_f + 1)} \quad (5\text{-}73)$$

and the Nyquist plot of this equation is roughly given by Fig. 7-6d. Mathematically, the plot is open because of the factor $(j\omega)$ in the denominator, since $KG(j\omega) \to \infty$ as $j\omega \to 0$. In terms of the complex, or s, plane used in setting up the Nyquist criterion, this corresponds to a pole at the origin; that is, $s = \Delta + j\omega = 0$, and the factor is in the denominator.

Since the pole cannot cause instability, it is not important to the Nyquist criterion and mathematically the path on the s plane should be

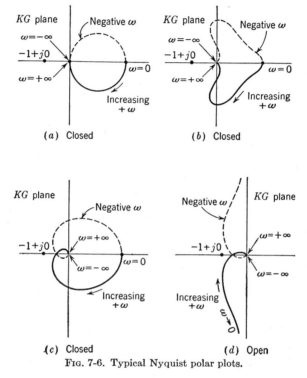

FIG. 7-6. Typical Nyquist polar plots.

reshaped to avoid it, as shown in Fig. 7-7a, so that the new contour would be $ABCDEFA$-, where BCD is an infinitesimal semicircle. This means, in terms of frequency response, that $j\omega$ never reaches zero, and so $KG(j\omega)$ never reaches infinity. The small semicircle BCD on the s plane expands to the almost infinite semicircle on the $KG(j\omega)$ plane (Fig. 7-7b), thus closing the plot. Mathematical methods are available for making this change but are not very practical and will not be discussed.

Practically the infinite semicircle may be drawn in by inspection, and the rule for doing this may be determined from Fig. 7-7. On the s-plane contour the variable is assumed to move clockwise. This in general transforms on the KG plane into a locus along which the variable also moves clockwise. In both cases then the area enclosed by the contour

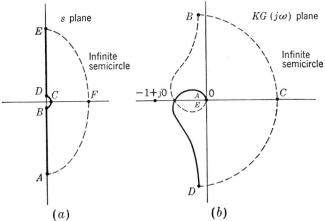

FIG. 7-7. Graphical closure of open plots.

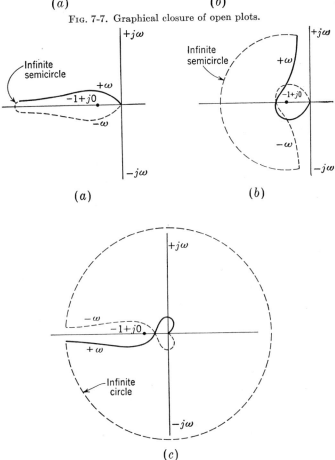

FIG. 7-8. Graphical closure of typical KG plots.

lies always to the right of the variable point as it moves along the contour. Then on any open $KG(j\omega)$ plot the variable may be assumed to start at $j\omega = 0+$, then move along the $+j\omega$ locus to $j\omega = \mp \infty$, then along the $-j\omega$ locus to $j\omega = 0-$. The locus is then closed by moving *clockwise* along an infinite semicircle so that the enclosed area lies always to the right of the variable point.

Figure 7-8 shows a number of illustrative open plots. Some of these are not necessarily practical plots, but they are inserted to show the principle involved. It is readily seen that the $-1 + j0$ point is enclosed by Fig. 7-8a and the system is unstable. Conversely, in Fig. 7-8c the $-1 + j0$ point is obviously not enclosed, and so the system is stable. In Fig. 7-8b, however, the interpretation requires care. It must be remembered that the enclosed area lies always to the *right* of the path when the variable moves clockwise. If this test is applied to Fig. 7-8b, it is seen that the $-1 + j0$ is never to the right of the locus and is therefore not enclosed; so the system is stable.

7-8. Relative Stability—General Discussion. Once it has been shown by application of the Nyquist criterion that a system is stable, the next point of interest in an analysis is the question of transient performance. Even though a servomechanism may be absolutely stable, *i.e.*, does not oscillate indefinitely, it is certainly possible that the system may be greatly underdamped and have excessive overshoot or too long a duration of oscillation to be acceptable practically and thus is only relatively stable. Since the transfer-function locus would be available from the stability check, it is only sensible to obtain as much information as possible about relative stability from this curve.

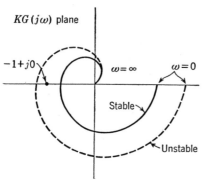

Fig. 7-9. Stable and unstable KG loci.

A little thought about the $KG(j\omega)$ locus shows that the difference between a stable and an unstable system is really just a small displacement of the locus. This is illustrated in Fig. 7-9, where two loci of the same general shape are shown (only plus frequency half). The solid-line curve passes slightly to the right of $-1 + j0$ and therefore represents a stable system, while the broken-line curve passes slightly to the left of $-1 + j0$ and therefore represents an unstable system. It is apparent that both loci must represent the same type of system and that only a slight difference in parameters can exist because the two loci are almost identical in size and shape. It is true that one system is unstable and the other stable; yet common sense says that there cannot be a tremendous difference in characteristics. Therefore the stable system should be nearly unstable, *i.e.*, greatly underdamped, because its locus passes so close to the $-1 + j0$ point.

It would seem, therefore, that the distance from the $-1 + j0$ point to the nearest point on the $KG(j\omega)$ locus should be an indication of the relative stability of the system. This is actually the case but is only of qualitative value; *i.e.*, loci which pass close to the $-1 + j0$ point are in general considerably underdamped, while those farther away have more damping, but measurement of the distance from the $-1 + j0$ point to the locus does not give a good quantitative index of damping.

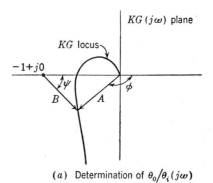

(*a*) Determination of $\theta_o/\theta_i(j\omega)$

It must be remembered that the transfer-function method of analysis is essentially a frequency-response method. It has been shown that the transfer-function curve may be interpreted graphically in terms of the frequency response, and it is known that the frequency response gives indication of the amount of damping. Therefore the vector relations on the transfer-function plot must be used to determine the relative stability. The following paragraphs show how these vector relationships may be used to determine the magnitude of the resonance peak of the frequency response and the frequency at which it occurs.

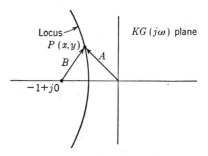

(*b*) Locus of $M=K$

Fig. 7-10. Derivation of constant-magnitude circles.

7-9. Relative Stability—Magnitude Circles. Figure 7-10*a* shows the vector relationships which exist on the transfer-function plot. The vector A is the transfer-function vector, $KG(j\omega)$, and the vector B is $1 + KG(j\omega)$. Thus the frequency-response function is given by

$$\frac{\theta_o}{\theta_i}(j\omega) = \frac{A/\phi}{B/\psi} = \frac{KG(j\omega)}{1 + KG(j\omega)}$$

It is obvious that there must exist a locus on the $KG(j\omega)$ plane such that the ratio $|A/B|$ is always a constant. This ratio is a magnitude ratio, *i.e.*, the phase angles are not considered, and may be defined as

$$M = \left|\frac{A}{B}\right| = \left|\frac{\theta_o}{\theta_i}\right| \tag{7-20}$$

where M is a constant number.

The locus-of-constant-magnitude ratio, M, may be shown to be a circle as follows: Fig. 7-10b shows a sketch of an assumed M locus on the KG plane with a point $P(x,y)$ selected on the locus. By definition,

$$M = \left|\frac{\theta_o}{\theta_i}\right| = \left|\frac{KG(j\omega)}{1 + KG(j\omega)}\right| = \left|\frac{A}{B}\right|$$

and

$$KG = A = x + jy$$

Therefore,

$$M = \frac{x + jy}{1 + x + jy} \tag{7-21}$$

$$M^2 = \frac{(x + jy)(x - jy)}{(1 + x + jy)(1 + x - jy)} = \frac{x^2 + y^2}{1 + 2x + x^2 + y^2} \tag{7-22}$$

$$y^2(M^2 - 1) + x^2(M^2 - 1) + 2xM^2 + M^2 = 0 \tag{7-23}$$

$$x^2 + y^2 + (2x + 1)\frac{M^2}{M^2 - 1} = 0 \tag{7-24}$$

and Eq. (7-24), upon completing the square, is the equation of a circle with center at

$$x = -\frac{M^2}{M^2 - 1} \qquad y = 0 \tag{7-25}$$

and radius

$$r = \frac{M}{M^2 - 1} \tag{7-26}$$

Since the locus of constant magnitude, M, of the frequency-response ratio is a circle, it is a simple matter to draw a number of circles on the KG plane such as are shown on Fig. 7-11a.

As the transfer-function locus is already on the KG plane from the stability test, and presumably it is a stable locus, it must somewhere be tangent to one of the M circles. If the point of tangency is located, the numerical value of M for the circle passing through this point is

$$M \text{ (tangency)} = M_p = \text{maximum ratio of } \left|\frac{\theta_o}{\theta_i}\right| \tag{7-27}$$

Likewise, the frequency parameter is used in plotting the transfer-function locus, so that a number of known frequency points, ω_1, ω_2, ω_3, etc., are marked, and the frequency at which the resonance peak, M_p, occurs can be picked from the curve.

$$\omega_r = \text{resonant frequency} = \text{frequency at which } M_p \text{ occurs} \tag{7-28}$$

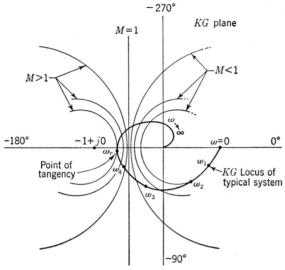

(*a*) Constant-magnitude, or *M*, circles

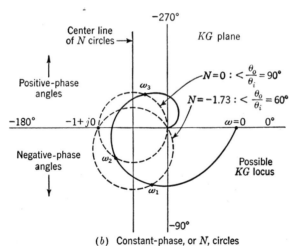

(*b*) Constant-phase, or *N*, circles

Fig. 7-11. *M* and *N* circles on the *KG* plane.

7-10. Constant-phase, or *N*, Circles. To facilitate the determination of the frequency-response function from the $KG(j\omega)$ plot, use may be made of a family of curves of constant phase-angle displacement between θ_o and θ_i. Such curves are known as *N* contours or *N* circles. These loci are also of much value in design problems which require reshaping of a locus to achieve desired servo performance, as the *N* circles provide a graphic picture of the approximate phase shift needed in the redesign.

The location of such contours and proof that they are a family of circles can be found by referring again to Fig. 7-10b. The angular portion of the frequency-response function is found to be

$$\underline{/\frac{\theta_o}{\theta_i}} (j\omega) = \tan^{-1}\frac{y}{x} - \tan^{-1}\frac{y}{1+x} \qquad (7\text{-}29)$$

Thus if N is defined as the tangent of this angle,

$$N = \tan\left(\tan^{-1}\frac{y}{x} - \tan^{-1}\frac{y}{1+x}\right) \qquad (7\text{-}30)$$

This last equation is of the form

$$\tan(A - B) = \frac{\tan A - \tan B}{1 + \tan A \tan B} \qquad (7\text{-}31)$$

so that an expression for N becomes

$$N = \frac{\dfrac{y}{x} - \dfrac{y}{1+x}}{1 + \left(\dfrac{y}{x}\dfrac{y}{1+x}\right)} \qquad (7\text{-}32)$$

This expands to

$$N(x^2 + x) + N\left(y^2 - \frac{y}{N}\right) = 0 \qquad (7\text{-}33)$$

It can readily be shown that the expansion of Eq. (7-33) is the equation of a circle whose center is defined by the coordinates

$$x = -\frac{1}{2} \qquad y = +\frac{1}{2N} \qquad (7\text{-}34)$$

The radius of the circle is defined by

$$R = \sqrt{\frac{1}{4} + \left(\frac{1}{2N}\right)^2} \qquad (7\text{-}35)$$

It may be noted that the N circles and the M circles are both independent of the family parameter, frequency.

Thus a family of circles may be drawn on the KG plane as shown in Fig. 7-11b. A sample transfer-function plot is superimposed on the plane to illustrate the use of N circles. A few typical frequencies are indicated at which the transfer-function locus intersects the few N contours drawn.

Note that at the frequency ω_1, where the KG plot intersects the $N = -1.73$ circle, the phase angle is -60 deg, $i.e.$, the output lags the input by slightly more than 1 radian. At the frequency ω_2, where the transfer-function plot intersects the $N = 0$ circle, the phase angle is -90

deg, the output again lagging the input. Finally at the frequency ω_3, where the KG plot intersects the $N = 0$ circle in the second quadrant, the output leads the input by 90 deg or lags by 270 deg.

When both M and N circles are drawn on the same axes with a system transfer-function plot, rapid determination of the frequency-response curves is made possible by merely noting the intersections and points of tangency with the various contours and the frequency at which they occur.

7-11. Correlations between Transient Response and Frequency Response. No exact mathematical relationship has been derived between the resonance peak, M_p, and the transient overshoot, or between the resonant frequency, ω_r, and the transient oscillating frequency, or between ω_r and the speed of response to a transient. However, there is ample evidence that such relationships exist.[10−12,16,21,22] Empirical relationships are normally used, based on the comparison between transient and transfer-function responses of known systems. Since the relationships are empirical, they will merely be stated here.

1. Relationship between peak overshoot and M_p. In general the peak overshoot of the transient response of a servomechanism is slightly less than the resonance peak M_p of the frequency response. It has been found from experience that a satisfactory transient performance is usually obtained if M_p is made less than $1\frac{1}{3}$. Under these conditions the over-all damping is normally $0.5 < \zeta < 0.8$.

2. Relationship between ω_r and the transient oscillating frequency. In general, ω_r is approximately the same as the base frequency of the transient oscillations. Of course, ω_r is lower than the undamped natural frequency of the system, ω_n.

3. Relationship between ω_r and speed of response. The resonant frequency ω_r is only a qualitative indication of the speed of response. Systems with a low ω_r respond slowly, and systems with a high ω_r respond quickly. Accurate determination of the speed of response usually requires a transient analysis, or an actual test, or considerable experience.

Certain additional empirical relationships exist between the transient performance of systems and the phase angle of the transfer-function response. It is not convenient to introduce these at this point.

7-12. Steady-state Performance from the KG Locus. The question of the steady-state performance of a servomechanism may be conveniently divided into two parts:

1. Existence of steady-state error
2. Magnitude of steady-state error

The first of these, the existence of error, is readily determined from the transfer-function equation or from the locus. In addition it will be shown that the criteria for existence of error also provide a convenient means for classifying systems. The magnitude of the steady-state error as a function of operating conditions may be readily indicated by what are commonly called *figures of merit*.

Various transfer functions of components and systems have already been derived in this text, as, for example, Eqs. (5-30), (5-35), (5-46), (5-74). It has also been indicated that the denominator of the frequency-response function $(1 + KG)$ may be expressed as the ratio of two polynomials as in Eq. (7-18). Therefore, it may readily be seen that the general expression for the transfer function may be written as the ratio of two polynomials,

$$KG(j\omega) = \frac{A(j\omega\tau_a + 1)(j\omega\tau_b + 1) \cdots}{(j\omega)^N(j\omega\tau_1 + 1)(j\omega\tau_2 + 1) \cdots} \qquad (7\text{-}36)$$

Equation (7-36) is readily applied to the problem of interpreting the shape of the transfer-function locus in terms of the existence of a steady-state error.

In general, the relationship

$$KG(j\omega) = \frac{\theta_o}{\varepsilon}(j\omega)$$

relates the output *position* to the error between output and input. Also, in general the term "steady state" means that the input is of constant form (constant position, constant velocity, constant acceleration) and that it has retained its constant property for a sufficient length of time so that the transient period is completed. If the input signal is a position, the steady-state output is also a position and the steady-state error is obviously a position error. However, if the input is a velocity or an accleration, the steady-state output is also a velocity or an acceleration (since the basic purpose of a servomechanism is to reproduce an input according to some definite law); yet the error is still a *position* error if the servomechanism is properly designed for the application. This is so because a true servomechanism compares the instantaneous value of the input and output positions (or corresponding variables) and attempts to reduce any discrepancy to zero. Thus for a constant-velocity or -acceleration input the system reaches steady state in the sense that the output velocity or acceleration is in direct proportion to the input, and any error is in the form of an instantaneous displacement between input and output reference points, *i.e.*, a position error. It is possible, of course, to operate servomechanism systems so that the above criteria are not met, *i.e.*, a system may be designed for zero position error and if used with constant-velocity input will reproduce the velocity with a position error but if used with a constant-acceleration input will not reproduce the acceleration and will have a continuously increasing position error.

The transfer-function equation of a servomechanism, when expressed with the $j\omega$ operator, indicates the ability of the system to transfer energy when a sinusoidal error signal of angular frequency, ω, is applied to the error terminals. The mathematical expression is therefore in the frequency domain. The steady-state performance of the servomechanism is, in physical terms, the behavior of the system a long time after a disturbance. Thus steady-state performance is basically a function of the time domain. To interpret the transfer function in terms of the steady-state performance requires a mathematical relationship between the frequency domain and the time domain. One relationship, which is sufficient for the purposes of this text, is the final value theorem of the Laplace transformation. It states in brief that

$$\lim_{s \to 0} sF(s) = \lim_{t \to \infty} f(t) \qquad (7\text{-}37)$$

This theorem is stated for an assumed sudden disturbance in the system. When used to determine the steady-state time performance from the transformed equation, it is assumed that $F(s)$ contains the transform of the disturbance.

The transfer-function equation of a servomechanism does not contain any term relating to a sudden disturbance, and thus Eq. (7-37) does not apply directly. It may be noted, however, that the transfer function could be modified to include the effect of a sudden disturbance by multiplying it by the transform of a step-displacement function, which is $\mathcal{L}[u(t)] = 1/s$. This, however, would only cancel the multiplying factor, s, in Eq. (7-37). Therefore, to interpret the steady-state performance of a servomechanism from its transfer function, Eq. (7-37) may be modified and rewritten as

$$\lim_{s \to 0} F(s) = \lim_{t \to \infty} f(t) \qquad (7\text{-}38)$$

and of course the $j\omega$ notation may be substituted for the s notation.

7-13. Interpretation of Transfer Function for Positioning Systems. If a servomechanism system is to indicate a position, i.e., if the input signal is a position, then in order that the steady-state error, $\mathcal{E}_{ss}$, be zero, it is necessary that

$$\frac{\theta_o}{\mathcal{E}}(j\omega) \underset{\omega \to 0}{=} \frac{A(j\omega\tau_a + 1)(j\omega_b\tau + 1) \cdots}{(j\omega)^N(j\omega\tau_1 + 1)(j\omega\tau_2 + 1) \cdots} \underset{\omega \to 0}{=} \infty \qquad (7\text{-}39)$$

where $N = 0, 1, 2, \ldots$.

It is obvious that if $\theta_o \neq \infty$ then $\mathcal{E}$ must be zero in order that $\theta_o/\mathcal{E} = \infty$. Then the ratio of polynomials must be infinite, and by inspection all of the terms $(j\omega\tau_a + 1)$ and $(j\omega\tau_1 + 1)$ approach unity as ω approaches zero, so that a positioning system has zero steady-state error if, and only if, $N \geq 1$.

Inspection of Eq. (7-39) shows that if $N = 0$, $\theta_o \rightarrow A$ (some constant) as $\omega \rightarrow 0$, and therefore $\varepsilon \neq 0$, and there is a position error.

For $N = 1$: $\dfrac{\theta_o}{\varepsilon} \rightarrow -j\infty$ as $\omega \rightarrow 0$ $\therefore \varepsilon = 0$

$N = 2$: $\dfrac{\theta_o}{\varepsilon} \rightarrow -\infty$ as $\omega \rightarrow 0$ $\therefore \varepsilon = 0$

$N = 3$: $\dfrac{\theta_o}{\varepsilon} \rightarrow +j\infty$ as $\omega \rightarrow 0$ $\therefore \varepsilon = 0$

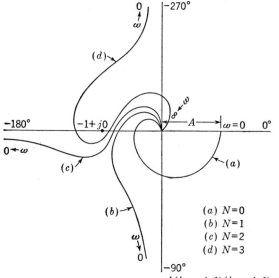

(a) $N=0$
(b) $N=1$
(c) $N=2$
(d) $N=3$

Fig. 7-12. Transfer-function loci for $KG \dfrac{A(j\omega\tau_a + 1)(j\omega\tau_b + 1) \cdots}{(j\omega)^N(j\omega\tau_1 + 1)(j\omega\tau_2 + 1) \cdots}$.

In terms of the polar plot of the transfer function these characteristics are easily seen by inspection. Figure 7-12 shows a number of possible transfer-function loci which illustrate the problem. Curve a shows a plot for $N = 0$, which is a closed plot since $\theta_o = A$ when $\omega = 0$. Curve b shows a plot for $N = 1$, which is open with $\theta_o/\varepsilon \rightarrow -j\infty$ as $\omega \rightarrow 0$. Curve c is for $N = 2$, and again the plot is open with $\theta_o/\varepsilon \rightarrow -\infty$ as $\omega \rightarrow 0$. Likewise curve d for $N = 3$ is an open plot with $\theta_o/\varepsilon \rightarrow +j\infty$ as $\omega \rightarrow 0$. Thus in general a system with a closed transfer-function plot has a position error when used as a positioning system, but all servomechanisms with open transfer-function plots inherently have zero position error when used as positioning systems.

7-14. Classification of Servomechanism Systems. Because of the form of the general transfer-function equation, the corresponding transfer-function loci have a definite relationship to the steady-state error, and because there is no such definite relationship for transient performance, it is convenient to classify servomechanism systems in terms of Eq. (7-39). This will be done before discussing other steady-state conditions in order to simplify terminology in the following discussions.

Definitions

Type 0 system, one for which $N = 0$ in the transfer-function equation
Type 1 system, one for which $N = 1$ in the transfer-function equation
Type 2 system, one for which $N = 2$ in the transfer-function equation
Type 3 system, one for which $N = 3$ in the transfer-function equation

The type of locus which is characteristic of each system so defined may be seen from Fig. 7-12. It should be noted that the fundamental locus characteristic is the behavior of the curve as $\omega \to 0$; the shape of the locus at other frequencies depends on the other factors in Eq. (7-39).

7-15. Interpretation of Transfer Function for Systems with Constant-velocity Input. When a servomechanism is operated with a constant-velocity input, the transfer function requires a somewhat different interpretation. It is first desired to know whether a steady-state error exists and what is the nature of this steady-state error. Equation (7-39) must be modified to account for the fact that the output is a velocity. This is done by taking a derivative, *i.e.*,

$$\frac{d}{dt}\left[\frac{\theta_o}{\varepsilon}(j\omega) \right] = \frac{d}{dt}\left[\frac{A(j\omega\tau_a + 1)(j\omega\tau_b + 1) \cdots}{(j\omega)^N(j\omega\tau_1 + 1)(j\omega\tau_2 + 1) \cdots} \right] \qquad (7\text{-}40)$$

and since the transfer function itself actually consists of transformed functions rather than time functions, it is necessary to transform the operator so that Eq. (7-40) becomes

$$j\omega \frac{\theta_o}{\varepsilon}(j\omega) = j\omega \frac{A(j\omega\tau_a + 1) \cdots}{(j\omega)^N(j\omega\tau_1 + 1) \cdots}. \qquad (7\text{-}41)$$

The expression obtained in Eq. (7-41) is actually another transfer function. It is the ratio of the velocity output to the position input.

If Eq. (7-41) is examined as $\omega \to 0$, the steady-state performance with constant-velocity input is determined,

$$j\omega \frac{\theta_o}{\varepsilon}(j\omega) = j\omega \frac{A(j\omega\tau_a + 1) \cdots}{(j\omega)^N(j\omega\tau_1 + 1) \cdots}. \qquad (7\text{-}42)$$
$$\quad\;\; {\scriptstyle \omega \to 0} \qquad\qquad\quad {\scriptstyle \omega \to 0}$$

From this examination, for a type 0 system, $j\omega(\theta_o/\varepsilon) \to 0$; therefore $\varepsilon \to \infty$ as $j\omega\theta_o \to$ a constant value since the output operates at some constant velocity in steady state. This means that the output velocity is different from the input velocity since this is the only way in which it is possible for ε to approach infinity.

For a type 1 system, $j\omega(\theta_o/\mathcal{E}) \to A$; therefore the output velocity is equal to the input velocity, but there is a constant position error between output and input. The magnitude of this error depends on the value of A.

For type 2, 3, and higher-order systems, $j\omega(\theta_o/\mathcal{E}) \to \infty$; therefore $\mathcal{E}$ is zero, and the system operates with exact input and output correspondence.

Thus it is seen that inspection of the transfer-function plot also indicates the steady-state performance when the input is a constant velocity. The existence of a steady-state error is readily determined by inspection. The magnitude of such an error, if one exists, unfortunately is not available from the plot.

7-16. Interpretation with Constant-acceleration Input. If the servomechanism is operated with constant-acceleration input, a second derivative of Eq. (7-39) is needed for interpretation, which gives

$$\frac{d^2}{dt^2}\left[\frac{\theta_o}{\mathcal{E}}(j\omega)\right] = \frac{d^2}{dt^2}\left[\frac{A(j\omega\tau_a + 1) \; \cdots}{(j\omega)^N(j\omega\tau_1 + 1) \; \cdots}\right] \tag{7-43}$$

which after transformation and taking the limit becomes

$$(j\omega)^2 \frac{\theta_o}{\mathcal{E}}(j\omega) = (j\omega)^2 \frac{A(j\omega\tau_a + 1) \; \cdots}{(j\omega)^N(j\omega\tau_1 + 1) \; \cdots} \tag{7-44}$$
$$\omega \to 0 \qquad\qquad\qquad \omega \to 0$$

and for type 0 and type 1 systems

$$(j\omega)^2 \frac{\theta_o}{\mathcal{E}} = 0$$

Therefore the acceleration is not reproduced, and the error, $\mathcal{E}$, increases continuously.

For a type 2 system,

$$(j\omega)^2 \frac{\theta_o}{\mathcal{E}} = A$$

and the acceleration is reproduced, but there is a constant position error.

For a type 3 or higher system,

$$(j\omega)^3 \frac{\theta_o}{\mathcal{E}} = \infty$$

and the error is zero.

Thus the existence of an error for a constant-acceleration input is readily seen from the transfer-function equation or plot.

Table 7-1 summarizes the preceding discussion. In general the complexity of equipment, cost, and difficulty in design increase greatly with the more advanced type of systems. Type 1 systems are therefore

TABLE 7-1

Type system	Locus characteristic	Error characteristic	Application
0	Closed.	Position error at all times.	Static positioning systems where high accuracy is not important. Some regulator systems.
1	Open. The low-frequency end of the locus goes to infinity along the negative imaginary axis.	No static error. Lag error when operated at constant velocity.	High-accuracy static and dynamic positioning systems.
2	Open. The low-frequency end of the locus approaches infinity along the negative real axis.	No static error. No position error at constant velocity. Constant error in acceleration.	High-accuracy dynamic positioning systems. Control acceleration errors.
3	Open. The low-frequency end of the locus goes to infinity along the positive imaginary axis.	No static error. No position error at constant velocity or acceleration.	

commoner than any of the others. Occasionally accuracy requirements will justify the type 2 system, and in other cases where high accuracy is not essential a type 0 system is more economical.

7-17. Figures of Merit. As in any design problem, it is desirable to have available methods which will quickly check the important performance features of a servomechanism, in order to eliminate unnecessary calculations. The preceding equations used to indicate the existence of a steady-state error may also be conveniently used to check the steady-state error quantitatively. It may be noted that in every case where a finite and constant error exists, the evaluation of the transfer function at $j\omega = 0$ results in a constant number. This number always represents the ratio of the steady-state output to the steady-state error. Thus

$$\frac{\text{Output}}{\text{Error}} = K \qquad (7-45)$$

from which

$$\text{Error} = \frac{\text{output}}{K} \qquad (7-46)$$

In the case of a type 0 system used as a positioning system,

$$KG(j\omega) \underset{\omega \to 0}{=} \frac{\theta_o}{\varepsilon}(j\omega) \underset{j\omega \to 0}{=} K_p \qquad (7\text{-}47)$$

and

$$\varepsilon \text{ (position)} = \frac{\theta_o}{K_p} \qquad (7\text{-}48)$$

For a Type 1 system operated with a constant-velocity input, the velocity-lag error may be determined from

$$j\omega KG(j\omega) \underset{j\omega \to 0}{=} \frac{j\omega\theta_o}{\varepsilon}(j\omega) \underset{j\omega \to 0}{=} \frac{\text{output velocity}}{\varepsilon} = K_v \qquad (7\text{-}49)$$

Thus the velocity-lag error is

$$\varepsilon \text{ (position)} = \frac{\text{output velocity}}{K_v} \qquad (7\text{-}50)$$

For a type 2 system there is an acceleration error at constant input acceleration, and

$$(j\omega)^2 KG(j\omega) \underset{j\omega \to 0}{=} \frac{(j\omega)^2\theta_o}{\varepsilon}(j\omega) \underset{\omega \to 0}{=} \frac{\text{output acceleration}}{\text{error}} = K_a \qquad (7\text{-}51)$$

from which the acceleration error is

$$\varepsilon \text{ (position)} = \frac{\text{output acceleration}}{K_a} \qquad (7\text{-}52)$$

The error in each case is a position error, *i.e.*, in terms of rotational systems it is an angular displacement (constant) between reference indices on the input and output shafts. The constants K_p, K_v, and K_a are in each case the gain constants of the system between the error terminals and the output. They are given different subscripts because they are peculiar to the type of system. That is, type 1 and type 2 systems inherently have no position error, and so for such systems K_p is infinite. From the equations it might be said that $K_p = K_v/j\omega$ or $K_p = K_a/(j\omega)^2$, both of which are seen to be infinite as $j\omega$ approaches zero.

Thus it may be seen that the gain constant of the system is a figure of merit which indicates the steady-state performance exactly. For example, assume that the equation of a type 1 system is

$$KG(j\omega) = \frac{37.5(0.8_j\,\omega + 1)}{j\omega(12j\omega + 1)(0.4j\omega + 1)(0.05j\omega + 1)} \qquad (7\text{-}53)$$

The gain constant of the system is readily seen to be

$$K_v = 37.5 \qquad (7\text{-}54)$$

If the system is to be operated at a constant input velocity of 9 rpm, then there will be a velocity-lag error and the magnitude of this error is

$$\varepsilon = \frac{\text{output velocity}}{K_v} = \frac{9 \times 6.28/60 \times 57.3}{37.5} = 1.44°$$

If the transfer-function equation of the system is not available, the gain constant may be evaluated from logarithmic plots. This procedure is discussed in Chap. 12.

Figures of merit for transient performance are not nearly so quantitative as those for steady-state performance. The figures of merit most commonly used for transient checks are M_p and ω_r, as previously discussed. To summarize their application, M_p is used as an indication of the peak transient overshoot and is usually kept below $M_p = 1.5$. The resonant frequency is an index of the speed of response, provided M_p is acceptable, and a large value for ω_r indicates a system with fast response. Practical application of these figures of merit is based largely on experience.

Other figures of merit which are used to estimate transient performance vary with the application. They are usually concerned with specific components rather than the over-all system. For example, maximum stalled torque and the torque-to-inertia ratio are vital in estimating the suitability of a motor in a system requiring definite transient-acceleration characteristics. Discussion of such figures of merit is beyond the scope of this text.

PROBLEMS

7-1. Check the following equations for the existence of positive real roots:
a. $2 \, dy/dt + 3 = 0$ b. $4 \, d^2y/dt^2 + 3 \, dy/dt + y + 6 = 0$
c. $5s^3 + 3s + 8 = 0$ d. $5s^3 + 6s^2 + s + 14 = 0$
e. $s^4 + 2s^3 + 11s^2 - 19s + 2 = 0$ f. $s^4 + 8s^3 - 3s^2 + 6s + 5 = 0$
g. $18s^5 + 3s^4 + 11s^2 + 9s^3 + s + 56 = 0$

7-2. Determine the poles and zeros of the following transfer functions, and plot them on the complex s plane:
a. $1/(s\tau + 1)$ b. $1/(s\tau + 1)(s\tau + 5)$
c. $1/s\tau(s\tau + 1)$ d. $(s\tau + 4)/s\tau(s\tau + 10)$
e. $(s\tau + 10)/[(s\tau)^2 + 6s\tau + 3]$

7-3. Determine the poles and zeros of the networks of Figs. 5P-1 to 5P-10.

7-4. Determine (by means of a Nyquist plot) which of the following transfer functions represent stable closed-loop systems:
a. $KG(j\omega) = 20/(j\omega + 1)(0.5j\omega + 1)$ b. $KG(j\omega) = 20/(j\omega + 1)^2(0.5j\omega + 1)$
c. $KG(j\omega) = 10/j\omega(j\omega + 1)$ d. $KG(j\omega) = 10/(j\omega)^2(j\omega + 1)$
e. $KG(j\omega) = 10(j\omega + 5)/j\omega(j\omega + 1)$
f. $KG(j\omega) = 5(j\omega + 10)/j\omega(j\omega + 3)(j\omega + 7)$
g. $KG(j\omega) = 5(j\omega + 10)/(j\omega)^2(j\omega + 1)$

7-5. Add M circles to the stable loci found in Prob. 7-4; determine M_p and ω_r.
7-6. For each of the stable loci of Prob. 7-4,

a. What is the steady-state position error if a step displacement of 5 deg is applied to the input?

b. What is the steady-state velocity-lag error if a step velocity of 1 radian/sec is applied to the input?

7-7. Given a system with the following transfer function:

$$KG(j\omega) = \frac{2(1 + 0.16j\omega)}{(0.02j\omega)(0.16j\omega)(1 + 0.02j\omega)}$$

a. Plot the transfer-function locus; determine M_p and ω_r.

b. Are there steady-state errors if used as a positioning system? As a velocity system? If so, how much error?

7-8. Using the transfer functions derived in Probs. 5-8 to 5-12, determine the steady-state velocity-lag error of each if a step velocity of 1 radian/sec is applied to their respective inputs.

7-9. Add M circles to the transfer-function curves on Prob. 6-11; determine M_p, ω_r, and the frequency-response function θ_o/θ_i. Compare the latter with that previously determined.

7-10. Add M circles to the transfer-function curves of Prob. 6-12. Determine M_p and ω_r.

7-11. Repeat Prob. 7-10 for the transfer-function curve of Prob. 6-13.

7-12. Repeat Prob. 7-10 for the transfer-function curves of Prob. 6-14. Add N circles, and determine the magnitude and phase curves for the frequency-response function.

7-13. Repeat Prob. 7-10 for the transfer-function curve of Prob. 6-15. Add N circles, and determine the magnitude and phase curves for the frequency-response function.

7-14. Add M circles to the transfer-function curve of Prob. 6-16. Determine M_p and ω_r.

7-15. Repeat Prob. 7-14 for the transfer-function curve of Prob. 6-17.

7-16. Add M and N circles to the transfer-function curve of Prob. 6-18. Determine M_p, ω_r, and the magnitude and phase curves for the frequency-response function.

7-17. Repeat Prob. 7-16 for the transfer-function curve of Prob. 6-19.

7-18. Add M circles to the transfer-function locus of Prob. 6-20. Determine M_p and ω_r.

7-19. Repeat Prob. 7-18 for the locus of Prob. 6-21.

CHAPTER 8

INTRODUCTION TO DESIGN

8-1. Introduction. The application of theoretical principles to the actual design of a servomechanism is not a simple procedure because of the relative complexity of most servomechanism systems. In addition, closed-cycle automatic controls are used in a great variety of applications, and the components available for use in such systems operate on many different principles. Thus it becomes impossible to specify a definite, universal approach to the problem of design. It is possible, however, to outline a general procedure which is helpful in most design work. In some specific cases, of course, departure from this procedure may be necessary as well as desirable.

The first step in any design work is to obtain certain minimum information about the desired system, preferably in the form of specifications. The form or manner in which these specifications are stated depends partly on the type of control problem and partly on the person writing the specifications and his familiarity with servomechanism or control theory. The designer certainly needs a fairly exact and explicit knowledge of the functions which are to be performed by the servomechanism. While all details may not be required initially, the following list indicates some of the items for which quantitative information is usually desirable:

1. The basic function of the system, *i.e.*, static positioning; positioning during velocity operation; speed duplication; temperature control; chemical-concentration control; etc.

2. The nature of any loading and the magnitude of such loads, *i.e.*, inertia; inertia plus friction; torque or force loading; etc. Also, any variations in loading must be known, the magnitude of such variations, and the frequency with which they occur. In many cases all of these data are not available quantitatively. Normal loading and intentional load variations are usually known, but in some applications extraneous loading effects may occur with unpredictable magnitudes and frequencies. For example, a radar antenna used for sweeping presents a known load, but any wind will produce additional loading the magnitude and frequency of which can only be estimated.

3. Desired accuracy, including time lags in response.

4. Maximum expected rates of change required in driving the output—maximum velocity and maximum acceleration.

5. Space, weight, and cost limitations, if any.

6. Disturbing influences external to the system itself—temperature and humidity; shock, as in naval service owing to the firing of big guns; accelerations, as in combat aircraft when pulling out of power dives; etc.

7. Type of power to be used in operating system (this may be optional in many applications).

The designer must be able to interpret such information in terms of servomechanism requirements. He must be able to express numerically:

1. Permissible steady-state error
2. Maximum allowable transient overshoot
3. Speed of response
4. Duration of transient period

Furthermore, if transfer-function methods are to be used in designing, the above criteria must be transferred into such criteria as the allowable resonance peak, M_p, the resonant frequency, ω_r, and the type of system (0, 1, 2, 3) required by the steady-state-error specification.

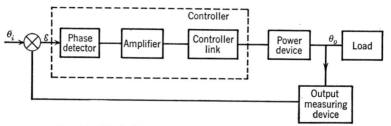

Fig. 8-1. Block diagram of servomechanism components.

The next step would probably be the construction of a basic block diagram and a tentative selection of components. Figure 8-1 shows a possible block diagram for an assumed type 1 system. The selection of components is at best arbitrary and depends not only on the requirements of the application but also on the experience and preference of the designer. A brief discussion of factors to be considered is given in the following paragraphs.

8-2. Powering Devices.[55-60],* The nature of the load and the nature of the available power supply normally dictate the physical nature of the powering device. Such a choice is then investigated to see whether or not a unit with acceptable performance is commercially available. Assuming that an apparently acceptable device is obtainable, the power and torque produced must be adequate not only to supply the load but to produce

---

* Superior numbers, when they appear in the text proper, are the numbers of references given in the Bibliography.

such velocities and accelerations as are required. Efficiency may be important, and finally the weight and space requirement of the power device must be checked. Again assuming that the power device is apparently acceptable, suitable elements for controlling it must be selected. Failure to obtain a suitable controller because of cost, performance requirements, etc., may require a different selection for a power device. Where weight and space are important, hydraulic and pneumatic devices have advantages, while high-speed systems frequently have electric motor drives.

8-3. Controllers. *Amplifying Devices.* The output of the selected amplifier must be of the proper physical nature to operate the powering device and must have ample power capacity. The amplifier need not be a single unit but may be several units in cascade. However, the over-all combination of units comprising the amplifier must have sufficient gain to raise the error signal to the power level required at the input to the power device. In the process of amplification some means should be incorporated for gain adjustment, and it may also be necessary to change the physical nature of the signal; for example, an electrical error signal at the amplifier input may be changed into a fluid-flow output in order to operate a hydraulic motor.

Phase Detectors, Modulators, and Demodulators. The phase detector may not be a distinct unit in itself but may often be incorporated in either the error detector or the amplifier. Since a continuous-control servomechanism is expected to apply corrective power under all error conditions, the error signal varies not only in magnitude but in direction or phase. The phase detector therefore tells the amplifier whether power should be increased, decreased, or reversed. A demodulator would be required when the feedback signal is superimposed on a carrier; for example, selsyn generators and transformers are typical carrier-type feedback links. A modulator might be required in an electrical system where the main transmission channel is operated at 400 cycles and the error signal is most conveniently obtained as a d-c voltage, or vice versa.

8-4. Sensing Elements—Output-measuring Devices and Error Detectors. The selection of sensing and measuring elements is to some extent an interdependent function. The error detector must be able to subtract the output measurement from the command signal and must produce an error signal which is a suitable input for the controller. Thus the output-measuring device should, if possible, be selected with consideration of available error detectors. The actual selection of the output-measuring device depends largely on the nature of the output, *i.e.*, rotation, translation, temperature, pressure, fluid flow, etc. Frequently the selection of this device is a vital factor in system performance. Most measuring devices inherently have some time lag in their response; some mechanical devices have backlash, and many types of measuring devices are linear only in a limited range of operation. Obviously a system cannot be controlled more accurately than its output can be measured so that the quality of the measuring device sets at least one limit on system performance.

8-5. Design Procedures for the System. After a preliminary selection of components, the characteristics of the devices selected must be determined quantitatively, either in terms needed for the differential equation or as transfer functions. In many cases the manufacturer can supply the desired information, but frequently tests must be run, and the result may be a curve rather than a number. The over-all transfer-function locus is then obtained, either by numerical or by graphical manipulation. Obvious errors are then apparent from the general shape of the locus, and other performance criteria may be determined by a more detailed study.

The first performance detail to be checked is normally the absolute stability. If the system is stable, M_p and ω_r are determined by adding M circles. Prediction of transient performance is then possible, using figures of merit. Steady-state performance (if not satisfactorily specified by the type of system used) cannot be obtained from the locus but must be calculated from the system gain. In general some changes will be required to obtain acceptable performance. The method generally used is gain adjustment or the insertion of corrective elements or both. Occasionally the desired results may be obtained by replacing one of the original components with a more suitable unit.

Either of the available adjustment methods (gain or compensation) may be used to provide stability, improve transient performance, or improve steady-state performance. Each, however, has its own advantages and disadvantages. Gain adjustment is usually the simplest and least expensive procedure; however, such adjustment cannot stabilize all types of systems. Type 0 and 1 systems may always be stabilized by gain reduction, but higher-order systems can rarely be stabilized by gain adjustment. In any case, gain adjustment always affects both the transient and the steady-state performance,* so that a suitable compromise between these items is not always possible by gain adjustment alone. In general, increased gain improves the steady-state performance but makes transient conditions more oscillatory.

Compensation devices, in general, change the shape of the transfer-function locus. They are generally frequency selective, so that the locus

---

* Except in those cases where the type of system automatically produces perfect steady-state performance. For example, a type 1 system inherently has no static position error, so that gain adjustment has no effect on this item. However, gain adjustment does affect the velocity-lag error of a type 1 system.

is changed only over a frequency band. Thus, if a system requires high gain for steady-state performance and if such gain would make the transient performance poor, it is possible to reshape the locus in the region of the resonant frequency so as to obtain good transient operation at high gain. Conversely, the same problem might be solved by reshaping the low-frequency range so as to obtain high gain in this region without affecting the transient region. The difficulties involved lie partly in the design of compensators to work with a given system, and partly in the additional cost, size, weight, etc.

Compensating components may be placed in series with the main transmission path or may be placed in a feedback path parallel to one or more of the main components. No definite rule can be stated as to the preferability of either method, since circumstances often dictate the choice. In general the required characteristics of a series compensator are somewhat easier to calculate, but the physical nature of the unit depends on the system in which it is to be used, and realization of a practical device having the proper characteristics may not be possible, whereas a feedback component to accomplish the same purpose might be easily obtained. In many practical cases the feedback loop is preferred because of the simplicity with which it may be inserted, low cost, etc. The following chapters treat the subjects of gain adjustment, series compensation, and parallel compensation in terms of the mathematical and graphical manipulations needed for analysis and design.

CHAPTER 9

GAIN ADJUSTMENT

9-1. Introduction. When a servomechanism system is found to be unstable, or when the over-all performance (transient and/or steady-state) is not completely satisfactory, the most direct means of altering the performance is gain adjustment. This is certainly the simplest adjustment when the system contains an electronic amplifier in the main transmission path, for changes in gain may then be accomplished by merely resetting a potential divider (volume control) in the amplifier, or perhaps by redesigning one or two stages. In those cases where amplification is not obtained by electronic means, some similar adjustment is usually available. For this reason gain adjustment is given first consideration when performance must be changed. Other means of altering the system response, as through the introduction of compensating devices in series or in parallel with the main servo loop, are considered only when mere gain adjustment will not satisfy specifications.

9-2. Effect of Gain Adjustment on Performance. In general any change in the gain of a system affects all of the system figures of merit; magnitude of the resonance peak, M_p (and therefore the peak transient overshoot); the damping ratio, ζ; the undamped natural frequency, ω_n; the actual resonant frequency, ω_r; and the steady-state error if any normally exists. That these performance criteria are affected may be seen by inspection of a few basic equations and typical transfer-function plots.

Equation (5-74) shows that the amplifier gain, μ_a, for a specific system is part of the over-all gain constant, K, but is not included in the frequency-variant portion, $G(j\omega)$,

$$KG(j\omega) = \frac{\mu_a K_g}{R_f K_v} \frac{1}{j\omega(j\omega\tau_m + 1)(j\omega\tau_f + 1)} \tag{5-74}$$

Thus any change in μ_a affects the magnitude of the transfer-function vector but does not affect the phase angle. Therefore the magnitude ratio

$$\left|\frac{\theta_o}{\theta_i}\right| = \left|\frac{KG}{1 + KG}\right| = M$$

182

is dependent on the amplifier gain,* and when μ_a is changed, the magnitude of M_p is also changed.

The effect of varying the amplifier gain is shown in Fig. 9-1. The loci shown are typical for systems with equations similar to Eq. (5-74).

Curve a shows the locus for a relatively high gain, producing a resonance peak $M_p = 2.0$ and resonant frequency ω_{ra}. Doubling this gain by adjusting μ_a produces curve b and an unstable system. Reducing the gain by proper adjustment of μ_a produces curve c with a resonance peak $M_p = 1.5$ and a *new* resonant frequency ω_{rc}. Note that for a given frequency, ω_1, the transfer-function vector is located at an angle ψ from the reference axis, and only the magnitude of the vector is changed.

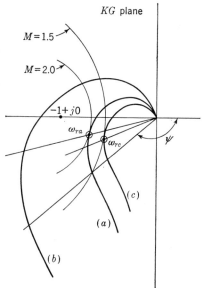

It is readily seen from Fig. 9-1 that the M_p and ω_r of the system are changed by gain adjustment. That the steady-state error is also affected may be seen from the system equation. There obviously is

FIG. 9-1. Effect of gain adjustment on KG locus.

no position error, because the system under discussion is a type 1 system, but there is a velocity-lag error, which is

$$\lim_{j\omega \to 0} (j\omega)KG(j\omega) = (j\omega)\frac{\mu_a K_g}{R_f K_v}\frac{1}{j\omega(j\omega\tau_m + 1)(j\omega\tau_f + 1)}\bigg|_{j\omega \to 0} = \frac{\mu_a K_g}{R_f K_v} \quad (9\text{-}1)$$

and this is changed by adjusting μ_a.

The effect of gain adjustment on the damping ratio, ζ, and the natural frequency, ω_n, is most readily seen from the transient equations. For a simple servomechanism,

$$K\varepsilon = J\frac{d^2\theta_o}{dt^2} + f\frac{d\theta_o}{dt} \quad (9\text{-}2)$$

where K is the system gain and contains μ_a as a factor. It is then apparent that if μ_a is altered the natural frequency $\omega_n = \sqrt{K/J}$ is changed.

---

* The same result may be obtained by varying any of the factors (K_g, R_f, K_v) included in the gain constant K. However, changes in amplifier gain are usually more convenient, and a wider (though not unlimited) range of variation is possible.

Furthermore, since $\zeta = f/2 \sqrt{KJ}$, the damping ratio is also changed and the system resonant frequency, $\omega_r = \sqrt{1 - \zeta^2}\, \omega_n$, is altered. This last statement is verified by Fig. 9-1.

To summarize, an increase in gain increases M_p, ω_n, and ω_r but decreases ζ and decreases the steady-state error, while a decrease in gain has the opposite effect on each of these system characteristics. In general an increase in gain produces a faster response with less steady-state error but makes the system more oscillatory (less stable) and thus gives undesirable transient characteristics.

9-3. Design Methods for Proper Gain Adjustment. The problem of determining the proper gain setting for a given servomechanism application can be solved in several ways. Graphical methods are preferred because of the relative ease with which they may be applied. Two methods are presented here. The first is purely a trial-and-error one and is presented only because it gives a clear picture of the principles involved. The second method obtains the desired information without trial and error and would be preferred in actual design. Both methods assume that the desired performance may be obtained with gain adjustment alone. If it is necessary to compensate the system, compensation devices would be inserted before adjusting the gain, since such devices normally introduce attenuation and phase shift, which would have to be considered in the gain adjustment.

9-4. Gain Adjustment by Trial and Error. In adjusting any devices, the desired result is known in advance, at least qualitatively and more often quantitatively. In adjusting the gain of a servomechanism the desired values of M_p and the steady-state error are usually specified precisely, with tolerances. The desired resonant frequency, ω_r, must also fall within a given range of values. Setting the gain of the system determines one of these factors (usually M_p), and the other two must then be checked. If either of the two remaining specifications is not satisfied, then the system must be compensated or some compromise agreed on.

To set the gain for a given M_p by trial and error, the over-all locus $KG(j\omega)$ is first plotted, and the M circle for the desired M_p is added. Such a locus and circle might be the curve a and the $M = 1.3$ circle in Fig. 9-2. Inspection shows that the gain must be reduced. Since each point on the locus represents the tip of a vector, and since a gain reduction decreases the length of each vector by some fraction, x, it is necessary only to determine the proper value of x. This may be done by inspection as follows:

1. Select the point on the locus which probably will be tangent to the M circle after gain reduction.

2. Draw the vector $KG(j\omega)$ from the origin to this point.

3. Measure the lengths $KG(j\omega)$ and $K'G'(j\omega)$ (*see* Fig. 9-2). Then $x = K'G'(j\omega)/KG(j\omega)$.

4. Multiply the original locus by x, and replot. If the result is not tangent to the M circle, another trial must be made.

When the proper reduction ratio, x, is determined, then

$$K'G'(j\omega) = xKG(j\omega)$$

from which

$$K' = xK \qquad (9\text{-}3)$$

and

$$\mu_a' = x\mu_a$$

The resonant frequency, ω_r, may then be checked from the locus and the steady-state error calculated from the equation.

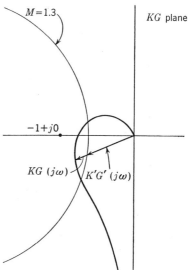

FIG. 9-2. Graphical determination of system gain.

Example. For the positioning servomechanism shown in Fig. 9-3, determine the proper amplifier gain for $M_p = 1.3$.

Component data:

1. D-C motor: 220 volts, 1,570 rpm, 1.75 amp. $R_a = 0.667$ ohm, $T = 0.833$ ft-lb, J (motor + load) = 0.053 slug-ft².

2. D-C generator: 220 volts, 5,000 rpm. $I_f = 1$ amp, $R_f = 150$ ohms, $L_f = 6$ henrys.

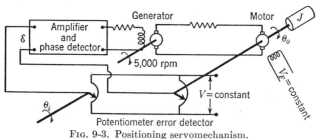

FIG. 9-3. Positioning servomechanism.

3. Phase detector and amplifier assumed ideal; original gain setting is $\mu_a = 3.12$.

Solution:

1. The equation of the system is

$$KG(j\omega) = \frac{\mu_a K_g}{R_f K_v} \frac{1}{j\omega(j\omega\tau_m + 1)(j\omega\tau_f + 1)} \qquad (5\text{-}74)$$

2. To determine K_g, assume operation on linear portion of curve; then

$$E_g \cong V_t = 220 \text{ volts} = K_g I_f$$

Therefore

$$K_g = 220 \text{ volts/amp}$$

3. To determine K_v, assume that the speed varies linearly with the load and that the armature inductance is negligible; then

$$V_t = E_b + I_a R_a = K_v \frac{d\theta_o}{dt} + I_a R_a$$

$$K_v = \frac{V_t - I_a R_a}{d\theta_o/dt}$$

But the motor current rating of 1.75 amp would be the total line current for self-excited operation; therefore

$$I_2 = I_a + I_f$$

$$I_a = I_2 - I_f = 1.75 - \frac{220}{R_f}$$

If the motor field resistance is 440 ohms, then

$$I_a = 1.75 - 220/440 = 1.25 \text{ amp}$$

and

$$K_v = \frac{220 - (1.25)(0.667)}{164} = 1.335 \text{ volts/radian/sec}$$

where $d\theta_o/dt = 1{,}570\pi/30$.

4. Then the gain constant, K, is

$$K = \frac{\mu_a K_g}{R_f K_v} = \frac{(3.12)(220)}{(150)(1.335)} = 3.42$$

5. The time constant of the motor is

$$\tau_m = \frac{J R_a}{K_t K_v} = \frac{(0.053)(0.667)}{(0.667)(1.335)} = 0.04 \text{ sec}$$

where $K_t = T/I_a = 0.833/1.25 = 0.667$.

6. The generator time constant is

$$\tau_f = \frac{L_f}{R_f} = \frac{6}{150} = 0.04 \text{ sec}$$

7. The transfer-function equation is

$$KG(j\omega) = \frac{3.42}{j\omega(0.04j\omega + 1)(0.04j\omega + 1)}$$

Numerical values for the locus are shown in Table 9-1.

TABLE 9-1

ω	$A = j\omega\tau + 1$	$j\omega A^2$	$G(j\omega) = \dfrac{1}{j\omega A^2}$	KG	$K'G'$
5	$1.02\underline{/11.3}$	$5.2\underline{/112.6}$	$0.192\underline{/-112.6}$	0.658	2.37
7	$1.04\underline{/15.6}$	$7.55\underline{/121.2}$	$0.132\underline{/-121.2}$	0.452	1.63
9	$1.06\underline{/19.8}$	$10.15\underline{/129.6}$	$0.0985\underline{/-129.6}$	0.337	1.21
10	$1.08\underline{/22}$	$11.7\underline{/134}$	$0.0854\underline{/-134}$	0.292	1.05
14.3	$1.15\underline{/30}$	$19\underline{/150}$	$0.052\underline{/-150}$	0.178	0.64
18	$1.21\underline{/35.7}$	$26.3\underline{/161.4}$	$0.038\underline{/-161.4}$	0.13	0.47
20	$1.28\underline{/38.6}$	$32.6\underline{/167}$	$0.031\underline{/-167}$	0.106	0.382
25	$1.414\underline{/45}$	$50\underline{/180}$	$0.020\underline{/-180}$	0.069	0.248
30	$1.56\underline{/50}$	$73\underline{/190}$	$0.0137\underline{/-190}$	0.047	
35	$1.72\underline{/54.4}$	$103.5\underline{/199}$	$0.00965\underline{/-199}$	0.033	
40	$1.89\underline{/58}$	$143\underline{/206}$	$0.007\underline{/-206}$	0.024	

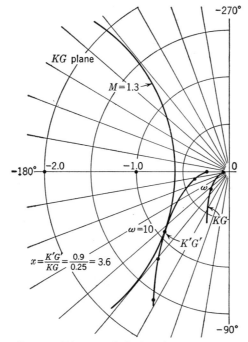

Fig. 9-4. Direct method of setting system gain.

The transfer-function locus is plotted as $KG(j\omega)$ in Fig. 9-4, and the gain is seen to be too low for $M_p = 1.3$. By inspection it is determined that the point of tangency with the $M = 1.3$ circle will occur at

$$\omega_r = 10 \text{ radians/sec}$$

and the vectors KG and $K'G'$ are laid off as in Fig. 9-4.   Then

$$x = \frac{K'G'}{KG} = \frac{0.9}{0.25} = 3.6$$

All values of KG in Table 9-1 are then multiplied by $x = 3.6$ and the results tabulated as $K'G'$.   These values are used to plot the $K'G'$ locus in Fig. 9-4.   This locus is seen to be sufficiently accurate; so another trial is not necessary.   Then the new amplifier gain setting should be

$$\mu_a' = x\mu_a = (3.6)(3.12) = 11.2$$

9-5. Direct Method of Gain Setting.   A somewhat simpler and much less laborious method for setting the gain of the system is obtained by plotting only the $G(j\omega)$ part of the transfer function (the gain constant K is assumed equal to unity).   A graphical construction is then used to determine a *scale* for this plot, and the new scale is then used to calculate the required system gain.

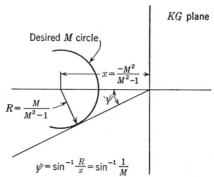

Fig. 9-5. Construction for system adjustment to specific M_p.

The graphical construction makes use of the easily proved fact (see Fig. 9-5) that (for $M > 1$) each M circle is tangent to a line drawn from the origin at an angle $\psi = \sin^{-1} 1/M$ with the negative real axis.

To obtain the proper gain setting for a specific M_p, this tangent line may be used as follows:

1. Plot the $G(j\omega)$ locus to any convenient scale.
2. Construct a line through the origin at an angle $\psi = \sin^{-1} 1/M_p$.
3. By trial and error draw in a circle with center on the negative real axis and tangent to both the ψ line and the $G(j\omega)$ locus.
4. The x coordinate of the center of this circle must be

$$x = -M^2/(M^2 - 1)$$

which determines a new scale for the plot.

5. Calculate the gain constant as the ratio of the new scale to the original scale.

6. The required adjustment of a system parameter (such as the amplifier gain μ_a) is then determined from the proper equation.

Example. The system tabulated in Table 9-1 may be used to check the procedure outlined. The $G(j\omega)$ locus is plotted in Fig. 9-6, and a ψ line is added for $M_p = 1.3$. The circle is constructed and its center

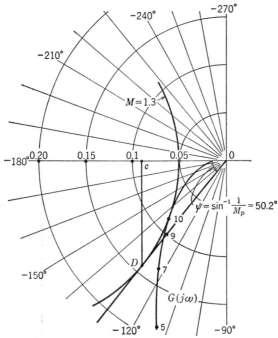

FIG. 9-6. Gain adjustment for numerical example.

located. If this circle is to be a true $M = 1.3$ circle, then its center must be located at $x = -2.45$, which fixes the new scale of the plot. From the original scale the coordinate of the circle center is $x = -0.22$, and therefore the required gain constant is

$$K = \frac{-2.45}{-0.22} = 11.13$$

The required amplifier gain setting is then

$$K = \frac{\mu_a' K_g}{R_f K_v}$$

$$11.13 = \frac{\mu_a' 220}{(150)(1.335)}$$

$$\mu_a' = \frac{(11.13)(150)(1.335)}{220} = 10.12$$

9.6. Alternate Direct Method. A method for obtaining the gain constant directly without considering a new scale is given by Brown and Campbell.[31,*] The procedure is illustrated in Fig. 9-7. The $G(j\omega)$ locus is drawn, the ψ line added, and the M circle constructed. The point of tangency between the circle and the ψ line is located at b and a perpen-

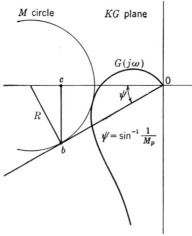

Fig. 9-7. Alternate gain-adjustment procedure.

dicular bc erected to locate point c. The distance oc is read to the original scale, and the required gain constant is

$$K = \frac{1}{oc} \tag{9-4}$$

Proof of this is left to the student.

Example. Point c may be located on the plot of Fig. 9-6. The distance oc, to the original scale, is

$$oc = 0.092$$

and

$$K = \frac{1}{oc} = \frac{1}{0.092} = 10.9$$

from which

$$\mu_a' = \frac{(10.9)(150)(1.335)}{220} = 9.92$$

Table 9-2 compares the three methods illustrated. It may be seen that the trial-and-error method is appreciably high in this case. The

* Superior numbers, when they occur in the text proper, are the numbers of references given in the Bibliography.

third method involves minimum labor and is therefore preferable.   Also, the use of a large scale is profitable if sufficient points are available for an accurate locus.

TABLE 9-2

Method	μ_a' for $M_p = 1.3$
Trial-and-error	11.2
Direct	10.12
Alternate direct	9.92

9-7. Summary.   The gain of a servomechanism may be set to produce a desired M_p by any of several simple methods.   After such adjustment is accomplished, the resonant frequency, ω_r, and the steady-state error must be checked against specifications.   Failure to meet specifications by means of gain adjustment usually leads to the insertion of compensating devices.

PROBLEMS

9-1. Given $KG(j\omega) = K/j\omega(0.1j\omega + 1)(0.05j\omega + 1)$; determine the values of K necessary to produce $M_p = 1.5; 2.0; 2.5$.   Indicate values of ω_r.   Use trial-and-error method.

9-2. Repeat Prob. 9-1, using a direct graphical method, and compare results.

9-3. For each of the following transfer functions, determine the gain, K, required to obtain an M_p of 1.3.   Note ω_r in each case. $\zeta = 0.3; 0.6; 0.9$.

a. $KG(j\omega) = \dfrac{K}{j\omega[(j\omega)^2 + 6\zeta j\omega + 1]}$

b. $KG(j\omega) = \dfrac{K}{j\omega[(j\omega)^2 + 6\zeta j\omega + 10]}$

c. $KG(j\omega) = \dfrac{K}{j\omega[(j\omega)^2 + 6\zeta j\omega + 10](0.05j\omega + 1)}$

d. $KG(j\omega) = \dfrac{K(0.2j\omega + 1)}{j\omega(0.1j\omega + 1)(0.05j\omega + 1)(2j\omega + 1)}$

e. $KG(j\omega) = \dfrac{K(0.02j\omega + 1)}{j\omega(0.1j\omega + 1)(0.05j\omega + 1)(0.002j\omega + 1)}$

9-4. a. For the system of Prob. 4-4, determine the gain required to limit M_p to 1.5.

b. If this system is operated at a constant velocity of 15 rpm, what gain is required to limit the steady-state error to 10 deg?   Is the system stable with this gain?   What are M_p and ω_r?   What is the value of gain which just causes instability?

9-5. Repeat Prob. 9-4 for the system of Prob. 4-5.

9-6. For the system of Fig. 4P-4, what value of gain is needed for $M_p = 1.3$? $M_p = 2.0$?

9-7. For the system of Fig. 4P-5, what is ω_r when M_p is 1.5?

9-8. For the system of Prob. 4-16, what value of gain is required for an M_p of 2.0? What is ω_r?

9-9. For the system of Prob. 4-21, what value of gain is required for an $M_p = 2.5$, and what is ω_r?

CHAPTER 10

SERIES COMPENSATION

10-1. Introduction—Compensation in General. There are many cases in which a servomechanism system needs compensation in order to meet performance specifications, and these cases do not fit into any single category. It is possible, however, to make a general classification of the cases in which compensation is needed. It is obvious from the preceding discussion of gain adjustment that need of compensation arises when control of gain alone does not provide a satisfactory compromise between steady-state and transient performance. This is in a sense a general classification which covers a majority of cases but is too general in the sense that it tacitly includes many cases in which the characteristics of the system preclude the possibility of a successful compromise by gain adjustment alone. The following paragraphs attempt to classify the applications of compensation into slightly more restricted divisions and illustrate the meaning of each division. After this general information some details on series compensation are presented.

10-2. Classification of Compensation Applications. It should be thoroughly understood that the term "compensation" as applied to servomechanisms means the reshaping of the $G(j\omega)$ locus to improve the system performance. In most, but not necessarily all, cases, a gain adjustment is also required because in general the introduction of a component to provide compensation reduces the gain of the system. The suggested classification for compensation applications is:

A. Solely to stabilize a system, when the system is unstable for all values of gain.

B. To improve transient performance in cases where gain control is not satisfactory and where neither gain control nor compensation appreciably affects the steady-state performance.

C. To provide (in conjunction with gain control) the possibility of a satisfactory compromise between steady-state and transient performance.

D. To make possible a satisfactory steady-state performance where gain control is not capable of doing so.

It will be shown that classes A, B, and C require compensation of the high-frequency portion of the transfer-function locus, while class D in general affects the low-frequency portion.

192

As a general illustration of class A compensation, consider Figs. 10-1a and b.   Figure 10-1a shows a type 3 transfer-function locus in curve a, and application of the Nyquist criterion shows that the locus represents an inherently unstable system.   It is also apparent that no adjustment of gain can possibly stabilize the system.   It is therefore necessary to reshape the high-frequency end of the locus in order to get the $-1 + j0$ point outside the loop and thus stabilize the system.   A possible

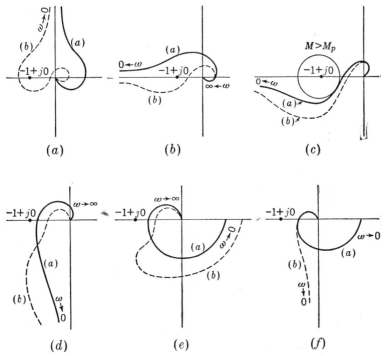

FIG. 10-1. Typical compensated and uncompensated KG plots.

reshaping, obtained by proper compensation, is illustrated by curve b in Fig. 10-1a.

Figure 10-1b, curve a, shows a typical locus for a type 2 system, which also is inherently unstable and therefore cannot be stabilized by gain adjustment.   Again it is necessary to use compensation to stabilize the system.   A possible stable locus obtained by compensation is illustrated by curve b, Fig. 10-1b.

Class B is intended to include cases of the type illustrated in Fig. 10-1c.   Curve a shows a possible type 2 system which is stable but has unsatisfactory transient performance because it is tangent to an M circle for which M is greater than the desired M_p.   It is obvious that gain adjustment is of little value since either increasing or decreasing the gain would essentially shift the locus horizontally and would only bring a different point on the locus into tangency with the same M circle, thus failing to decrease the transient overshoot. The only available way to provide acceptable transient performance is to insert a compensating component which might reshape the locus to a form such as curve b in Fig. 10-1c. It should be noted that the low-frequency response, which is indicative of steady-state performance, is essentially unaffected.

Class C probably includes the majority of compensation applications since it applies primarily to normal adjustment of type 1 and type 0 systems. Type 1 systems are frequently operated at constant velocity with the restriction that the velocity-lag error must be less than some specified value. Figure 10-1d, curve a, shows a typical locus for a type 1 system. In order to provide a small velocity-lag error it is normally necessary to use a high gain. There is obviously an upper limit to the gain which may be used with the locus of curve a, beyond which poor transient performance results. It is therefore necessary to reshape the locus to some form such as curve b in Fig. 10-1d. This makes it possible to use a higher gain without incurring poor transient performance, and thus the steady-state requirements may be met.

Type 0 systems are sometimes used rather than type 1 systems because, if some static error can be tolerated, it is frequently true that a properly designed type 0 system is cheaper than a type 1 system. Also, there may be conditions inherent in the application which make the type 0 system more desirable. In such cases the allowable steady-state error is specified, and, in general, the gain is made high enough to keep the error within specifications. If the shape of the locus is as shown in Fig. 10-1e, curve a, too high a gain may cause instability or poor transient perform-ance. It is then necessary to compensate the system, obtaining a locus such as curve b in Fig. 10-1e, thus permitting the required high gain to meet steady-state performance specifications.

Class D refers primarily to those cases in which it necessary to change a system from type 0 to type 1, or from type 1 to type 2, etc., in order to meet steady-state requirements. Figure 10-1f, curve a, shows a type 0 system, which inherently has a position error, and curve b shows a type 1 locus which may be obtained by compensating the type 0 system.

10-3. Series Compensation. Changes in the shape of the transfer-function locus, of the types illustrated in Fig. 10-1, may be obtained by placing the compensating unit in series with the main transmission path as shown in Fig. 10-2. The unit used to reshape the locus may be of any suitable physical nature. In the following discussion only electrical networks are used for illustration, but the use of nonelectrical compo-nents is based on the same general principles.

In general, the series location of the compensation device makes its transfer function multiply the system transfer function. If the compensating device has a transfer function $K_c G_c(j\omega)$, then the over-all transfer function becomes

$$K_0 G_0(j\omega) = K_c G_c(j\omega) KG(j\omega) \tag{10-1}$$

The evaluation of this over-all transfer function may be carried out by direct computation if all transfer functions are known algebraically, or

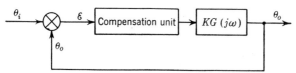

Fig. 10-2. Series-compensated single-loop servo.

it may be carried out by semigraphical methods. The semigraphical method is frequently preferable, since it permits some general estimates to be made before actual computation, and if the estimate shows that the final result is not likely to be satisfactory, then changes can be made in the compensating device before undertaking the actual computation of the over-all transfer-function locus.

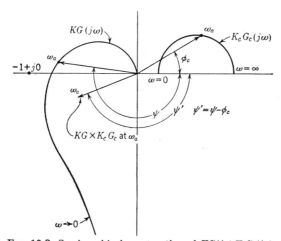

Fig. 10-3. Semigraphical construction of $KG(j\omega) K_c G_c(j\omega)$.

A semigraphical method for combining a transfer function $KG(j\omega)$ and a compensating function $K_c G_c(j\omega)$ is illustrated in Fig. 10-3. A number of discrete frequency points must be known on each locus. The vectors KG and $K_c G_c$ at a given frequency such as ω_a are determined by measurement (magnitude to scale and also phase angle). The magnitudes are then multiplied, and the phase angles are added algebraically. Thus the magnitude and phase of the resultant vector $KGK_cG_c(j\omega)$ are determined at the frequency ω_a.   This procedure is repeated for a sufficient number of frequencies to permit drawing of the resultant locus.

The advantage of this semigraphical method lies in the fact that it may be helpful in determining the design of the compensating unit (for analysis of a given system there is no advantage over normal computation).   The shape of the compensator locus is readily controlled by the designer, and one frequency point (in addition to $\omega = 0$ and $\omega = \infty$) can always be located arbitrarily.   The semigraphical method then permits computation of the effect of such compensation at the selected frequency (and over a reasonable range near that frequency).   The results of such rough computation may frequently be interpreted in terms of the desirability of the selected compensation locus.   If the locus is not satisfactory, it may be discarded without actually designing a unit which would produce it, while if it seems acceptable, its basic frequency-response and phase-shift characteristics have been determined and design is routine. Use of such a method depends somewhat on experience.

The compensation locus, K_cG_c, in Fig. 10-3 is arbitrarily located in the first quadrant and is shown as a semicircle.   Both the location and the shape of the locus actually depend on the nature of the compensating device, and considerable variation is possible.   In general, there are three classes of compensation devices,[45],* all in more or less common use. These are:

1. Phase-lead controllers
2. Phase-lag controllers
3. Compound controllers

Phase-lead controllers have transfer-function loci which are located in the first and second quadrants.   Thus the phase shift produced is positive, or leading.   In general they tend to accentuate the higher frequencies (*i.e.*, have many of the characteristics of high-pass filters), and they attenuate the lower frequencies.   In applying them to servomechanism compensation, they have proved most effective in changing the locus shape near the stability point, which is usually in the higher frequency range.   They therefore have a pronounced effect on both stability and transient performance and are used when these factors are to be improved.   The terms "derivative controller" and "differentiating unit" are sometimes applied to phase-lead devices because such devices inherently take an approximate derivative of the signal transmitted.

Phase-lag controllers have transfer-function loci which are located in the fourth and third quadrants, and they therefore produce a phase shift

* Superior numbers, when they occur in the text proper, are the numbers of references given in the Bibliography.

which is negative, or lagging. They have a predominant effect on the lower range of frequencies since they are essentially low-pass filters. Thus their effect on the servomechanism transfer locus is largely limited to the region which indicates the steady-state performance. They are therefore used when considerable reduction in steady-state error is required. Since such phase-lag devices tend to integrate the input signal, they are also referred to as "integral controllers" or "integrating devices."

Compound controllers are basically combinations of phase-lead and phase-lag units. Thus their loci always include the first and fourth quadrants and might (in extreme cases) extend into the second or third quadrants. They may consist simply of cascade combinations of phase-lead and phase-lag units but in general are better designed as a single unit. Their use may be required in systems which require low-frequency phase-lag compensation for steady-state performance but which cannot meet transient specifications without the high-frequency compensation of a phase-lead device. Such compound units are sometimes called "integrodifferential controllers."

10-4. Series Compensation with Phase-lead Controllers.[45,61—64] A lead controller may be thought of as any device having a transfer-function locus in the first or second quadrants, because its phase angle is then positive, or leading, and causes the compensated system locus to advance in phase with respect to the original system. The lead controller must meet several requirements if it is to be used for series compensation. It must have a suitable phase-shift characteristic primarily over the frequency range which is to be compensated, but the phase shift outside of this frequency band must not interfere with proper operation of the system. The same general restriction holds for the gain (or attenuation) characteristic of the lead controller. In addition to these restrictions, since the lead controller is in series with the system, it is important that the compensating device not only produce an output proportional to the derivative of the input signal but also transmit the input signal itself; *i.e.*, if the input to the compensating device is A, then the output must be proportional to $A + dA/dt$, not just to dA/dt alone. This is important because the actual error signal must be maintained in order to provide static alignment and proper steady-state performance. If only the derivative signal is transmitted, then the system has no output if the error is not changing, and it is also possible to reach a steady-state condition in which a continually changing error produces a constant output, in which case the system could hardly be called a servomechanism.

10-5. Ideal Lead Controller or True Differentiating Device. The basic mathematical requirement for an *ideal* lead controller may be derived from the notations of Fig. 10-4a. If the input and output are to be of the specified form, then the transfer function of the unit must be

$$K_cG_c(j\omega) = \frac{K(\mathcal{E} + j\omega\mathcal{E})}{\mathcal{E}} = K(1 + j\omega) \tag{10-2}$$

The vector locus of this transfer function on the polar plane is given in Fig. 10-4b.

Such characteristics cannot be obtained with a passive device but may be obtained with nonpassive units. A compensating unit having these ideal characteristics may be obtained by proper design of a feedback amplifier having a high-pass filter in the feedback loop. Such a combination is shown in Fig. 10-4c. The feedback must be positive, and the system equations then become

$$\frac{e_o}{e_y} = \mu \tag{10-3}$$

$$\frac{e_x}{e_o} = \frac{j\omega\tau}{j\omega\tau + 1} \tag{10-4}$$

where
$$\tau = RC$$

$$e_i + e_x = e_y \tag{10-5}$$

$$e_i + \frac{j\omega\tau}{j\omega\tau + 1} e_o = \frac{e_o}{\mu} \tag{10-6}$$

$$e_o\left(\frac{j\omega\tau}{j\omega\tau + 1} - \frac{1}{\mu}\right) = -e_i \tag{10-7}$$

$$\frac{e_o}{e_i} = \frac{-1}{j\omega\tau/(j\omega\tau + 1) - 1/\mu} = \frac{1}{1/\mu - j\omega\tau/(j\omega\tau + 1)} \tag{10-8}$$

$$\frac{e_o}{e_i} = \frac{\mu(j\omega\tau + 1)}{j\omega\tau + 1 - j\omega\tau\mu} = \frac{\mu(j\omega\tau + 1)}{1 + (1 - \mu)j\omega\tau} \tag{10-9}$$

If $\mu = +1$, then

$$\frac{e_o}{e_i} = K_cG_c(j\omega) = j\omega\tau + 1 \tag{10-10}$$

Thus if the circuit indicated is used, with the amplifier gain set exactly to unity, then the combination acts as an ideal phase-lead, or differentiating, circuit. It would be placed in series with the main transmission path of the servomechanism as shown in Fig. 10-4d. However, if the gain, μ, of the amplifier in the compensation unit is not kept at exactly unity, the transfer-function locus is no longer a straight line, as may be seen from Eq. (10-9) or from Fig. 10-4e.

Since the phase-lead locus for the ideal differentiating system of Fig. 10-4d is a straight line only when $\mu \equiv 1$, which is a difficult condition to meet and maintain practically, such a device is used only when absolutely necessary, which is seldom the case in compensating a servomechanism. The circular locus for $\mu < 1$ can be approximated to sufficient practical

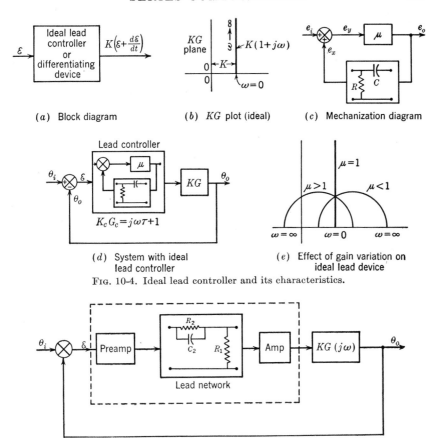

(a) Block diagram   (b) KG plot (ideal)   (c) Mechanization diagram

(d) System with ideal   (e) Effect of gain variation on
lead controller   ideal lead device

FIG. 10-4. Ideal lead controller and its characteristics.

FIG. 10-5. Series phase-lead compensation of a servomechanism.

accuracy by a passive network which is considerably less expensive than the feedback scheme. A simple form of passive network to produce phase lead is shown in Fig. 10-5 in its approximate location in a system. The transfer function of the lead network is

$$K_cG_c(j\omega) = \alpha \frac{j\omega\tau_2 + 1}{j\omega\alpha\tau_2 + 1} \tag{10-11}$$

where $\alpha = R_1/(R_1 + R_2)$
   $\tau_2 = R_2C_2$

The preamplifier and amplifier may or may not be needed, depending on the specific system, and the components within the dotted box may be built as a single unit.

The network of Fig. 10-5 cannot produce a phase lead of more than 90 deg, theoretically, and practically the limit is appreciably less for good performance. When larger phase leads are required, they may be obtained by using more complicated networks or by series combinations of simple networks and isolating amplifiers. Figure 10-6 shows a simple series system which can be made to provide a phase lead of more than 90 deg, as is indicated by its transfer function, given in Eq. (10-12).

$$\frac{e_o}{e_1} = \mu \left[\alpha \frac{j\omega\tau_2 + 1}{j\omega\alpha\tau_2 + 1} \right]^2 \tag{10-12}$$

It may be seen from Eq. (10-12) that the angle of the numerator is greater than that of the denominator for any value of ω. This produces a net phase lead which is doubled by the exponent. Proper choice of α and τ_2 can easily provide an over-all phase lead greater than 90 deg.

10-6. Example of Phase-lead Compensation—Type 2 System. A type 2 servomechanism, uncompensated, is shown in Fig. 10-7a. The components are somewhat idealized for simplicity in presentation. The system as shown is essentially two motor-speed controllers in series. The input shaft, θ_i, is driven at constant speed, and the output, θ_o, is supposed to duplicate the input speed and also maintain a fixed position correspondence with the input. It may be noted from Fig. 10-7a that the input and output position indicators (I and O) rotate continuously, and if their velocities and angular displacements are identical no error signal is fed to the first controller, μ_1. Under these conditions the motor M_1 is inactive, and the setting of N remains fixed. Thus the input to M_2 does not change, and its speed, $d\theta_o/dt$, is constant at the same value as the input speed. If an angular displacement exists between I and O, a signal is applied to μ_1, and M_1 moves N, thus changing the output speed so as to reduce the error. Thus constant-velocity operation with no velocity-lag error is attained. However, the system as shown is inherently unstable, as will be shown by deriving the transfer function and plotting its locus.

Let N = position of pilot motor M_1, volts or radians

    ε = output-input, volts or radians

    K_1 = generator constant of M_1, volts/radian/sec

    τ_{m1} = time constant of M_1, sec

    θ_o = output position, volts or radians

    K_2 = generator constant of M_2, volts/radians/sec

    τ_{m2} = time constant of M_2, sec

Then from Eq. (5-46),

$$\frac{N}{\varepsilon} = \mu_1 \left(\frac{1}{K_1}\right) \left[\frac{1}{j\omega(j\omega\tau_{m1} + 1)} \right] \tag{10-13}$$

and

$$\frac{\theta_o}{N} = \mu_2 \left(\frac{1}{K_2}\right) \left[\frac{1}{j\omega(j\omega\tau_{m2} + 1)} \right] \tag{10-14}$$

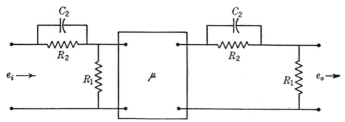

FIG. 10-6. Network to produce phase lead greater than 90 deg.

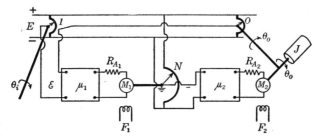

(a) Uncompensated system

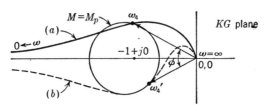

(b) Loci for compensation of system

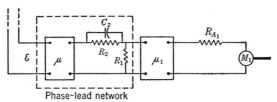

Phase-lead network

(c) Typical location of phase-lead compensator

FIG. 10-7. Type 2 servomechanism.

from which

$$\frac{\theta_o}{\varepsilon} = \frac{N}{\varepsilon} \frac{\theta_o}{N} = \frac{\mu_1 \mu_2}{K_1 K_2} \frac{1}{(j\omega)^2 (j\omega\tau_{m_1} + 1)(j\omega\tau_{m_2} + 1)} \qquad (10\text{-}15)$$

which is the over-all transfer function of the system.

Inspection of Eq. (10-15) shows that as $\omega \to 0$, the angle of $\theta_o/\varepsilon \to$ -180 deg, and as $\omega \to \infty$, the angle of $\theta_o/\varepsilon \to -360$ deg. For intermediate values of ω the phase angle is between these two limits. Furthermore, normal design would use a high-torque low-inertia motor for M_1 and the time constant τ_{m_1} would be very small so that the transfer-function locus for all practical frequencies would be between -180 and -270 deg. A sketch of the probable shape of the locus is shown in Fig. 10-7b, curve a.

The locus of Fig. 10-7b, curve a, represents an unstable system, as may be seen by applying the Nyquist criterion. To stabilize the system, the locus must be reshaped, and curve b represents a desirable locus. A positive phase shift is required to accomplish such a reshaping, and therefore phase-lead compensation may be used. A network of the type shown in Fig. 10-5 might be suitable and would be located as shown in Fig. 10-7c. The transfer-function equation of the compensated system then becomes

$$KG(j\omega) = \frac{\mu_1\mu_2}{K_1K_2}\frac{\alpha(j\omega\tau_2 + 1)}{(j\omega)^2(j\omega\tau_{m1} + 1)(j\omega\tau_{m2} + 1)(j\omega\alpha\tau_2 + 1)} \quad (10\text{-}16)$$

In order to calculate the proper constants for the phase-lead network (that is, R_1, R_2, C_2; or α and τ_2), the transfer-function locus of the uncompensated system must be known *quantitatively*, and several assumptions must be made. If the assumptions are not sufficiently accurate, then the resultant compensated locus will not be satisfactory and the computation must be repeated. A number of methods may readily be devised for carrying out such a design problem. Most of the difficulties encountered in designing such a compensator lie in the fact that the passive lead network has a variable gain as well as a variable phase shift. Because of this it is possible to set the magnitude and phase of the corrected transfer function at one frequency only. This condition must therefore be chosen so that the resulting locus is satisfactory at all frequencies. The procedure is accordingly one of trial and error, in which experience is quite helpful. The method outlined here is suitable for the simple phase-lead network chosen, because the locus of the network transfer function is known to be a semicircle. When more complex lead networks are used, portions of the method may require revision.

10-7. Procedure for Design of Phase-lead Network—Type 2 System

1. Draw the uncompensated locus and the desired M circle ($M = M_p$), and sketch in the expected compensated locus as in Fig. 10-7b.

2. From the known frequencies on the original locus (ω_1, ω_2, etc.) select a frequency which is to be the resonant frequency of the compensated system. This selection to a large extent determines the speed of response of the system. If the frequency selected is ω_4, then the same frequency is located on the compensated locus at approximately the point of tangency

with the M circle. This position, *i.e.*, the location of ω_4, is determined by inspection.

3. Measure the magnitudes of the vectors $0\omega_4$ and $0\omega_4'$, and also measure the phase angle ϕ. Then the combination of amplifier, μ, and phase-lead network must produce a phase lead of ϕ at frequency ω_4 and a net gain of $0\omega_4'/0\omega_4$. Thus

$$\mu K_c G_c(j\omega) = \mu\alpha \frac{j\omega_4\tau_2 + 1}{j\omega_4\alpha\tau_2 + 1} = \frac{0\omega_4'}{0\omega_4} \underline{/\phi} \qquad (10\text{-}17)$$

4. Equation (10-17) defines the compensation circle, but it contains three independent variables, μ, α, τ_2. Some assumption is therefore necessary in order to use the equation. The most logical assumption is to choose a value of α, basing the choice on the magnitude of the phase angle ϕ. If $\phi \cong 55$ deg, then a suitable value for α is $\alpha = 0.1$. (The reasons for this are given in detail immediately following this procedure outline.) A choice for α having been made, then τ_2 is determined approximately from

$$\text{Angle of } \frac{j\omega_4\tau_2 + 1}{j\omega_4\alpha\tau_2 + 1} = \phi \qquad (10\text{-}18)$$

5. Knowing α and τ_2, the value of μ is computed from Eq. (10-17).

6. Values of ω are then substituted in Eq. (10-17), and the compensation locus is plotted.

7. The over-all compensated locus is then calculated by vector multiplication of the original locus and the compensation locus. Corresponding values may be taken from tabulated data or measured from the curves.

8. If the resulting locus is not sufficiently close to the desired result, the calculations must be repeated, starting either with a change in resonant frequency or with an adjustment in the value of α.

10-8. Relationship between the Gain Constant and the Phase Shift of a Phase-lead Network. The choice of a value for α in step 4 of the procedure just given is based on known relationships between the gain constant, α, and the maximum phase shift, ϕ_{max}, of the phase-lead network considered. When the network alone is considered (no amplifier), the gain is unity when $\omega = \infty$, that is, the semicircle always passes through the $+1 + j0$ point. The gain constant α is the gain at $\omega = 0$. Thus increasing α decreases the diameter of the circle and reduces the maximum possible phase shift. Figure 10-8 shows a few examples of the relationship between α and ϕ_{max}. Similar relationships can be worked out for many networks.

The phase-lead network must produce a phase lead at least as great as the angle ϕ read from a plot equivalent to that of Fig. 10-7b. Therefore α must be small enough to make such a phase shift possible. In general, some frequency other than the resonant frequency may require a phase shift greater than ϕ (this can often be estimated from the curve), and therefore the choice of α need not be exact. If the required phase shift indicates a value of $\alpha < 0.1$, more satisfactory results will probably be obtained by using a different network.

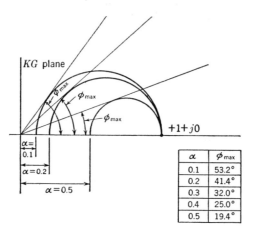

α	ϕ_{max}
0.1	53.2°
0.2	41.4°
0.3	32.0°
0.4	25.0°
0.5	19.4°

Fig. 10-8. Phase-shift characteristics for typical lead network.

10-9. Example of Series Compensation—Type 1 System. A simple positioning system is shown in Fig. 10-9a, and its transfer function is given in Eq. (10-19).

$$\frac{\theta_o}{\varepsilon}(j\omega) = \frac{\mu_1 K_g}{R_f K_v}\frac{1}{j\omega(j\omega\tau_f + 1)(j\omega\tau_m + 1)} \qquad (10\text{-}19)$$

It is seen from the equation that the positioning system may be classified as type 1. At $\omega = 0$, $\theta_o/\varepsilon = -j\infty$, and as $\omega \rightarrow \infty$, $\theta_o/\varepsilon \rightarrow 0$ at an angle of -270 deg. Thus the locus of the system transfer function is approximately as shown in Fig. 10-9b, curve A. It is obvious that the absolute stability depends on the gain of the system.

Compensation of a system such as is shown in Fig. 10-9 is never a matter of stability alone, since stability may always be obtained by reducing the gain. In general, such gain reduction produces poor steady-state operation, however, and the velocity-lag error becomes too large. Thus the obvious purpose of compensating a type 1 system is to improve the steady-state performance while maintaining stability and satisfactory transient performance. The type of compensation used depends on the steady-state requirements. If no velocity lag is permissible, then a phase-lag compensator which is a true integrating device must be used to create a pole at the origin and change the system from type 1 to type 2. If some velocity lag is permissible, then it is generally more practical to use a phase-lead device or a passive phase-lag device to reshape the locus and permit the use of sufficient gain for the required steady-state performance. The effects of phase-lead and phase-lag compensation are shown qualitatively in Fig. 10-9b by curves B and C, respectively. Discussion of phase-lag compensation is presented later in this chapter.

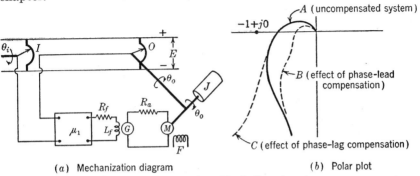

(a) Mechanization diagram   (b) Polar plot

FIG. 10-9. Compensation of basic Type 1 system.

10-10. Designing a Phase-lead Network for a Type 1 System. If the simple phase-lead network of Fig. 10-5 is used in conjunction with the type 1 system of Fig. 10-9, the locus may be reshaped to permit the use of sufficient gain for satisfactory steady-state performance. The compensating unit could be inserted in series with the error signal and preceding the system amplifier, but a preamplifier, μ, might be needed. The transfer-function equation of the compensated system then becomes

$$KG(j\omega) = \frac{\mu\mu_1\alpha K_g}{R_f K_v} \frac{j\omega\tau_2 + 1}{j\omega(j\omega\tau_f + 1)(j\omega\tau_m + 1)(j\omega\alpha\tau_2 + 1)} \quad (10\text{-}20)$$

Designing the network itself is inherently a trial-and-error process, since the network attenuation reduces the low-frequency gain and therefore impairs steady-state performance; yet increases in gain to cancel this effect also change the high-frequency portion of the locus and counteract in part the advantages gained by phase shift. Therefore any specified procedure for design, and interpretations of such procedure, must depend somewhat on experience. The following procedure is one of several which may be used successfully.

1. From the required steady-state performance determine the minimum permissible gain for the uncompensated system, including any desired safety margins. Further increase this gain constant by a factor intended to counteract the attenuation of the compensating network. (This is equivalent to selecting the gain of the amplifier, μ, based on an estimate of the probable value of α.)

2. Draw the locus of the uncompensated system, using the final value of gain determined in (1).   This locus will probably indicate an unstable system as shown in Fig. 10-10, curve a.

3. Draw the M circle for $M = M_p$.

4. Sketch in the expected compensated locus as in Fig. 10-10, curve b.

5. Select a value of ω which represents a desirable resonant frequency, ω_r', for the system.   This will be located on the compensated locus at the point of tangency with the M circle as shown.   Selection of such a value depends not only on the desired speed of response of the system but also on experience, which determines from the original locus the range of frequencies that can be shifted to the desired location on the compensated locus.

6. The frequency ω_r (numerically equal to ω_r') is marked on the original locus, and the magnitude of the vectors $0\omega_r$ and $0\omega_r'$ is measured, as well as the phase angle ϕ.

7. From the values in (6) one point on the locus of the compensation network is determined, $i.e.$,

$$K_c G_c(j\omega) = \frac{0\omega_r'}{0\omega_r} \quad (10\text{-}21)$$

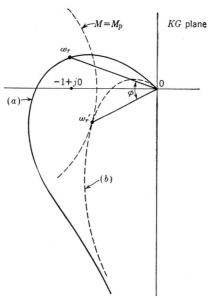

Fig. 10-10. Graphical determination of phase-lead compensator characteristics.

It should be noted that this is a point on the locus of the compensation network only and does not include the effect of amplifier gain.   It is therefore evident that $|0\omega_r'/0\omega_r| < 1.0$ is a necessary condition.

8. The compensation locus may then be constructed, since the center of the circle is known to lie on the positive real axis and $K_c G_c$ for $\omega = \infty$ is known to be $+1 + j0$.   The construction is illustrated in Fig. 10-11.

9. From the constructed locus determine the numerical value of α.

10. Calculate τ_2 from

$$\left|\frac{0\omega_r'}{0\omega_r}\right| \,\underline{/\phi} = \alpha \,\frac{j\omega_r'\tau_2 + 1}{j\omega_r'\alpha\tau_2 + 1}$$

11. Calculate values for the compensation locus; combine with the original locus, and obtain the corrected locus.

Inspection of the corrected locus indicates whether or not the transient performance is within acceptable limits, $i.e.$, indicates the true value of

M_p, which was approximately determined by the preceding design. The system velocity lag must be recalculated to determine the actual effect of α. If either the steady-state or the transient performance is unsatisfactory, it is sometimes possible to correct the trouble by gain adjustment. However, if the steady-state velocity lag is too great while M_p is close to the maximum permissible value, then the compensating network must be redesigned.

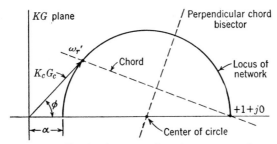

FIG. 10-11. Graphical construction of compensator locus.

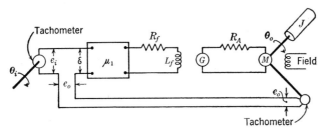

FIG. 10-12. Speed-control system, type 0.

10-11. Series Compensation—Type 0 System. An example of a type 0 system is the simple speed control shown in Fig. 10-12. The input speed is indicated by the voltage e_i produced by the input tachometer, and the output speed is given by e_o from the output tachometer. The transfer function of the system is

$$\frac{e_o}{\varepsilon}(j\omega) = \frac{\mu_1 K_g K_n}{R_f K_v} \frac{1}{(j\omega\tau_f + 1)(j\omega\tau_m + 1)} \qquad (10\text{-}22)$$

where K_n is the output-tachometer transfer constant.

Physically there is no positional relationship between the output and input since both e_i and e_o are functions of velocity and not of position. Also, it may be seen that there can never be an exact speed duplication, since no voltage is supplied to the motor unless $\varepsilon \neq 0$, and the existence of an error signal depends on a difference between input and output speeds. However, the speed error may be kept small by making the gain, μ_1, a large number.

From the transfer function of Eq. (10-22), it may be seen that as $\omega \to 0$, $e_o/\mathcal{E}(j\omega) \to \mu_1 K_g K_n / R_f K_v$, a constant at a phase angle of 0 deg. As $\omega \to \infty$, $e_o/\mathcal{E}(j\omega) \to 0$, and the phase angle approaches -180 deg.

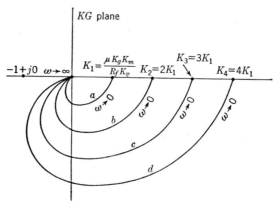

FIG. 10-13. Effect of gain increase on type 0 characteristic.

For all intermediate frequencies the magnitude and phase are between these limiting values. The transfer-function locus may therefore be sketched roughly as in Fig. 10-13, curve a. Inspection of this curve shows that steady-state error can be reduced by gain control, as previously mentioned, or by converting to a type 1 system, which will be considered later. The effect of increasing the gain is shown in curves b, c, and d of Fig. 10-13. It may be seen that increasing the gain cannot make the system unstable but may alter the transient conditions sufficiently to cause unsatisfactory performance.

When a large value of gain must be used with such a system to reduce steady-state error, the high-frequency portion of the locus may be compensated with a phase-lead network to provide acceptable transient performance. The effect of such compensation on the locus is shown qualitatively, in Fig. 10-14. The phase-lead network may be designed by application of the same procedure outlined for the type 1 system.

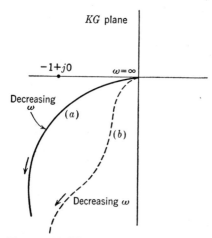

FIG. 10-14. Phase-lead compensation of type 0 system. (a) High-frequency portion of locus at high gain, (b) compensated locus.

10-12. Phase-lag, or Integral, Compensation.[28-31,45] When the steady-state performance of a servomechanism is not satisfactory and cannot be improved sufficiently to meet specifications by the use of phase-lead compensation and gain adjustment, then phase-lag, or integral, compensation may be used. The steady-state errors which are normally eliminated or minimized by such compensation are the steady-state position error of a type 0 system and the velocity-lag error of a type 1 system. In either case, if the error is to be completely eliminated, a true integral device must be used to produce a pole at the origin. If complete elimination of

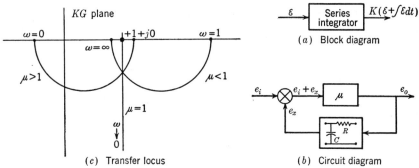

(c) Transfer locus   (b) Circuit diagram

Fig. 10-15. Regenerative integrator and its KG characteristics.

the steady-state error is not necessary or if it is not practical for the particular system, considerable improvement may be obtained by using a passive phase-lag device which does not introduce a pole but produces appreciable phase shift in the low-frequency portion of the transfer-function response.

A true integrating device cannot be a passive component. Figure 10-15a shows the basic transfer requirement of an integrating device. The transfer-function equation of such a device is then

$$KG(j\omega) = \frac{K(\varepsilon + \varepsilon/j\omega)}{\varepsilon} = K\left(\frac{j\omega + 1}{j\omega}\right) \tag{10-23}$$

One means of obtaining such a transfer function is shown in Fig. 10-15b. If an amplifier of gain μ is connected to a feedback path containing a low-pass filter (RC as shown), and if the feedback is regenerative, the resulting over-all transfer function has the desired form as shown in the following derivation:

$$\frac{e_o}{e_i + e_x} = \mu \tag{10-24}$$

$$\frac{e_x}{e_o} = \frac{1/j\omega C}{R + 1/j\omega C} = \frac{1}{j\omega CR + 1} \tag{10-25}$$

Substituting,

$$\frac{e_o}{e_i + e_o/(j\omega CR + 1)} = \mu \tag{10-26}$$

$$e_o = \mu e_i + \frac{\mu e_o}{j\omega CR + 1} \tag{10-27}$$

$$\frac{e_o}{e_i} = \frac{\mu}{1 - \mu/(j\omega CR + 1)} = \frac{j\omega CR\mu + \mu}{1 - \mu + j\omega CR}$$

$$= \mu\left(\frac{j\omega CR + 1}{1 - \mu + j\omega CR}\right) \tag{10-28}$$

and if the amplifier gain is adjusted to give $\mu \equiv +1$, then

$$\frac{e_o}{e_i} = \frac{j\omega CR + 1}{j\omega CR} \tag{10-29}$$

which is the desired form of transfer function.

In practice the problem of adjusting and maintaining the amplifier gain at the exact desired value is a difficult one, although practical use is made of regenerative feedback amplifiers in some applications.[178] There

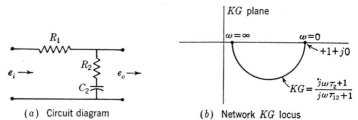

(a) Circuit diagram   (b) Network KG locus

FIG. 10-16. Phase-lag network and its KG characteristics.

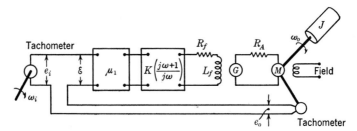

FIG. 10-17. Speed-control system with added integrator.

are three possible forms of equation (10-28), depending on the value of μ, and the transfer-function plots are illustrated in Fig. 10-15c. If $\mu > 1$ or if $\mu < 1$, the locus is a semicircle. A more detailed study of this may be found in the literature.[45]

If a true integrating device is used, the pole introduced at the origin changes the classification of the system, i.e., type 0 plus integrator results in a type 1 system, etc. On the other hand, passive devices may be used to give a close approximation of the locus for $\mu < 1$. Such devices (including the regenerative system when $\mu \neq 1$) do not introduce a pole at the origin and thus do not change the basic classification of the system but do improve the steady-state performance considerably. A simple passive phase-lag device is shown in Fig. 10-16a, and its transfer function is sketched in Fig. 10-16b. The transfer-function equation of the network is

$$\frac{e_o}{e_i} = \frac{R_2 + 1/j\omega C_2}{R_1 + R_2 + 1/j\omega C_2}$$
$$= \frac{j\omega C_2 R_2 + 1}{j\omega C_2(R_1 + R_2) + 1} \qquad (10\text{-}30)$$

Letting $C_2 R_2 = \tau_2$ and

$$C_2(R_1 + R_2) = \tau_{12},$$

$$\frac{e_o}{e_i} = \frac{j\omega\tau_2 + 1}{j\omega\tau_{12} + 1} \qquad (10\text{-}31)$$

It is evident that $\tau_{12} > \tau_2$, so that for any value of ω the angle of the denominator is greater than the angle of the numerator so that the net phase angle is always lagging. The effect of phase-lag compensation on simple systems will now be illustrated.

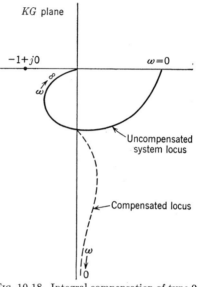

FIG. 10-18. Integral compensation of type 0 system.

10-13. Series Compensation—Type 0 System. *True Integral Device.* Consider the system of Fig. 10-17, which is the simple speed control of Fig. 10-12 plus a series integrating device. The transfer-function equation is then

$$\frac{e_o}{\varepsilon} = \frac{\mu_1 K_g K_n}{R_f K_v} \frac{1}{(j\omega\tau_f + 1)(j\omega\tau_m + 1)} K\left(\frac{j\omega + 1}{j\omega}\right) \qquad (10\text{-}32)$$

$$\frac{e_o}{\varepsilon} = \frac{\mu_1 K_g K_n K}{R_f K_v} \frac{j\omega + 1}{j\omega(j\omega\tau_f + 1)(j\omega\tau_m + 1)} \qquad (10\text{-}33)$$

It is readily seen from Eq. (10-33) that $e_o/\varepsilon \to \infty$ as $\omega \to 0$, and since $e_o \neq \infty$, then $\varepsilon \to 0$. Thus the output speed must duplicate the input speed exactly. Inspection of Eq. (10-33) also shows that the integrator affects only the low-frequency portion of the transfer-function locus; so the locus of the compensated system might be as sketched in Fig. 10-18.

Passive Network Providing an Approximate Integration. If a passive integrating device (of the type shown in Fig. 10-16) is substituted for the true integrator, the transfer function becomes

$$\frac{e_o}{\varepsilon} = \frac{\mu_1 K_o K_n}{R_f K_v} \frac{1}{(j\omega\tau_f + 1)(j\omega\tau_m + 1)} K \left(\frac{j\omega\tau_2 + 1}{j\omega\tau_{12} + 1}\right) \qquad (10\text{-}34)$$

This obviously does not create a pole at the origin, so as $\omega \to 0$, $\varepsilon \not\to 0$. However, the attenuation at high frequencies decreases the length of the vector in the third quadrant, and the phase shift (lagging) changes the shape of the locus in the fourth quadrant so that additional gain may be used to improve steady-state performance without affecting the peak overshoot. This is illustrated in Fig. 10-19a and b.

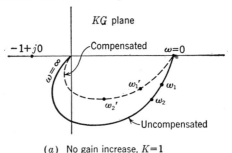

(a) No gain increase, $K=1$

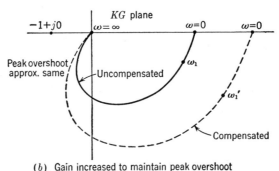

(b) Gain increased to maintain peak overshoot

Fig. 10-19. Compensated locus for various gain settings.

Use of a Reset Device (Position-error Detector).   Neither of the above systems maintains a position correspondence between input and output. For example, if the input is stopped, the output will gradually slow down but, in general, reference points on the input and output will not be in correspondence. This is normal in speed-control systems since there usually is no need for a position correspondence. However, if a position correspondence is established by replacing the tachometers with a reset-type error detector such as a selsyn generator-control transformer system, an effective integration is obtained and the system becomes type 1. Thus it can operate at constant velocity with exact speed duplication.

The change in the actual system is illustrated in Fig. 10-20.

It should be noted that in this case the error equation is $\varepsilon = \theta_i - \theta_o$ rather than $\varepsilon = d\theta_i/dt - d\theta_o/dt$ as was the case when tachometers were used. The transfer function of the system becomes

$$\frac{\theta_o}{\varepsilon} = \frac{K_g \mu_1}{R_f K_v} \frac{1}{j\omega(j\omega\tau_f + 1)(j\omega\tau_m + 1)} \tag{10-35}$$

which denotes a type 1 system.

10-14. Series Integral Compensation—Type I System. In some applications nearly perfect position correspondence is required of servomechanisms operating at constant velocity. For such cases a normal type 1 system is not satisfactory because the gain usually cannot be increased

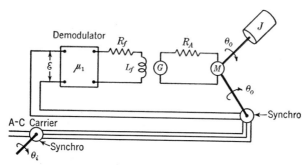

FIG. 10-20. Positioning servomechanism, type 1.

sufficiently without impairing transient performance. If position correspondence must be exact, then a true integral device must be added to introduce an additional pole at the origin and thus change the type 1 system to a type 2 system. A fundamental type 1 system which might be compensated in this fashion has been shown in Fig. 10-9a and is reproduced in Fig. 10-21a with the integral compensator indicated. The resultant transfer-function equation is

$$\frac{\theta_o}{\varepsilon} = \frac{\mu_1 K_g K}{R_1 K_v} \frac{j\omega + 1}{(j\omega)^2 (j\omega\tau_f + 1)(j\omega\tau_m + 1)} \tag{10-36}$$

The effect on the transfer-function locus is indicated in Fig. 10-21b.

Frequently it is difficult to obtain satisfactory transient performance with such compensation, because some phase shift in the region of the resonant frequency is virtually unavoidable, and in general this phase shift tends to produce a larger transient overshoot. In general it is advisable to design the integral device so as to keep the phase shift at ω_r to a few degrees. If this is not possible, sometimes an additional phase-*lead* compensator is added to cancel the lagging phase shift produced by the integral device in the critical frequency range. This would then be a compound, or integrodifferential, controller.

In most velocity-operated servomechanisms where high position accuracy is specified, the velocity-lag error may be reduced to the order of magnitude of the system noise level by a passive phase-lag compensator.[45]

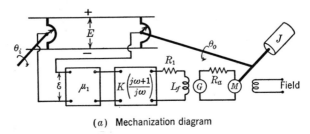

(a) Mechanization diagram

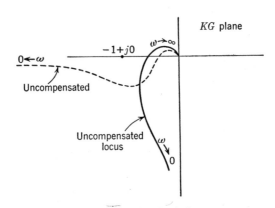

(b) Transfer-function loci

FIG. 10-21. Type 1 system with true integral compensation.

Such compensation is indicated by the system of Fig. 10-22a, and its transfer-function equation is

$$\frac{\theta_o}{\varepsilon} = \frac{\mu_1 K_g K}{R_f K_v} \frac{j\omega\tau_2 + 1}{j\omega(j\omega\tau_f + 1)(j\omega\tau_m + 1)(j\omega\tau_{12} + 1)} \qquad (10\text{-}37)$$

Since the passive network does not produce a pole at the origin, the system is still type 1, but the gain, K, may be adjusted to reduce the velocity-lag error, and K, τ_2, and τ_{12} must all be considered in adjusting the transient performance. The effect on the transfer-function locus is indicated in Fig. 10-22b.

It should be reasonably obvious that phase-lead compensation may sometimes be needed in addition to the integrating device in order to obtain acceptable transient performance. It should also be clear that the same methods may be applied to type 2 systems when acceleration errors are important. In general, however, as the complexity of the system increases, more difficulty is encountered in obtaining good transient performance while meeting steady-state requirements.

10-15. Summary. Compensation is required in servomechanisms to obtain satisfactory transient and steady-state operation. In some few cases the purpose of the compensation is solely to stabilize or to improve transient performance, and in these cases phase-lead (differentiating) devices are generally used. In most cases the compensation is used to

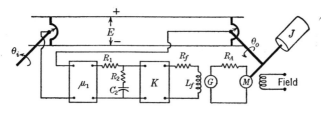

(*a*) Mechanization diagram

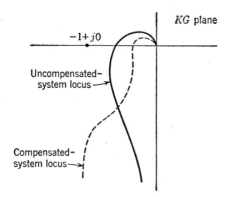

(*b*) Transfer-function loci

FIG. 10-22. Type 1 system with approximate integral compensation.

permit improved steady-state performance without appreciably interfering with transient performance. For these cases either phase-lag or phase-lead devices may be used, depending on the specifications of the particular problem. If the steady-state error must be entirely eliminated, then a true integral device must be used. However, if specifications do not require the *elimination* of steady-state error, then the general procedure is to increase the system gain and at the same time reshape the transfer-function locus. Passive phase-lead devices, in general, distort the high-frequency portion of the transfer-function locus so that a higher gain may be used without producing instability. Passive phase-lag devices, on the other hand, are low-pass filters and permit the low-frequency portion of the locus to be amplified while attenuating the high frequencies. It is normally true that phase-lag, or integral, controllers are most effective in adjusting steady-state performance, while phase-lead, or derivative, controllers are best suited to correcting transient deficiencies. It therefore follows logically that many systems may require the use of both types of devices.

The effects of compensation on the steady-state error is checked from the transfer-function equation. The procedure is to let $j\omega = 0$ (after rearranging the equation to show the position, velocity, or acceleration error). This evaluates the system gain, which is a figure of merit for the steady-state performance. The transient performance is verified from the transfer-function locus, which need be plotted only in the region of the resonance frequency ω_r.

PROBLEMS

10-1. For the system of Fig. 10-7a, in the text, assume the following values for the constants: E is 200 volts; allowable rotation of potentiometers, I, O, N, is 800 deg; K_1 is 0.4 volt-sec/radian; τ_{m1} is 0.05; K_2 is 0.6 volt-sec/radian; τ_{m2} is 0.1 (including load inertia); μ_2 is 5.0; $\tau_g = 0.08$.

  a. Plot $G(j\omega)$.

  b. Although (*a*) shows an unstable system, set the gain, μ_1, so that the locus is tangent to the $M = 4.0$ circle.

  c. Insert a phase-lead network of the type shown in Fig. 10-7c, and calculate the values of μ, α, and τ_2 required to just stabilize the system.

  d. Determine whether this type of lead network can stabilize the system to an M_p of 2.0.

  e. Use two identical phase-lead networks in series (isolated), and determine whether or not an M_p of 1.5 is possible.

10-2. For the system of Fig. 10-9a, in the text, τ_f is 0.10, and τ_m is 0.05.

  a. Determine the system gain for $M_p = 1.3$.

  b. Calculate the velocity-lag error if the input is 10 deg/sec.

  c. Calculate the improvement in velocity performance if a phase-lead network of the type used in Prob. 10-1 is inserted, if $\alpha_2 = 0.2$ and if $M_p = 1.3$.

  d. Repeat (*b*) and (*c*) for an input of 1 radian/sec.

  e. Repeat (*b*) and (*c*) for an input of 5 radians/sec.

10-3. For the system of Prob. 10-2, it is specified that the input velocity may be as great as 5 radians/sec, that the velocity-lag error may not exceed 10 deg, and that an M_p of 1.5 is permissible.

  a. Calculate the required system gain.

  b. Design a phase-lead compensator to permit use of such gain with the system.

10-4. For the system of Fig. 10-12, in the text, τ_f is 0.1, and τ_m is 0.5.

  a. Calculate the gain for an M_p of 2.0.

  b. What is the steady-state velocity error? What is ω_r?

  c. Design a phase-lead network to reduce M_p to 1.3.

  d. What are the steady-state velocity error and ω_r of the compensated system?

  e. Is it possible to obtain an M_p of 1.0 or less with the type of compensator used and without appreciably changing the velocity error?

10-5. For the system of Fig. 10-20, in the text, τ_f is 0.1, and τ_m is 0.05.

a. Calculate the required gain for a steady-state velocity-lag error of 25 deg with an input velocity of 5 radians/sec.

b. What are M_p and ω_r?

c. Design a phase-lead network to reduce M_p to 1.3 while maintaining the same steady-state error. What is the effect on ω_r?

d. Repeat for a velocity-lag requirement of 10 deg.

10-6. Determine the effect of the differentiating term in the amplifier of Fig. 4P-4 by means of a polar study.

10-7. Repeat Prob. 10-6 for the system of Fig. 4P-5.

10-8. Repeat Prob. 10-6 for the system of Prob. 4-16.

10-9. Find the effect of the integrating term in the system of Prob. 4-20 by preparing a polar locus study.

10-10. Select and design a compensating circuit to be used with the computer servo of Prob. 4-21 which will allow a 50 per cent reduction in the velocity-lag error.

CHAPTER 11

PARALLEL COMPENSATION

11-1. Introduction.[29-31,65,66,203,*] The compensation of a servomechanism system to meet performance specifications need not be accomplished by a device in series with the main transmission path: it is usually possible and often desirable to use a device which is in parallel (schematically)

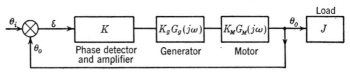

(a) Uncompensated system

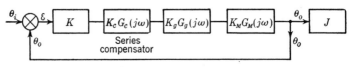

(b) Series-compensated

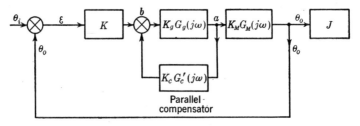

(c) Parallel-compensated

Fig. 11-1. Block diagrams of uncompensated and compensated servomechanisms.

with one or more components of this path. In Fig. 11-1a is shown the block diagram of an uncompensated servo whose performance may be assumed to fall short of specifications. In Figs. 11-1b and c, the same system is series- and parallel-compensated, respectively, to improve the

* Superior numbers, when they appear in the text proper, are the numbers of references given in the Bibliography.

218

system performance. Because the compensating element in Fig. 11-1b is connected in cascade with the main signal-transmission path, the compensation achieved is described as series compensation.

In Fig. 11-1c the compensating element is connected in parallel with one of the system elements in the main signal-transmission path; hence the compensation accomplished by this physical arrangement is known as parallel compensation. Because the output of the parallel compensating device, connected to point b, feeds backward and modifies an input signal derived at point a of the main transmission path, this is often called *feedback* compensation.

The parallel compensator functions to improve the steady-state or transient performance (or both) of the system by introducing phase lead or lag as desired. Thus the existence of a subsidiary feedback loop in a system such as that of Fig. 11-1c should not be confused with those parallel circuits which may necessarily be included in a specific system to allow for remote control from several stations (see Chap. 4) or with those parallel circuits which transmit energy in the same direction as the entire main transmission path (for example, the input velocity and acceleration circuits of Chap. 4). If the purpose of the added feedback loop or loops is to *alter* one or more of the servo performance characteristics, then obviously the device is a parallel compensator.

It will be seen that either series or parallel compensation may theoretically be used to accomplish a given purpose. Often the decision as to which method to use is difficult to make. But several important factors should be kept in mind in deciding upon the type of compensation.

1. The physical nature of the system and application. In electrically operated servos usually either type is possible (though in a specific system one type may be definitely more practical). In a hydraulic, pneumatic, or mechanical servo a suitable device for series (or for parallel) compensation may not exist.

2. The availability of a suitable signal. The design of any compensating device depends largely on the type of signal which is to be applied to its input. Obviously, if an electrical servo is operated at 400 cycles its power components have different characteristics from those of a d-c system which might be able to do the same job. In one case a series compensator might be simpler and better than a parallel device, while for the other case the reverse might be true.

3. Economic factors. In many cases either series or parallel compensation might be practically feasible, but one might require more equipment than the other, or more expensive equipment. In general a feedback device is likely to require less equipment if a suitable signal is available, because the energy transfer is from a high power level to a lower level and amplifiers, etc., may not be necessary. In using series

compensation, however, an additional amplifier is frequently required to increase gain or to provide isolation.

Thus, in general, the choice of a method of compensation depends on the specific system involved, available practical components, economic considerations, and the designer's experience and preferences.

11-2. Requirements of Equivalent Series and Parallel Compensators. It has been shown that the basic means for servo-system adjustment is the use of derivatives and/or integrals of one or more signals which are conveniently available. It is readily seen that true differentiators or integrators are not always possible, and more often are not practical, so that compensating devices are normally approximate differentiators or integrators. In the following sections the equations for series and parallel compensators which provide true derivatives and integrals will be derived. It will be shown that, in terms of frequency response, such devices effectively produce a phase lead or a phase lag, and thus the important feature of an approximate differentiator or integrator is its phase-shift characteristic. Simple illustrations are then used to make the discussion more concrete.

11-3. Ideal Differentiator. It has previously been shown that ideal derivative control can be obtained by adding to a system a series-compensating device whose output signal is of the form

$$\theta_2 = K_1\theta_1 + K_2\frac{d\theta_1}{dt} \tag{11-1}$$

where θ_1 is the input signal to the series device.

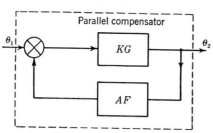

FIG. 11-2. Block diagram of parallel compensator.

The transfer function of the device must be

$$\frac{\theta_2}{\theta_1} = K_cG_c(s) = K_1 + K_2s$$

or $\hspace{6em}$ (11-2)

$$K_cG_c(j\omega) = K_1 + K_2j\omega$$

For a feedback network [as, for example, in (11-2)] to simulate ideal differentiation, it must be so designed that

$$\frac{\theta_2}{\theta_1} = \frac{KG}{1 + KGAF} \tag{11-3}$$
$$= K_1 + K_2s$$

where KG is the transfer function of the main transmission elements about which the feedback loop closes and AF is the transfer function of

the device in the feedback path.   From (11-3) it is readily shown that
the required form of the feedback network is

$$AF(s) = \frac{1}{K_1 + K_2 s} - \frac{1}{KG(s)}$$

or   (11-4)

$$AF(j\omega) = \frac{1}{K_1 + j\omega K_2} - \frac{1}{KG(j\omega)}$$

In general, the phase shift of the feedback device is negative, or lagging,
as may be seen by substituting typical equations for $KG(j\omega)$ in Eq. (11-4).

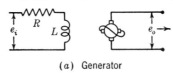

(a) Generator

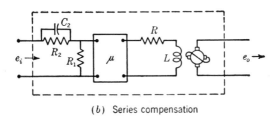

(b) Series compensation

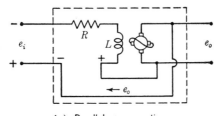

(c) Parallel compensation

FIG. 11-3. Derivative compensation of a generator.

However, the term $AF(j\omega)$ appears only in the denominator of the net
transfer function [see Eq. (11-3)] so that the effect of phase lag in $AF(j\omega)$
is to produce phase lead in the main transmission path.   It is evident,
therefore, that the basic characteristic of an ideal differentiator is that of
phase lead, and when a parallel device is used the signal feedback must
have a phase lag.   These, then, are the minimum requirements of
approximate differentiators which may be used practically.

11-4. Illustration of Approximate Derivative Compensation.   Assume
that the main series component denoted by $K_o G_o$ in Eq. (11-5) below is

the electromagnetic rotating amplifier shown in Fig. 11-3a.   Then

$$K_g G_g(j\omega) = \frac{K}{j\omega\tau_g + 1} \qquad (11\text{-}5)$$

Furthermore assume that series compensation in the form of a passive derivative network would be acceptable as shown in Fig. 11-3b.   Then for the series arrangement the over-all transfer function is

$$K_s G_s(j\omega) = \alpha\mu\,\frac{j\omega\tau + 1}{j\omega\alpha\tau + 1}\,\frac{K}{j\omega\tau_g + 1} \qquad (11\text{-}6)$$

where $K_s G_s$ is enclosed by dotted lines and all constants are as previously defined.

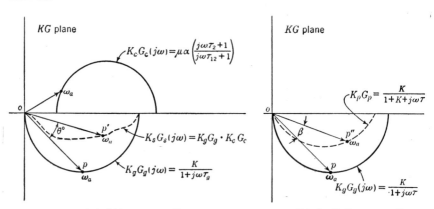

(a) Series compensation   (b) Feedback compensation

FIG. 11-4. Graphical procedures for phase-lead compensation.

An equivalent parallel compensation may be obtained as shown in Fig. 11-3c.   The transfer function of this simple system (no network in the feedback path) is

$$K_p G_p(j\omega) = \frac{K_g G_g}{1 + K_g G_g} = \frac{K/(j\omega\tau_g + 1)}{1 + \dfrac{K}{j\omega\tau_g + 1}} = \frac{K}{1 + K + j\omega\tau_g} \qquad (11\text{-}7)$$

The effect of the feedback connection upon the generator transfer function is essentially the same as that of the added series network in Fig. 11-3b, as can be shown graphically or deduced from the mathematical expressions.

In Fig. 11-4a are plotted the probable transfer-function locus of the dynamoelectric amplifier, the transfer locus of the cascade compensating network, and the over-all transfer function of the combination $K_s G_s(j\omega)$. The latter is obtained by the usual vector methods.   For the sake of comparison, a single angular frequency, ω_a, is selected; the vector representing the transfer function of the generator alone at ω_a is op, the vector representing K_sG_s at ω_a is op'. Obviously, the effect of the series network is to accomplish a phase advance through the angle θ.

In Fig. 11-4b are drawn the original dynamoelectric amplifier locus $K_gG_g(j\omega)$ and the transfer-function locus of the parallel-compensated system described by Eq. (11-7). A single frequency ω_a is again selected to illustrate the effect of compensation. op is K_gG_g at ω_a, and op'' is K_pG_p at ω_a. The net effect, then, is a phase advance through an angle β. Thus the addition of the specific feedback loop is qualitatively equivalent to the series phase-lead compensator.

Proof of the phase advance introduced by the series and parallel devices shown in Figs. 11-3b and c can also be derived from the mathematical expressions for the respective transfer functions. The series-compensating device produces an over-all series transfer function, as in Eq. (11-6),

$$K_sG_s = \alpha\mu K \frac{j\omega\tau + 1}{(j\omega\alpha\tau + 1)(j\omega\tau_g + 1)} \qquad (11\text{-}6)$$

and thus introduces a phase angle in both numerator and denominator. However, both of these phase angles are positive, and for any given value of $j\omega$, the phase angle in the numerator is the larger. So the net effect is a positive phase shift.

While the simple inverse feedback loop does not introduce an additional phase angle in the over-all transfer function equation (11-7),

$$K_pG_p(j\omega) = \frac{K}{(1 + K) + j\omega\tau_g} \qquad (11\text{-}7)$$

it does change the real part of the existing complex denominator. Thus for a given value of $j\omega$ the angle of the denominator is reduced, which is effectively a positive phase shift in the net transfer function.

It may thus be seen that in this case a very simple parallel connection produces the same general effect as a more complex series compensator. Quantitative adjustments would be necessary in either case to obtain a specified result. In the case of the feedback compensation, the magnitude of voltage fed back may be varied with a potentiometer, or if additional phase shift is required, a network may be inserted in the feedback channel. Such adjustments become more apparent in dealing with specific systems.

11-5. Ideal Integration. Series methods for obtaining true integration have already been discussed. If it is desired to produce ideal integration by feedback compensation, then the output of the compensated unit in Fig. 11-2 must be of the form

$$\theta_2 = K_1\theta_1 + K_3\int\theta_1\,dt \qquad (11\text{-}8)$$

where θ_2 and θ_1 are output and input signals of the compensated unit. Thus the transfer function of the compensated unit must be of the form

$$K_p G_p(s) = \frac{\theta_2(s)}{\theta_1(s)} = K_1 + \frac{K_3}{s}$$

$$K_p G_p(j\omega) = \frac{\theta_2(j\omega)}{\theta_1(j\omega)} = K_1 + \frac{K_3}{j\omega} \tag{11-9}$$

and the feedback network must be designed so that

$$\frac{KG}{1 + KGAF} = K_1 + \frac{K_3}{j\omega} \tag{11-10}$$

From (11-10), the required form of the feedback network is

$$AF(j\omega) = \frac{1}{K_1 + K_3/j\omega} - \frac{1}{KG(j\omega)} = \frac{j\omega}{j\omega K_1 + K_3} - \frac{1}{KG(j\omega)} \tag{11-11}$$

For a given transfer function, $KG(j\omega)$, the mathematical requirements of the feedback component $AF(j\omega)$ may be derived from Eq. (11-11). In general, however, the dominant characteristic of the feedback device will be that of phase lead, and usually it is more convenient to use a practical phase-lead device than to synthesize one with the necessary characteristics for a true integrator.

11-6. Illustration of Approximate Integral Compensation. Assume that the main series component which is to be compensated by an integrating device or network is the generator shown in Fig. 11-5a. Approximate integral compensation may be obtained by introducing a series net as shown in Fig. 11-5b. The transfer function of the net is

$$K_c G_c = \frac{j\omega\tau_2 + 1}{j\omega\tau_{12} + 1} \tag{11-12}$$

where $\tau_{12} > \tau_2$.

The amplifier, μ, would be desirable for isolation purposes. The transfer function of the series combination is then

$$K_s G_s = \mu KG K_c G_c = \frac{\mu K(j\omega\tau_2 + 1)}{(j\omega\tau_{12} + 1)(j\omega\tau_g + 1)} \tag{11-13}$$

Approximate integration by feedback compensation may be obtained by connecting the RC high-pass filter combination in the feedback loop as shown in Fig. 11-5c. The transfer function of the feedback net (to realize approximate integration) is

$$AF = \frac{j\omega\tau}{j\omega\tau + 1} \tag{11-14}$$

and for Fig. 11-5c the over-all transfer function is then

$$K_f G_f = \frac{K/(j\omega\tau_g + 1)}{1 + \dfrac{Kj\omega\tau}{(j\omega\tau_g + 1)(j\omega\tau + 1)}} \qquad (11\text{-}15)$$

Figures 11-6a and b indicate the effective phase lag (approximate integration which is caused by the series- and parallel-compensating net-

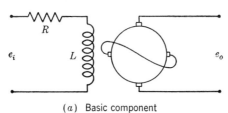

(a) Basic component

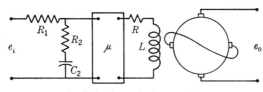

(b) Series integral compensation

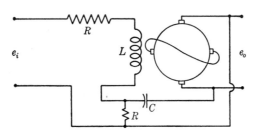

(c) Feedback integral compensation

FIG. 11-5. Integral compensation of a generator.

works). In Fig. 11-6a, op is $K_g G_g$ at ω_a; op' is $K_c G_c$ at ω_a; op'' is the over-all transfer function found by ordinary graphical methods. The angle of lag introduced is θ.

In Fig. 11-6b, op is $K_g G_g$ at ω_a, and op' is $K_p G_p$ at ω_a. (Determination of the graphical plot of $K_p G_p$ is somewhat more involved here.) The angle of phase lag is denoted by β.

11-7. Summary. Several generalizations may be drawn and extended from the previous graphical and mathematical investigations:

1. A derivative controller effectively produces a phase lead, while an integrating controller introduces a phase lag in a system. Devices or networks for producing phase lead or lag, and therefore approximate differentiation and integration devices (over a selected frequency range), may be obtained by either series or parallel connection of chosen elements. Parallel, or feedback, compensation introduces a phase change into a system by altering the over-all transfer function between the points to which it is connected.

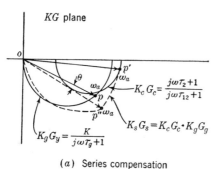

(*a*) Series compensation

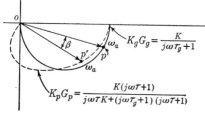

(*b*) Parallel compensation

Fig. 11-6. Graphical procedures for phase-lag compensation.

2. In general, for series compensation, approximate differentiation is obtained by adding a phase-lead network, and approximate integration is realized by adding a phase-lag network. But for parallel compensation the addition of a phase-lag network in the feedback path produces effective differentiation. Conversely, the use of a phase-lead network in the feedback path results in approximate integration.

11-8. Manipulations in Parallel Compensation. The mathematical and graphical manipulations required for the design of series compensators are straightforward, if sometimes laborious. The effect of the compensator on the system transfer-function locus is readily determined, since a simple vector multiplication is all that is normally required. When feedback compensation is to be used, however, the effect of the compensator is not readily determined by direct transfer-function methods as will now be shown.

When a compensation device is inserted in a feedback path, the net effect is to change the transfer function of the section between the connected points from a simple KG to $KG/(1 + KGAF)$. For example, if the over-all transfer function of an uncompensated system is

$$K_u G_u = K_1 G_1 K_2 G_2 K_3 G_3 \qquad (11\text{-}16)$$

and if a compensating loop is closed around the element $K_3 G_3$ with an element AF in the feedback path, then the compensated system has an over-all transfer function

$$K_cG_c = K_1G_1K_2G_2\left(\frac{K_3G_3}{1 + K_3G_3AF}\right)$$

$$= K_1G_1K_2G_2K_3G_3\left(\frac{1}{1 + K_3G_3AF}\right) \qquad (11\text{-}17)$$

It is reasonably obvious that numerical computations with Eq. (11-17) are laborious and *simple* graphical methods do not obtain. Furthermore, there is considerable additional labor if trial-and-error methods must be used to find a suitable compensator AF. Some desirable simplifications in computation are obtained if the *inverse* transfer functions and frequency-response functions are used rather than the direct functions. These are illustrated in later sections.

11-9. Outline of Typical Parallel-compensation Procedures. The steps outlined assume that a plot of the transfer function of the uncompensated servo has been made and that the desired form and location of the compensated locus have been determined:

1. Select the proper type of network for compensation (phase lead or phase lag or both), and evaluate its transfer function.

2. Determine the direct transfer-function equation of the servomechanism with the compensation added. Then invert the transfer function.

3. Plot each factor of the inverse transfer-function equation to a convenient scale (on the same coordinate axis) except those related to the compensating network (AF).

4. Carry out such vector multiplications, additions, or subtractions as are invariant with changes in the compensating-network parameters.

5. Estimate parameters for the chosen parallel compensator, and draw its transfer function to the same scale as above, on the same axis as (3).

6. Perform such graphical vector operations with the compensator transfer function as are denoted by the equation to get the locus of the complete inverse transfer function.

7. Compare this locus with the desired locus. Adjust the compensator parameters if necessary, and repeat (5) and (6). If a satisfactory alteration is not obtained, then the type of compensator must be changed.

8. Add inverse M circles, determine M_p and ω_r, and calculate the proper gain setting.

9. Evaluate performance.

11-10. Vector Algebra for Parallel Compensation. To illustrate the common graphical manipulations necessary for the analysis of parallel compensation, consider the simple case of a single main-loop component, KG, with a paralleled feedback component, AF (*see* Fig. 11-2). The inverse transfer function is

$$\frac{\varepsilon}{\theta_o} = \frac{1}{KG} + AF = KG^{-1} + AF \qquad (11\text{-}18)$$

Possible plots for the direct transfer functions KG and AF are shown in Fig. 11-7a. The inverse KG plot and the direct AF plot, as required by Eq. (11-18), are shown in Fig. 11-7b, together with a curve for their

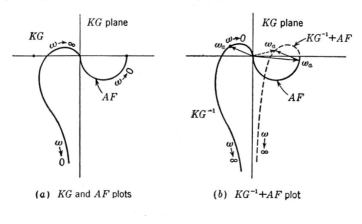

(a) KG and AF plots   (b) $KG^{-1}+AF$ plot

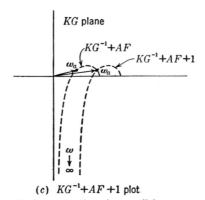

(c) $KG^{-1}+AF+1$ plot

Fig. 11-7. Graphical constructions for parallel compensation.

vector sum. The vector addition is indicated on the plot at a selected frequency, ω_a. The inverse frequency-response function is

$$(\theta_i/\theta_o) = KG^{-1} + AF + 1 \tag{11-19}$$

which represents merely a shift in the origin of the inverse transfer-function locus. This is shown in Fig. 11-7c.

For a more complicated case such that expressed by Eq. (11-17), the graphical procedure is still much the same. The inverse transfer-function equation is then

$$\frac{\varepsilon}{\theta_o} = \frac{1}{K_1G_1K_2G_2}\left(\frac{1}{K_3G_3} + AF\right) = K_1G_1^{-1}K_2G_2^{-1}(K_3G_3^{-1} + AF) \tag{11-20}$$

which indicates a vector addition followed by a multiplication. The inverse frequency-response equation is

$$\frac{\theta_i}{\theta_o} = K_1 G_1^{-1} K_2 G_2^{-1}(K_3 G_3 + AF) + 1 \tag{11-21}$$

again representing simply a shift in origin of the inverse transfer-function locus.

Several important advantages in the use of inverse-function representation for parallel-compensated systems may now be pointed out.

1. The transfer function of the feedback component is usually separated from the other factors in the inverse equation, so that the effect of variations in feedback is more readily studied.

2. Graphical studies are made practical through this procedure. The effect of adjusting the parameters of the type of network may be readily investigated, though the procedures are more involved than for series compensation.

The advantages noted above assume that more than just a single locus is required, as for optimum adjustment of compensating-network constants. It should also be noted that the advantages of inverse loci are not limited to the study of feedback compensation. They have been applied to the study of relay servomechanisms[72] and to multiloop systems.[203] The following specific example is intended to illustrate the principles involved in applying the inverse functions to parallel compensation.

11-11. Illustration of Parallel Compensation. Consider the simple uncompensated servomechanism of Fig. 11-8a. Assuming somewhat idealized components, the block diagram of the system would be as shown in Fig. 11-8b. The direct transfer function is then

$$\frac{\theta_o}{\varepsilon} = \frac{KK_g K_m}{j\omega(j\omega\tau_g + 1)(j\omega\tau_m + 1)} \tag{11-22}$$

If the system is to be operated at constant velocity, the velocity-lag error may be excessive and phase-lag compensation may be needed. Such compensation may be added as indicated in Fig. 11-8c (an isolation amplifier might be needed), and the equation of the compensated system would then be

$$\frac{\theta_o}{\varepsilon} = \frac{KK_g K_m}{j\omega(j\omega\tau_g + 1)(j\omega\tau_m + 1)} \frac{j\omega\tau_2 + 1}{j\omega\tau_{12} + 1} \tag{11-23}$$

where τ_2 and τ_{12} are as previously defined. It is readily seen that for series compensation the transfer function is essentially isolated in the equation, so that calculations (either numerical or graphical) are easily carried out even though trial-and-error methods may be required.

To effect a comparable integration by feedback the circuit shown in Fig. 11-8d might be used. Figure 11-8e is the block diagram of this system.   The direct transfer function of the system becomes

$$\frac{\theta_o}{\varepsilon} = \frac{KK_gK_m/(j\omega\tau_g + 1)}{j\omega(j\omega\tau_m + 1)\left[1 + \dfrac{K_g j\omega\tau}{(j\omega\tau_g + 1)(j\omega\tau + 1)}\right]}$$

$$= \frac{KK_gK_m(j\omega\tau + 1)}{j\omega(j\omega\tau_m + 1)\left[(j\omega\tau_g + 1)(j\omega\tau + 1) + j\omega\tau K_g\right]} \qquad (11\text{-}24)$$

It is apparent that this expression does not separate the compensating device parameters from those of the other factors.   Therefore, analytic

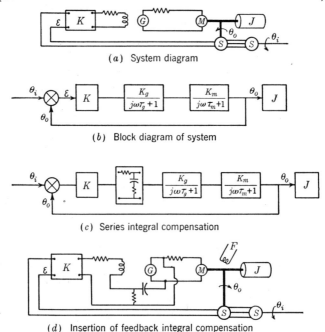

(a) System diagram

(b) Block diagram of system

(c) Series integral compensation

(d) Insertion of feedback integral compensation

(e) Block diagram of system with feedback compensation

Fig. 11-8. Series and parallel compensation of a typical system.

study of the compensating effect from the equation is difficult.   Furthermore, there are no graphical methods available for convenient study of the effects of varying the compensation.

When the inverse transfer function is written as

$$\frac{\varepsilon}{\theta_o} = \frac{j\omega(j\omega\tau_m + 1)}{KK_m}\left[\frac{j\omega\tau_g + 1}{K_g} + \frac{j\omega\tau}{j\omega\tau + 1}\right] \qquad (11\text{-}25)$$

the feedback transfer function is isolated.   Note that numerical calculations using this expression would entail essentially the same amount of
labor as the use of the direct transfer function, if only one locus is to be
calculated.   But if the time constant, τ, of the feedback unit is to be
adjusted for optimum system performance, the successive loci required
are more readily obtained using Eq. (11-25) and graphical procedures.

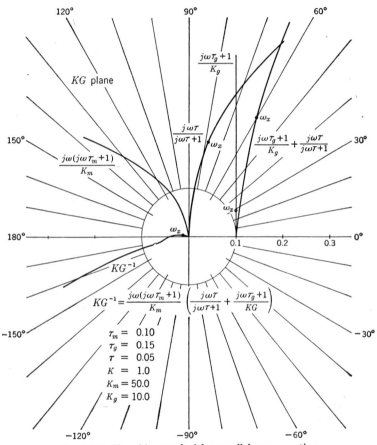

FIG. 11-9. Use of inverse loci for parallel compensation.

11-12. Graphical Procedure.

From Eq. (11-25) two basic curves may
first be drawn on the KG plane.   These would be plots of $j\omega(j\omega\tau_m + 1)/K_m$
and $(j\omega\tau_g + 1)/K_g$.   A third curve, or family of curves, would be constructed for the feedback unit $j\omega\tau/(j\omega\tau + 1)$.   An intermediate locus
would then be constructed by vector addition of the $(j\omega\tau_g + 1)/K_g$ and
the selected $j\omega\tau/(j\omega\tau + 1)$ curve.   The final inverse transfer-function
locus could be obtained by vector multiplication of this intermediate
locus and the $j\omega(j\omega\tau_m + 1)/K_m$ curve.   These operations are indicated in
Fig. 11-9 for a single value of τ.   (Note that the curves are drawn assum-

ing gain constant $K = 1$. Adjustment of gain is not usually attempted until after the compensation-network parameters have been found.)

The curves for $j\omega(j\omega\tau_m + 1)/K_m$ and $(j\omega\tau_g + 1)/K_g$ are invariant because they represent the selected motor and generator. The compensation locus of $j\omega\tau/(j\omega\tau + 1)$ will, of course, be altered by any change in τ. The approximate effect of variation in τ can be determined quickly, by plotting the transfer function of the compensator for several values of τ over just the frequency range in the region of the desired ω_r and repeating the graphical procedure. The over-all locus selected may then be adjusted by the gain-constant procedures outlined in the next section.

11-13. Gain-adjustment Procedures with Parallel Compensation. Before interpretation of the transfer-function locus can be carried out, it is necessary that the locus (Fig. 11-9) be modified by introducing the actual system gain constant K. This modification merely expands or contracts the locus depending upon the gain setting. The system M_p and ω_r must then be determined in order to get a comparison with the desired performance characteristics.

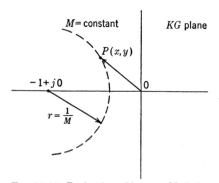

An obvious procedure for determining the resonance peak of the compensated system, and the corresponding resonant frequency ω_r, is to invert the KG^{-1} to find KG and then use the methods already developed in Chaps. 7 and 9. But a considerably simpler approach is to retain the inverse transfer-function locus and invert the M circles.

Fig. 11-10. Derivation of inverse M circles.

From a family of inverse M circles the resonance peak and resonant frequency of the servo can be picked off directly without the labor of replotting the direct transfer-function locus.

The inverse M circles may be derived as follows: Consider a point, $P(x,y)$, on the KG plane in Fig. 11-10. This point may be considered as one point on the inverse transfer-function locus. Then the vector op is

$$op = KG^{-1} = x + jy \qquad (11\text{-}26)$$

but

$$\frac{\theta_i}{\theta_o} = KG^{-1} + 1 = x + jy + 1 \qquad (11\text{-}27)$$

and

$$M^{-1} = \left|\frac{\theta_i}{\theta_o}\right| = |x + jy + 1| = \sqrt{(x + 1)^2 + y^2} \qquad (11\text{-}28)$$

or

$$\frac{1}{M^2} = (x + 1)^2 + y^2 \qquad (11\text{-}29)$$

Equation (11-33) is the equation of a circle with center at $-1 + j0$ and radius $1/M$. Thus a family of concentric circles may be drawn, with $-1 + j0$ as a center, where for each circle the value of M is the reciprocal of the radius. By trial and error, then, the maximum over-shoot and resonant frequency of the servomechanism can be found by constructing an inverse M circle which is tangent to the compensated transfer-function locus. This would correspond to merely locating the point on the KG^{-1} locus nearest to $-1 + j0$.

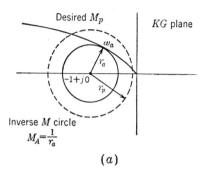

If the overshoot determined is not satisfactory, as is often the case, the gain may be adjusted to obtain the desired value of M_p. A simple con-struction may be used to determine the required gain setting. In Fig. 11-11a is shown the parallel-com-pensated inverse locus and the in-verse M circle which locates the resonant frequency ω_a and deter-mines the resonance peak $1/r_a$. The circle corresponding to the desired M_p is dotted. It is obvious, for the assumed conditions, that gain adjustment is necessary because the reso-nance peak is too large;

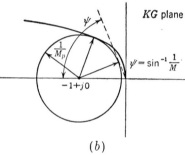

Fig. 11-11. Use of M^{-1} circles to set the resonance peak.

$$M_p = \frac{1}{r_p} < M_a = \frac{1}{r_a}$$

Therefore gain must be decreased.

A line is drawn from the origin at an angle $\psi = \sin^{-1} 1/M$ and a circle constructed with its center on the negative x axis so as to be tangent to both the constructed line and the KG^{-1} locus (see Fig. 11-11b). The circle will have a radius $1/M_p$ if the coordinate of its center is defined to be $-1 + j0$. The gain, K, by which the original locus must be multi-plied to obtain the desired condition is given by the coordinate of the center of the M_p^{-1} circle; read from the original scale. Proof of this is left to the student.

11-14. Parallel Compensation of System Requiring Phase Lead. The following example is intended to illustrate the general use of the inverse transfer function and inverse loci in the design of parallel-compensating devices. To simplify the presentation, numerical calculations have not been included. The discussion is carried out with the help of a series of sketched loci. Figure 11-12a shows a block diagram of an uncompen-

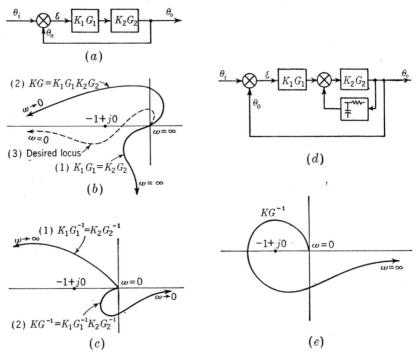

Fig. 11-12. Direct and inverse loci for a type 2 system. (a) Block diagram, (b) direct transfer-function locus, (c) inverse transfer-function loci, (d) insertion of parallel compensator, (e) required inverse locus.

sated servo system. If this system is to be type 2 (*i.e.*, no velocity-lag error), the over-all transfer function might be

$$KG = K_1G_1K_2G_2 = \frac{K_1}{j\omega(j\omega\tau_1 + 1)} \frac{K_2}{j\omega(j\omega\tau_2 + 1)} \qquad (11\text{-}30)$$

To simplify the sketches, it is assumed that $K_1 = K_2 = \sqrt{K}$ and $\tau_1 = \tau_2 = \tau$, giving the over-all equation

$$KG = \frac{K}{(j\omega)^2(j\omega\tau + 1)^2} \qquad (11\text{-}31)$$

The direct transfer-function locus of each component is represented by curve 1 in Fig. 11-12b, and the over-all locus by curve 2. The corresponding inverse loci are sketched in curves 1 and 2 of Fig. 11-12c.

In order to stabilize the system, it is necessary to introduce a sufficient amount of phase lead over the proper range of frequencies to produce a compensated locus such as curve 3 of Fig. 11-12b. Such compensation probably could be obtained by either series or parallel means, but in this example parallel compensation is assumed as shown in Fig. 11-12d. The equation of the feedback transfer function is then

$$AF = \frac{1}{j\omega\tau_f + 1} \tag{11-32}$$

The transfer function of the compensated system is

$$KG = \frac{K_1 K_2 / (j\omega)^2 (j\omega\tau + 1)^2}{1 + \dfrac{K_2}{(j\omega)^2 (j\omega\tau + 1)^2 (j\omega\tau_f + 1)}} \tag{11-33}$$

and so the inverse transfer function is

$$KG^{-1} = \frac{j\omega(j\omega\tau + 1)}{K_1} \left[\frac{j\omega(j\omega\tau + 1)}{K_2} + \frac{1}{j\omega\tau_f + 1} \right] \tag{11-34}$$

The required inverse locus, which is to be obtained by compensation, is the reciprocal of curve 3 in Fig. 11-12b and is shown in Fig. 11-12e.

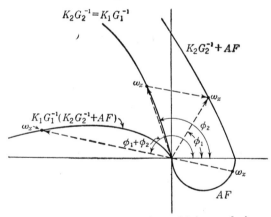

Fig. 11-13. Vector operations with inverse loci.

It is apparent from Eq. (11-34) that the graphical manipulations involved are vector addition of the loci $K_2 G_2^{-1}$ and AF, then the multiplication of the resulting locus by $K_1 G_1^{-1}$. The first of these manipulations is indicated in Fig. 11-13. The second step, multiplication, is carried out on the same curve sheet by inserting the $K_1 G_1^{-1}$ locus (in this case $K_1 G_1^{-1} = K_2 G_2^{-1}$) and performing the operation point by point. This is also illustrated in Fig. 11-13. While it is not obvious from the completed curves, if the feedback time constant, τ_f, has not been properly chosen, the direction of the needed adjustment in τ_f is easily determined during the multiplication process. Thus readjustment involves only the recalculation of the feedback locus and repetition of the graphical manipulations. Normally the M_p^{-1} circle would also be added and adjustments in gain or compensation used to obtain the desired performance. Figure 11-14 shows a calculated plot of a first trial computation on a system corresponding to the one just discussed.

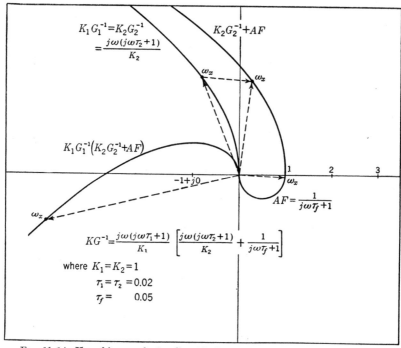

Fig. 11-14. Use of inverse loci. Graphical procedure for parallel compensation.

11-15. Parallel Compensation of Multiloop Systems.

When a control system is sufficiently complex to require multiple parallel loops for proper compensation, a quantitative analysis of performance involves considerable labor. Ordinarily the simplest procedure is to start with the innermost loop, reduce it to an equivalent series component, then add the next loop, and so on. Such algebraic manipulations have already been outlined in Chap. 5. These manipulations are reasonably simple once all of the transfer functions have been determined. However, each feedback loop is normally inserted as a specific compensation device and is separately designed to modify some performance characteristic. Thus the transfer functions are often dependent upon each other. If the compensation devices cannot be designed independently, trial-and-error methods are necessary to obtain proper compensators and, ultimately, proper performance. In any event, the use of inverse transfer-function plots will be found laborsaving in the design of each compensating device and the combining of multiple loops.

11-16. Nyquist Stability Criterion for Multiloop Systems. The simplified Nyquist stability criterion presented in Chap. 7 assumes that there are no poles in the positive real half of the complex plane. This is normally true for simple single-loop systems. In multiloop systems, however, if an interior loop is unstable, the effect of this instability is to produce a pole with a positive real part. This pole does not make the system unstable but will make the locus encircle the $-1 + j0$ point. Thus inspection of the locus would apparently indicate an unstable system, and the number of poles has to be calculated in order to complete the stability test. It should be true, however, that if the internal loops are known to be stable, no encirclements should result unless a zero exists, in which case the simplified criterion may still be used. Of course, the stability of the subordinate loops may be checked with successive Nyquist plots.

11-17. Summary. Parallel compensation reshapes the $KG(j\omega)$ locus and thus may be used to obtain improved transient and steady-state performance. In many cases parallel compensation may be preferred to series compensation because of the nature of the specific problem or for economic reasons. In such cases the use of the inverse transfer function is preferred because it reduces the labor of repeated numerical calculations and also permits graphical studies which would not be practical with the direct transfer function. Inverse magnitude circles may be added and used in the graphical determination of proper gain adjustment in much the same fashion as the direct magnitude circles are used with the direct transfer function.

PROBLEMS

11-1. Compute the transfer functions for the units shown in Figs. 11P-1 to 11P-4, and plot on the same polar chart. Let $R_f = 100$ ohms; $L_f = 4$ henrys; $\mu = 1.0$; K_g = generator voltage constant = 100 volts/amp; $R = 0.5$ megohm; $C = 0.08$ μf.

11-2. Compute the inverse transfer functions for the units shown in Figs. 11P-1 to 11P-4, and plot on the same polar chart. Use the component constants specified in Prob. 11-1.

11-3. For the unit of Fig. 11P-3, compute the transfer function for $C = 0.16$ μf and $C = 0.04$ μf. All other constants are in Prob. 11-1. Plot the results on a polar chart, and add the curve (from Prob. 11-1) for $C = 0.08$ μf.

11-4. Repeat Prob. 11-3, using inverse transfer functions.

11-5. For the units of Figs. 11P-2 to 11P-4, study the effect of varying μ by means of direct and inverse polar plots.

11-6. For the system of Fig. 11P-5, the motor time constant is $\tau_m = 0.5$, and the motor transfer constant is $K_m = 0.131$. The synchro sensitivity is $K_s = 57.3$ volts/radian, $K_1 = 2$, and this tachometer constant is $K_t = 8.5$.

a. Study the effect of variations in the gain of the amplifier, K.   Check both the steady-state and the transient performance.

b. Set K at some convenient value, and study the effect of varying the tachometer constant, K_t.

c. Show (by means of curves) the effect of reversing the polarity of the tachometer.

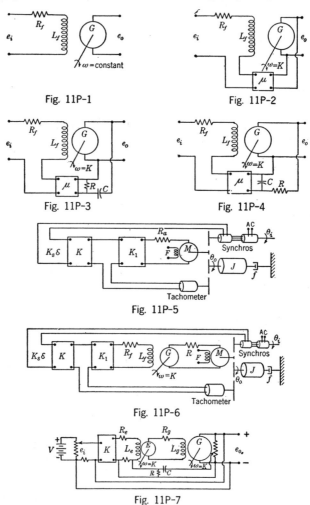

Fig. 11P-1

Fig. 11P-2

Fig. 11P-3

Fig. 11P-4

Fig. 11P-5

Fig. 11P-6

Fig. 11P-7

11-7. For the system of Fig. 11P-6, the component constants are:

$$K_1 = 0.5 \text{ amp/volt}$$
$$K_g = 250 \text{ volts/amp}$$
$$\tau_m = 0.8, \ \tau_g = 0.3$$
$$K_m = 1 \text{ rpm/volt (referred to the load)}$$
$$K_s = 1 \text{ volt/deg}$$
$$K_t = 0.01 \text{ volt/rpm}$$

a. Derive the direct and inverse transfer functions of the system.

b. By means of an inverse polar plot, determine a value of K which will limit the resonance peak to $M = 1.5$.   Vary K_t if necessary.

c. Prepare inverse polar loci showing the effects of variations in K, K_1, and K_t.

d. Determine the effect of reversing the polarity of the tachometer.

11-8. In the system of Fig. 11P-7, the values of the constant are

$$K_e = 30$$
$$K_g = 0.6$$
$$K = 1.0$$
$$\tau_e = 0.2$$
$$\tau_g = 0.5$$
$$\tau = RC = \text{variable}$$

The potentiometer tap on the output is also variable.

a. Derive the system transfer function.

b. Prepare inverse polar loci showing the effect of variations in τ, and also the effect of varying the potentiometer tap.

CHAPTER 12

LOGARITHMIC COORDINATES IN ANALYSIS AND DESIGN[29,31,67—69,*]

12-1. Introduction. The analysis of a servomechanism's performance is readily carried out through the use of the polar plot of its transfer function and certain stability criteria. The labor involved in carrying out such an analysis is not excessive, and results are dependable. But often, where gain adjustment, compensation, or general redesign of a system is required to meet given performance specifications, the manipulations of polar transfer-function plots become tedious.

If the transfer function of the servomechanism, and such auxiliary components as needed, are plotted on a logarithmic or semilogarithmic basis rather than on polar plots, simple and less laborious methods become available for determining steady-state performance, adjusting gain, and selecting compensating devices. Not only is direct parametric determination of series- and parallel-compensation networks made possible, but design of entire single and multiloop systems is facilitated. In addition certain convenient correlations with transient performance (maximum overshoot, speed of response, etc.) are established through the use of logarithmic coordinates.

Much of a system's polar transfer-function locus is of little value outside of two narrow bands of frequencies: in the region of the critical $-1 + j0$ point, for transient performance and stability determination, and the low-frequency portion, which is indicative of steady-state performance. Yet a relatively large number of points must be determined to obtain an accurate plot. Logarithmic plots of system transfer functions require graphing of only a few important frequencies out of the entire frequency spectra, because straight-line or asymptotic approximations of the actual transfer-function loci can be made with determinable accuracy.

Other advantages of the logarithmic approach are that the many manipulations of polar transfer functions, which required vector multiplication and division, reduce to simple addition and subtraction opera-

* Superior numbers, when they appear in the text proper, are the numbers of references given in the Bibliography.

240

tions. Also, the use of semilog paper serves to expand the low-frequency range, which often is of the most interest.

The information required for analysis and design using logarithmic methods is basically the same as that required for the polar plot. The transfer function of the system is needed, together with the numerical values associated with the system parameters. Gain constants would be required for analysis, but not for design, just as in using the polar plot.

12-2. Mathematical and Graphical Relationships. The general equation for the transfer function of a servomechanism can be written as the ratio of two polynomials,

$$KG(j\omega) = K \frac{(j\omega\tau_1 + 1)(j\omega\tau_2 + 1) \cdots}{(j\omega)^N(j\omega\tau_a + 1)(j\omega\tau_b + 1) \cdots} \qquad (12\text{-}1)$$

Taking logarithms of both sides of this equation, and expressing the results in decibels, gives

$$20 \log_{10} KG(j\omega) = 20 \log_{10} K + 20 \log_{10} (j\omega\tau_1 + 1)$$
$$+ 20 \log_{10} (j\omega\tau_2 + 1) + \cdots - 20 \log_{10} (j\omega)^N - 20 \log_{10} (j\omega\tau_a + 1)$$
$$- 20 \log_{10} (j\omega\tau_b + 1) - \cdots \qquad (12\text{-}2)$$

so that the logarithm of the transfer function is merely the algebraic sum of the logarithms of its factors.

Equation (12-2) contains the logarithms of complex quantities and so is more conveniently handled as two separate relationships, one involving magnitudes and a second involving just the phase angle. These relationships are

$$20 \log_{10} |KG(j\omega)| = 20 \log_{10} K + 20 \log_{10} |j\omega\tau_1 + 1| + \cdots$$
$$- 20 \log_{10} |\omega^N| - 20 \log_{10} |j\omega\tau_a + 1| - \cdots \qquad (12\text{-}3)$$
$$\underline{/KG(j\omega)} = 0 + \tan^{-1} \omega\tau_1 + \tan^{-1} \omega\tau_2 + \cdots - N(90°)$$
$$- \tan^{-1} \omega\tau_a - \tan^{-1} \omega\tau_b - \cdots \qquad (12\text{-}4)$$

Equation (12-3) relates the logarithm of the magnitude of the transfer function to the frequency, while (12-4) relates the phase angle of the transfer function to the frequency.

These equations may then be plotted as separate curves which are functions of the frequency, ω;

    a. Log of the magnitude of $KG(j\omega)$ (in decibels) vs. log ω.

    b. Phase angle of $KG(j\omega)$ (in degrees or radians) vs. log ω.

Alternatively, a single curve may be plotted with frequency as a parameter.

    c. Log of magnitude of $KG(j\omega)$ (in decibels) vs. phase angle of $KG(j\omega)$ in degrees or radians.

    d. Log of magnitude of $KG(j\omega)$ in decibels vs. phase margin of $KG(j\omega)$. Curve *d* is identical with *c* except for the abscissa scale.

Curves *a* and *b* are of primary value in *analyzing* servomechanism performance and obtaining a qualitative understanding of the logarithmic approach to the design or modification of a system and are also used to a large extent in quantitative design. The concepts of gain margin and phase margin, used for stability determination, are also most conveniently defined if the logarithms of the magnitude and the phase angle are plotted

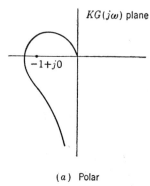

(*a*) Polar

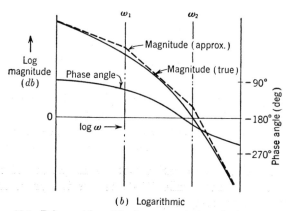

(*b*) Logarithmic

FIG. 12-1. Polar and logarithmic representation of a type 1 system.

versus log ω. Curves of type *c* and *d*, however, are of value in carrying out the quantitative design of a servomechanism to more precise specifications.

Figures 12-1*a* and *b* illustrate the polar plot of a type 1 system and its equivalent logarithmic plots. The asymptotic approximation to the actual log-magnitude curve is shown dotted. Methods for determining the location of frequencies, ω_1 and ω_2, and the slope of asymptotes as in Fig. 12-1*b* are discussed in the following section. A method for predicting stability from the logarithmic plot will also be established. Discussion of log of magnitude vs. phase-angle and phase-margin curves is reserved until later.

12-3. Linear Asymptote Approximation of Log-magnitude Curves. Perhaps the prime advantage of using logarithmic plots of the system transfer functions is that linear asymptotic approximations can be made to the actual curves. This greatly reduces the labor of plotting curves, for a few "significant" frequencies may be selected and connected together by appropriately sloping lines. The selection of these important frequencies and the determination of the slope of the lines are dependent upon the number, nature, and weight of each transfer-function factor. These are now considered for several typical system factors. The accuracy of approximate curves is subsequently studied.

a. For frequency invariant factors as K, $\log_{10} K = C$; then

$$20 \log_{10} K = 20C \qquad \text{db}$$

This plots as a horizontal straight line, independent of ω, as shown in Fig. 12-2a.

b. For terms of the form $(j\omega\tau_1 + 1)$, if $j\omega\tau_1 \ll 1$,

$$20 \log_{10} |j\omega\tau_1 + 1| = 20 \log_{10} 1.0 = 0 \text{ db}$$

and if $j\omega\tau_1 \gg 1$,

$$20 \log_{10} |j\omega\tau_1 + 1| = 20 \log_{10} |j\omega\tau_1| = +6 \text{ db/octave*}$$

so that the term $(j\omega\tau_1 + 1)$ may be represented by two straight-line asymptotes: a horizontal line at 0 db for low frequencies, and a line of $+6$ db/octave at high frequencies. These two lines intersect, or "break," at a frequency ω_1 such that $\omega_1\tau_1 = 1$, as shown in Fig. 12-2b.

c. For terms of the form $1/(j\omega\tau_a + 1)$, if $\omega\tau_a \ll 1$, then

$$-20 \log_{10} |j\omega\tau_a + 1| = -20 \log_{10} 1.0 = 0 \text{ db}$$

and if $\omega\tau_a \gg 1$,

$$-20 \log_{10} |j\omega\tau_a + 1| = -20 \log_{10} |j\omega\tau_a| = -6 \text{ db/octave}$$

which plots as two straight lines, intersecting at $\omega = 1/\tau_a$, as shown in Fig. 12-2c.

d. For terms of the form, $j\omega\tau$ or $1/j\omega\tau$, then $\pm 20 \log_{10} |j\omega\tau|$ has a ± 6 db/octave slope with a value of 0 db at some frequency, ω, such that $\omega\tau = 1$ as shown in Fig. 12-2d.

---

* It is readily shown that the slope is 6 db/octave:
If $\omega\tau_1 = 1$, then $20 \log_{10}(1) = 0$ db
If $\omega\tau_1 = 2$, then $20 \log_{10}(2) = 6.02$ db
If $\omega\tau_1 = 4$, then $20 \log_{10}(4) = 12.05$ db
which is a change, or slope, of 6 db/octave.

e. If any of the frequency-dependent factors is repeated, *i.e.*, if there are two or more identical time constants in the system, then the slope of

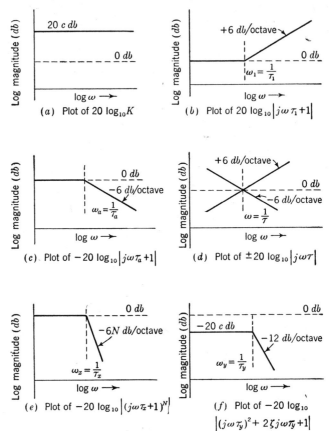

Fig. 12-2. Typical asymptotic log-magnitude vs. log-frequency plots.

the high-frequency asymptote is multiplied by the number of such factors; *i.e.*, if $\omega\tau_x \ll 1$, then

$$-20 \log_{10} |j\omega\tau_x + 1)^N| = -20 \log_{10} 1 = 0 \text{ db}$$

but for $\omega\tau_x \gg 1$,

$$-20 \log_{10} |(j\omega\tau_x + 1)^N| = -20 \log_{10} |j\omega\tau_x|^N$$
$$= -20N \log_{10} |j\omega\tau_x| = -6N \quad \text{db/octave}$$

so that the high-frequency asymptote has a slope of $-6N$ db/octave as shown in Fig. 12-2e.

f. For terms of form $1/[(j\omega\tau_y)^2 + 2\zeta j\omega\tau_y + 1]$, whose roots ordinarily are complex, several points must be plotted in order to obtain an accurate approximation.

1. If $\omega\tau_y \ll 1$ (where $\zeta < 1$),

$$-20 \log_{10} |(j\omega\tau_y)^2 + 2\zeta j\omega\tau_y + 1| \cong -20 \log_{10} 1.0 = 0 \text{ db}$$

2. For $\omega\tau_y \gg 1$, the value becomes

$$-20 \log_{10} |(j\omega\tau_y)^2| = -12 \text{ db/octave}$$

The typical plot of such a quadratic factor is illustrated in Fig. 12-2f.

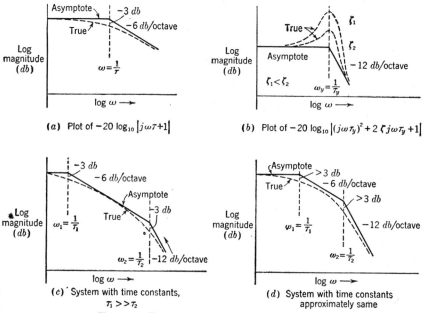

(a) Plot of $-20 \log_{10} |j\omega\tau + 1|$

(b) Plot of $-20 \log_{10} |(j\omega\tau_y)^2 + 2\zeta j\omega\tau_y + 1|$

(c) System with time constants, $\tau_1 \gg \tau_2$

(d) System with time constants approximately same

Fig. 12-3. Errors in asymptotic approximations.

12-4. Accuracy of Asymptotic Representation.

The accuracy with which the asymptotes approximate the true plot is readily checked:

a. A term such as $20 \log_{10} K$ is exact.

b. Terms such as $\mp 20 \log_{10} |j\omega\tau + 1|$ are not exact, and have their greatest error at the break frequency, which is $\omega = 1/\tau$. At this frequency the true value of the term is

$$\mp 20 \log_{10} |j1 + 1| = \mp 20 \log_{10} \sqrt{2} = \mp 3 \text{ db}$$

The true plot is then as shown in the dotted curve of Fig. 12-3a. At 1 octave above and below the break frequency the error is 1 db.

c. When quadratic terms are encountered, the greatest error is also at the break point. The magnitude of the quadratic term is in general $\mp 20 \log_{10} \sqrt{(1 - \omega^2\tau_y^2)^2 + (2\zeta\omega\tau_y)^2}$, and the value of this obviously depends on the value of ζ. The general shape of the true curve is indicated by the dotted line in Fig. 12-3b. It should be noted that appreciable error from the asymptotes exists over a considerable frequency range, and therefore the straight-line approximation is not too satisfactory.

d. When a system has several time delays, so that its equation is of the form

$$20 \log_{10} |KG(j\omega)|$$
$$= 20 \log_{10} K - 20 \log_{10} |j\omega\tau_1 + 1| - 20 \log_{10} |j\omega\tau_2 + 1| - \cdots$$

then in general if $\tau_1 \gg \tau_2$, the asymptotes are sufficiently accurate for most purposes, as shown in Fig. 12-3c. On the other hand, if τ_1 and τ_2 are not greatly different, the curves may not approach their asymptotes rapidly enough and the error at the break points may be greater than 3 db, as shown in Fig. 12-3d. (This would also be true if factors appeared in the numerator.)

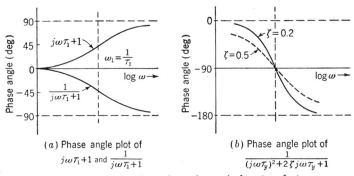

(a) Phase angle plot of
$$j\omega\tau_1 + 1 \text{ and } \frac{1}{j\omega\tau_1 + 1}$$

(b) Phase angle plot of
$$\frac{1}{(j\omega\tau_y)^2 + 2\zeta j\omega\tau_y + 1}$$

Fig. 12-4. Phase angle vs. log ω for typical system factors.

12-5. Plotting of Phase Angle vs. log ω. No simple linear approximations can be made to plot the phase angle of the respective transfer-function factors considered. Some short cuts may be realized in the case of complicated transfer functions, however, by weighing the various time constants. The labor in obtaining a composite phase-angle plot is not excessive, anyway, as the phase angles of the various factors need only be added algebraically. A few examples are:

1. For terms of the form $(j\omega\tau_1 + 1)$ and $1/(j\omega\tau_1 + 1)$ the phase-angle plots are indicated in Fig. 12-4a. Note that at $\omega\tau_1 = 1$, the phase angle is ± 45 deg; at low frequencies, the phase angle approaches zero while at high frequencies it approaches 90 deg.

2. For factors of the form $1/[(j\omega\tau_y)^2 + 2\zeta j\omega\tau_y + 1]$ typical phase-angle plots are shown in Fig. 12-4b. Note that the phase angle is a function of ζ.

12-6. Plotting and Basic Interpretation of Log-magnitude vs. log ω and Phase-angle vs. log ω Curves. The determination of stability and of general servomechanism performance from log-magnitude vs. log ω plots requires that the phase-angle vs. log ω curve be drawn on the same coordinate axis and that the 0-db axis of the log-magnitude curve coincide with the -180-deg phase-angle axis. An illustration of such a plot is given in Fig. 12-5.

The location of the phase-angle plot in Fig. 12-5 is fixed by the system $G(j\omega)$ equation and can be altered only by changes in the frequency-dependent components of the system. Such changes are usually accomplished by compensation when needed. The log-magnitude locus, on the other hand, is controlled by the gain of the system as well as by the components. For example, if curve a in Fig. 12-5 represents the system

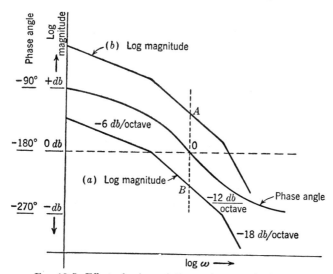

Fig. 12-5. Effect of gain variation on log-magnitude plot.

locus for unity gain, then a gain increase would shift the entire log-magnitude locus upward to a location such as curve b, because multiplying by a gain constant greater than 1 is equivalent to adding decibels to the log magnitude.

Two valuable concepts readily defined from logarithmic plots of magnitude and phase vs. log ω are the concepts of gain margin and phase margin. The concept of phase margin is perhaps more useful than that of gain margin. Referring to the polar plot (see Fig. 12-6a), phase margin is defined as the angle between the KG vector of unit length and the negative real axis. Thus in Fig. 12-6a the phase margin for curve a is ϕ_a and is defined to be positive, while for curve b the phase margin is ϕ_b and is defined to be negative. In other words, the phase margin is the amount of negative phase shift which would have to be introduced into the system to set the performance at the stability limit (assuming no additional attenuation). Since $|KG| = 1$ corresponds to 0 db on the logarithmic plot, the phase angle of the system for the frequency corresponding to 0 db gain, subtracted from 180 deg, is the phase margin of the system as shown in Fig. 12-6b, *i.e.*, the phase margin is the minimum amount of phase shift required to make a stable system unstable. For satisfactory performance the phase margin should be greater than 30

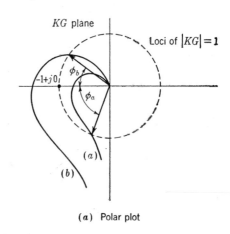

(*a*) Polar plot

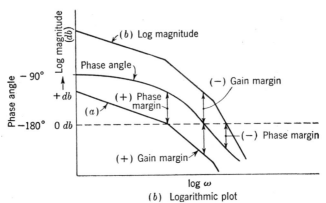

(*b*) Logarithmic plot

FIG. 12-6. Polar and logarithmic plots of stable and unstable single-loop servo.

deg, usually more than 45 deg. Critical damping is normally obtained with a phase margin of about 60 deg.

Gain margin may be defined as the factor by which the gain must be raised to make the system unstable (positive gain margin) or the factor by which the gain must be decreased to make the system stable (negative gain margin). In terms of Fig. 12-6a, the system represented by curve *a* is stable but can be made unstable by increasing the gain until the locus point on the negative real axis falls on the $-1 + j0$ point.

This is equivalent to saying that the system becomes unstable when the transfer function vector having 180 deg phase lag also has unit length.

In terms of the logarithmic plot of Fig. 12-6b, the gain margin is the number of decibels by which the magnitude curve must be raised (or lowered) to make the gain crossover coincide with the phase crossover. If these crossover points coincide, then at the frequency corresponding to the crossover point the phase angle is 180 deg and the magnitude of the vector is unity.

Once the control system has been found stable, meaning that positive gain and phase margins exist, attention must be given to the system accuracy, errors, speed of response, etc. The existence and approximate magnitude of steady state and transient errors can be found from a study of the log-magnitude vs. log ω plots. In general, the steady-state errors may be determined with reasonable accuracy from the log plots, but only approximate values of certain transient errors can be found. Hence, where accurate determination of transient performance is required, the differential equations of the system must be set up and solved. Ordinarily the demands on system performance data are not so exacting as to require the latter. If the system is complex and accurate transient data are required, the system may be referred to an analogue computer.

12-7. Steady-state Performance—Existence of Steady-state Errors. The existence of steady-state errors can be determined directly from the log-magnitude vs. log ω curve by noting the initial slope of the log-magnitude plot. This may be proved by taking the logarithm of the general servomechanism equation and letting $\omega \to 0$. Interest is focused on the low-frequency spectra much the same as was done for the polar plots. The general equation of any servomechanism is of the form

$$KG(j\omega) = \frac{K(j\omega\tau_1 + 1)(j\omega\tau_2 + 1) \cdots}{(j\omega)^N(j\omega\tau_a + 1)(j\omega\tau_b + 1) \cdots} \qquad (12\text{-}1)$$

If the system is type 0, then $N = 0$, and as $\omega \to 0$, the equation reduces to $KG(j\omega) = K$. Then $20 \log_{10} K$ is a constant, and the slope of the low-frequency end of the log-magnitude vs. log ω plot is zero. Thus a horizontal line at lowest frequencies represents a type 0 system with inherent position error. For a type 1 system, $N = 1$, and as $\omega \to 0$, the transfer function reduces to $20 \log_{10} |KG(j\omega)| = 20 \log_{10} K - 20 \log_{10} |j\omega|$, so that the slope is -6 db/octave. Thus a negative 6 db/octave slope at lowest frequencies indicates a type 1 system with no static position error but with velocity-lag error and acceleration errors. In like manner it can be shown that a -12 db/octave initial slope represents a type 2 system; a -18 db/octave represents a type 3 system, etc. Figure 12-7 shows the typical initial slopes.

12-8. Steady-state Performance—Magnitude of Steady-state Errors.
Type 0.   For a type 0 system a static position error is known to exist.

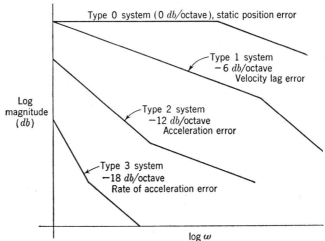

Fig. 12-7. Steady-state error identification from log plots.

The approximate position error accompanying an input displacement, θ_i, may be calculated as follows:

1. The system gain in decibels is read from the curve—this is the value of gain for the low-frequency portion of the locus.

2. The gain constant, K, is obtained by taking the antilog.

3. At $\omega = 0$ the transfer function is

$$KG(j\omega) = \frac{\theta_o}{\varepsilon} = K$$

but

$$\theta_o = \theta_i - \varepsilon$$

and so

$$\varepsilon = \frac{\theta_i}{K + 1} \tag{12-5}$$

Then for a known input displacement, θ_i, the static position error may be calculated.

Type 1.   For a type 1 system there is inherently no static position error, but if the system is operated at constant velocity, it has a position error which is called a velocity-lag error.   The magnitude of this error is of course dependent on the input velocity.   In general, then, for constant-velocity operation

$$\frac{d\theta_o/dt}{\varepsilon} = \frac{d\theta_i/dt}{\varepsilon} = \frac{\omega_i}{\varepsilon} = K \tag{12-6}$$

In the notation of the Laplace transform, $d\theta_o/dt = j\omega\theta_o$, and constant-velocity operation (at any velocity) corresponds to $j\omega = 0$ for the transform variable. Then

$$K = \frac{\omega_i}{\varepsilon} = \frac{j\omega\theta_o}{\varepsilon} = j\omega[KG(j\omega)]_{j\omega\to0} = j\omega\frac{K(j\omega\tau_a + 1)\cdots}{j\omega(j\omega\tau_1 + 1)\cdots}\bigg|_{j\omega\to0} = K_v \quad (12\text{-}7)$$

where the notation K_v is used to represent a *velocity* constant, since a type 1 system inherently operates at a constant velocity when an error signal of constant magnitude is applied. The steady-state velocity-lag error is then

$$\varepsilon_{ss} = \frac{j\omega\theta_o}{K_v} = \frac{\omega_i}{K_v} \quad (12\text{-}8)$$

and if K_v is determined from the log-magnitude vs. log ω plot, the steady-state velocity-lag error may be calculated.

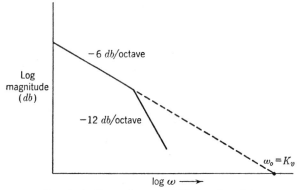

Fig. 12-8. Determination of K_v from log plot.

The velocity constant, K_v, may be obtained by extrapolating the -6 db/octave initial segment of the locus until it intercepts the 0-db axis. The value of the frequency intercept, ω_o, is read from the scale, and numerically $\omega_o = K_v$. This is shown in Fig. 12-8. The justification of this is as follows: At low frequencies ($j\omega \to 0$), which region indicates the steady-state performance of the system, and the transfer function reduces to

$$KG(j\omega) = \frac{K_v}{j\omega} \quad (12\text{-}9)$$

In logarithmic notation then

$$20 \log_{10} |KG(j\omega)| = 20 \log_{10} K_v - 20 \log_{10} |j\omega| \quad (12\text{-}10)$$

Arbitrarily setting $20 \log_{10} |KG(j\omega)| = 0$ gives

$$0 = 20 \log_{10} K_v - 20 \log_{10} |j\omega| \quad (12\text{-}11)$$

from which K_v equals that value of ω which makes

$$20 \log_{10} |KG(j\omega)| = 0 \text{ db} \qquad (12\text{-}10)$$

in the low-frequency equation. This is obviously the intercept of the -6 db/octave segment with the 0-db axis. Therefore

$$K_v = \omega_o \qquad (12\text{-}12)$$

Type 2. A type 2 system inherently has no static-position error and no velocity-lag error. Under constant acceleration, however, there is a position error which may be called an acceleration-lag error. By applying the same methods used for the type 1 system it is readily seen that

1. The low-frequency portion of the locus has a -12 db/octave slope.
2. The intercept of this portion of the locus (extrapolated if necessary) with the 0-db axis is at some frequency ω_a.
3. This frequency, ω_a, is numerically equal to the square root of the gain constant K_a; $(\omega_a{}^2 = K_a)$.
4. Then the acceleration-lag error under constant-acceleration operation is

$$\varepsilon_{ss} = \frac{A}{K} = \frac{A}{\omega_a{}^2} \qquad (12\text{-}13)$$

where A is the numerical value of the applied acceleration.

12-9. Transient Performance[29,67,69]—**Magnitude of Transient Error.** In any system, practical or hypothetical, transient errors are presupposed to exist whenever there is an input or output disturbance. In many applications, errors during transient periods are as important as steady-state errors. This is particularly true for type 1 systems, which operate at essentially constant velocity but undergo periods of acceleration. During such accelerations the error includes not only the velocity-lag error but an additional component due to the acceleration. An estimate of the error during such periods may be obtained by another simple manipulation on the log-magnitude vs. log ω plot. But first it will be shown that the total error is approximately the sum of the velocity lag and acceleration errors; then the graphical means for determining the error will be presented.

The general equation for a type 1 system is

$$KG(j\omega) = \frac{K_v(j\omega\tau_a + 1)(j\omega\tau_b + 1) \cdots}{j\omega(j\omega\tau_1 + 1)(j\omega\tau_2 + 1) \cdots} \qquad (12\text{-}14)$$

where in general τ_1 is the largest time constant in the denominator and usually is larger than any time constant in the numerator. Then for small values of ω this equation reduces approximately to

$$KG(j\omega) \cong \frac{K_v}{j\omega(j\omega\tau_1 + 1)} \cong \frac{\theta_o}{\varepsilon}(j\omega) \qquad (12\text{-}15)$$

Solving Eq. (12-15) for the error gives

$$\varepsilon(j\omega) \cong \frac{j\omega(j\omega\tau_1 + 1)}{K_v} \theta_o = \frac{(j\omega)^2\theta_o\tau_1}{K_v} + \frac{j\omega\theta_o}{K_v} \qquad (12\text{-}16)$$

By inverse Laplace transformation this reduces to

$$\varepsilon(t) \cong \frac{1}{K_v} \frac{d\theta_o}{dt} + \frac{\tau_1}{K_v} \frac{d^2\theta_o}{dt^2} \qquad (12\text{-}17)$$

which relates the error to the output velocity and acceleration. However, in any specific case the *input* velocity and acceleration are much more readily determined; so a desirable simplification is obtained by assuming $\theta_i \cong \theta_o$. Thus the error equation becomes

$$\varepsilon(t) \cong \frac{1}{K_v} \frac{d\theta_i}{dt} + \frac{\tau_1}{K_v} \frac{d^2\theta_i}{dt^2} \cong \frac{\omega_i}{K_v} + \frac{\tau_1 A_i}{K_v} \qquad (12\text{-}18)$$

where ω_i = input velocity
A_i = input acceleration

It is thus seen that the total error may be considered a sum of a velocity component and an acceleration component.

To evaluate the error, the input velocity ω_i and the input acceleration, A_i, must be known. The velocity constant K_v is evaluated as previously shown, so that $K_v = \omega_o$ is determined by extrapolating the $(-6$ db/octave) initial section of the locus to the 0-db axis. The only remaining factor to be evaluated is the time constant τ_1. It has already been shown that each time constant causes a break, or change, in slope in the log-magnitude vs. log ω plot. Since τ_1 is the largest time constant in the system, it causes the first, or lowest frequency, break in the locus. The value of τ_1 is then readily determined since $\omega_1 = 1/\tau_1$, where ω_1 is the frequency at which the initial break occurs. Thus by determining ω_o and ω_1 from the plot, the error is evaluated as

$$\varepsilon = \frac{\omega_i}{\omega_o} + \frac{A_i}{\omega_1\omega_o} \qquad (12\text{-}19)$$

If the curve is the result of experimental data so that the break point is not readily determined, the -12 db/octave slope may be extrapolated to the 0-db axis as shown in Fig. 12-9. It is readily shown that the frequency read at this intercept is $\omega_2 = \sqrt{\omega_o\omega_1}$, so that the error is then

$$\varepsilon = \frac{\omega_i}{\omega_o} + \frac{A_i}{\omega_2{}^2} \qquad (12\text{-}20)$$

This approximation of the total error is not accurate except under special conditions. For example, if the system is at rest and a step-velocity function is applied, then presumably the input acceleration is zero and the total error calculated from Eq. (12-19) or (12-20) would be just the velocity-lag error, which obviously is not correct for the transient condition. However, it is readily seen from the equations that if ω_o and ω_1 are large numbers, then the velocity error and the acceleration error must be small, and therefore the total error even during transient periods must be small. Thus the higher the intercept frequencies ω_1, ω_o, the more accurately are Eqs. (12-19) and (12-20) indicative of the transient error. (This implies that the system must have very high gain.)

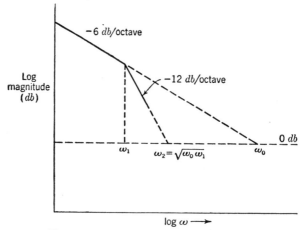

FIG. 12-9. Determination of transient error.

12-10. Transient Performance—System Damping and Resonant Frequency. If Eqs. (12-19) and (12-20) are to indicate transient errors, then the frequencies determined from the plot (ω_o, ω_1, ω_2) must be related to the coefficients of the differential equation, and it should therefore be possible to evaluate ζ and ω_n approximately from the log-magnitude vs. log ω plot. That this may be done for simple systems at least is shown as follows: Equation (12-17) is

$$\varepsilon = \frac{1}{K_v}\frac{d\theta_o}{dt} + \frac{\tau_1}{K_v}\frac{d^2\theta_o}{dt^2} \tag{12-17}$$

Substituting $\theta_o = \theta_i - \varepsilon$ and rearranging gives

$$\frac{d^2\varepsilon}{dt^2} + \frac{1}{\tau_1}\frac{d\varepsilon}{dt} + \frac{K_v}{\tau_1}\varepsilon = \frac{d^2\theta_i}{dt^2} + \frac{1}{\tau_1}\frac{d\theta_i}{dt} \tag{12-21}$$

But the normal form of the differential equation is

$$\frac{d^2\varepsilon}{dt^2} + \frac{f}{J}\frac{d\varepsilon}{dt} + \frac{K}{J}\varepsilon = \frac{d^2\theta_i}{dt^2} + \frac{f}{J}\frac{d\theta_i}{dt} \tag{12-22}$$

and upon equating coefficients it is seen that

$$\frac{1}{\tau_1} = \omega_1 = \frac{f}{J} \tag{12-23}$$

and

$$\frac{K_v}{\tau_1} = \omega_2{}^2 = \omega_o\omega_1 = \frac{K}{J} \tag{12-24}$$

from which

$$K_v = \left(\frac{K}{J}\right)\left(\frac{J}{f}\right) = \frac{K}{f} \tag{12-25}$$

Using the basic relationships for ζ and ω_n, it is seen that

$$\zeta = \frac{f}{2\sqrt{KJ}} = \frac{\omega_1 J}{2\sqrt{\omega_o\omega_1 J^2}} = \frac{1}{2}\sqrt{\frac{\omega_1}{\omega_o}} = \frac{\omega_1}{2\omega_2} \tag{12-26}$$

$$\omega_n = \sqrt{\frac{K}{J}} = \omega_o\omega_1 = \omega_2 \tag{12-27}$$

12-11. Gain Adjustment on Plots of Log Magnitude and Phase Angle vs. log ω. As seen in Fig. 12-5, the system depicted by curve b is unstable. This system could be stabilized by reducing the gain to some value corresponding to curve a. The gain adjustment required is determined by adding (arithmetically), the negative gain margin to the desired positive gain margin. That is, in Fig. 12-5, the desired gain reduction will be $AO + OB = AB$ db. The actual gain corresponding to this is then found by merely taking the antilog of $AB/20$.

It is obvious that a reduction in gain, though producing a stable condition, will result in an increase in existing steady-state and transient errors. At the same time the speed of response will be decreased, since the entire log-magnitude curve would be shifted downward (no change in shape), reducing the intercept frequencies ω_o, ω_1, and ω_2, which are indicative of the performance quality.

12-12. Series Compensation on the Log-magnitude Plot. When gain adjustment alone cannot provide stability or a desired compromise between transient and steady-state performance, the transfer-function locus must be reshaped by compensation. The principles of compensation are not changed by the use of logarithmic coordinates, but when log coordinates are employed, certain interpretations are available which are not readily shown by polar plots. In addition most of the methods used with polar diagrams are still applicable. The effect of compensating devices must be understood in terms of the changes they produce in the logarithmic loci. Therefore the logarithmic loci of typical compensating networks are derived first. Subsequently the change in shape of system loci when compensation is added will be studied. Suggested design methods for the selection of types of compensating networks and their parameters are presented in a later section.

The effect of compensating networks on system loci are best understood from their log-magnitude vs. log ω characteristics. The simple phase-lead and phase-lag devices have log-magnitude vs. log ω loci which may be approximated by linear asymptotes. This, of course, greatly simplifies the graphical constructions which are used in selecting a corrective network for a given situation.

(a) Circuit diagram

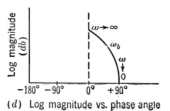

(d) Log magnitude vs. phase angle

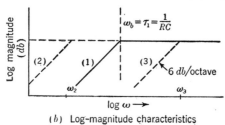

(b) Log-magnitude characteristics

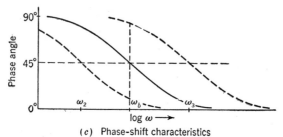

(c) Phase-shift characteristics

Fig. 12-10. Logarithmic characteristics of simple phase-lead network.

In general the simple phase-lead and phase-lag devices have log-magnitude loci which are characterized by two break points, with corresponding phase-shift characteristics limited to a small range of frequencies. Generally the shift is less than 90 deg. More complex compensating devices may have more break points, cover a larger frequency range, and produce much larger phase shifts. Only simple networks are discussed here since they are sufficient to illustrate the principles involved.

The simplest possible phase-shifting network consists of a single capacitor and a single resistor. It may be used as in Fig. 12-10a to produce a phase lead or as in Fig. 12-11a for phase lag. Ordinarily it would not be used in series compensation because it does not transmit the error signal under all conditions when used for phase lead. The main break point is at $\omega_b = 1/RC$, as shown in Fig. 12-10b. For frequencies above ω_b full output is obtained, but below ω_b the output is attenuated at 6 db/octave. The frequency of the break point may be shifted by changing the value of either R or C. Additional break points are indicated in Fig. 12-10b. The phase-shift curve of the phase-lead net is

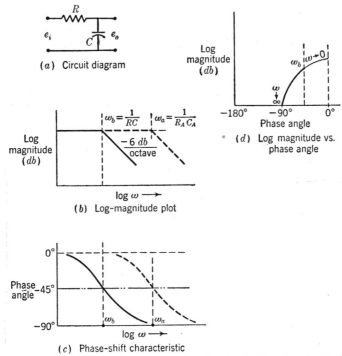

(a) Circuit diagram

(b) Log-magnitude plot

(c) Phase-shift characteristic

(d) Log magnitude vs. phase angle

FIG. 12-11. Logarithmic characteristics of a simple phase-lag circuit.

shown in Fig. 12-10c. It should be noted that the phase shift is approximately $+90$ deg for $\omega \ll \omega_b$, is $+45$ deg at $\omega = \omega_b$, and is 0 deg for $\omega \ll \omega_b$. The locus on the log-magnitude vs. phase-angle plot constructed from curves b and c is shown in Fig. 12-10d.

If the simple RC circuit is used for phase lag, the arrangement of Fig. 12-11a produces a break point at frequency ω_b, as shown in Fig. 12-11b. Again the break point may be shifted in frequency by varying R or C. In any case, for $\omega \ll \omega_b$ full output is obtained, and the slope of the locus is 0 db/octave. For $\omega \gg \omega_b$ the output decreases at -6 db/octave. A phase-shift curve is shown in Fig. 12-11c, and the log-magnitude vs. phase-angle plot is given in Fig. 12-11d.

A phase-lead circuit, suitable for series compensation, is shown in Fig. 12-12a. The attenuation vs. frequency, phase vs. frequency, and attenuation vs. phase characteristics are shown in Fig. 12-12b, c, and d. It may be seen from Fig. 12-12b that two finite break points occur at ω_1 and ω_2. Between these frequencies the output rises at $+6$ db/octave, while below ω_1 and above ω_2 the output is constant. It may also be seen from Fig. 12-12b that if the same time constant ($\tau_1 = R_1 C_1$) is used with various

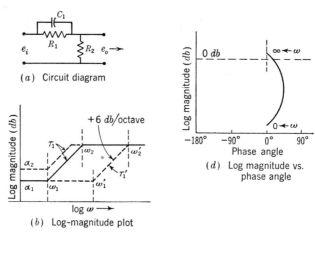

(a) Circuit diagram

(b) Log-magnitude plot

(d) Log magnitude vs. phase angle

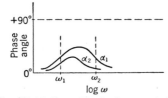

Fig. 12-12. Logarithmic characteristics of a practical phase-lead network.

values of $\alpha = R_1/(R_1 + R_2)$ the first break point does not shift frequency, whereas a change in time constant shifts the break point. Figure 12-12c shows that the phase angle is a function of α rather than τ_1, although changes in τ_1 affect the frequency range in which the phase shift occurs. It should be noted that there is appreciable phase shift at the break frequencies. Figure 12-12d shows the locus of the network on the log-magnitude vs. phase-angle plot.

Figure 12-13a shows a phase-lag circuit, suitable for series compensation. Its characteristics are shown in Figs. 12-13b, c, and d. Note that two break points exist, that their frequencies may be adjusted by altering the time constant, and that the attenuation between break points is -6 db/octave.

12-13. Generalized Method for Selecting Compensation from Log-magnitude vs. log ω Plots. The steps outlined below assume that log-magnitude vs. log ω and phase-angle vs. log ω plots have been made for the uncompensated servomechanism.

1. Select the proper type of network for the compensation desired (phase lead or lag) by noting the phase and gain margins existing and those desired.

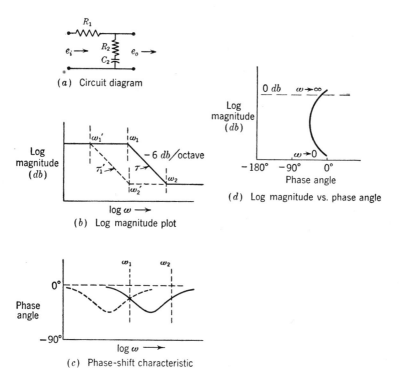

(a) Circuit diagram

(b) Log magnitude plot

(c) Phase-shift characteristic

(d) Log magnitude vs. phase angle

Fig. 12-13. Logarithmic characteristics of a practical phase-lag network.

2. Determine the frequency range over which compensation is needed. This is generally the range extending between the gain and phase cross-overs.

3. Construct the log-magnitude and phase-angle vs. log ω characteristics of the network selected (using the same scales as for the uncompensated loci).

4. Add, algebraically, the log-magnitude plots and phase-angle plots of compensator and servo system to get the compensated loci. Simple algebraic combination assumes that the compensating network characteristics are not altered by cascading with the system, and isolating amplifiers may be required in the actual system.

5. Compare resultant gain and phase margins with desired, and increase gain as much as is consistent with specified steady-state and transient performance.

6. Change the type of network if the compromise between desired steady-state performance and transient performance cannot be reached.

12-14. Effect of Phase-lead Compensation on System Loci. Consider the system of Fig. 10-9, and assume that the gain is sufficiently

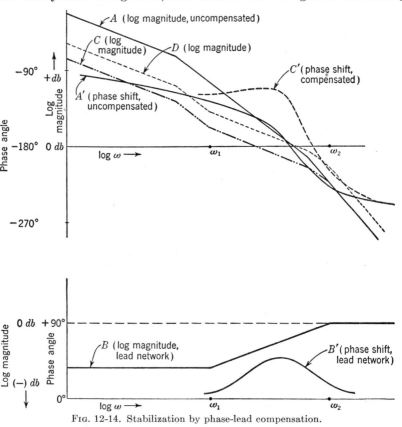

FIG. 12-14. Stabilization by phase-lead compensation.

high to make the system unstable. The loci of the uncompensated system are shown in Fig. 12-14, curves A and A'. The fact that the system is unstable may be seen from the phase margin. If a series phase-lead network such as that of Fig. 12-12 is chosen for compensation, it would normally be designed to produce a positive phase shift in the frequency range of the gain and phase crossovers. This phase shift moves the phase crossover to a higher frequency, while the attenuation of the lead network moves the gain crossover to a lower frequency, thus tending to produce a reasonable phase margin. Curves B and B' show possible loci for a phase-lead compensator. By algebraically combining A and B, A' and B', the loci for the compensated system C and C' are obtained. In general, it is possible to increase the gain of the system to counteract some of the attenuation introduced by the compensator. This does not alter the phase characteristic but moves the gain locus to a new position, such as curve D, which gives an acceptable phase margin.

Inspection of curves A and D in Fig. 12-14 readily shows that the compensated system has been stabilized by the addition of the phase-lead network. However, the velocity-lag error has been increased and the natural frequency decreased; thus both transient and steady-state performance have been slightly impaired in obtaining stability. This may be seen by checking the intercepts of the -6 db/octave and -12 db/octave sections of the loci. For the compensated system both intercepts have moved to lower frequencies. This would be expected for the particular case shown in Fig. 12-14, as the over-all gain could not be returned to its original value and still maintain a suitable phase margin. This net decrease in gain is the reason for the increased velocity-lag error and decreased natural frequency.

In the more usual case of phase-lead compensation the system may not be completely unstable but might have an excessive resonance peak as indicated by inadequate phase and gain margins. Under these conditions phase-lead compensation is used to increase the phase margin; then, in general, it is possible to increase the over-all loop gain so as to reduce the velocity-lag error, increase the natural frequency, and decrease acceleration errors. Figure 12-15 shows the loci for a stable system with a small phase margin. The system represented is essentially that considered in Fig. 12-14, but with different time constants. In Fig. 12-15, curves A and A' are the original magnitude and phase loci, B and B' are the loci of the chosen phase-lead compensator, and C and C' represent the compensated system. The remaining curve, D, is the magnitude locus of the compensated system with increased gain.

The increase in phase margin, which was the objective of compensation, is apparent by comparing the compensated and uncompensated phase and gain crossovers. The intercepts of the -6 db/octave and -12 db/octave asymptotes have been shifted to higher frequencies (ω_o compensated $> \omega_o$ uncompensated; ω_1 compensated $> \omega_1$ uncompensated); therefore the steady state and transient errors are reduced. The system natural frequency is raised accordingly so that the response is speeded up.

12-15. Effect of Phase-lag Compensation on System Loci. In many cases the specification of minimum velocity-lag error cannot be satisfied through the use of phase-lead compensation, and so phase-lag compensation similar to that of Fig. 12-13 is frequently used. The phase-lag network is generally designed to alter the phase characteristics of the system at the low-frequency end of the spectrum as illustrated by the dotted curve in Fig. 12-13c and so does not shift the phase crossover appreciably. The attenuation of the compensator will, however, be greatest in the higher frequency range, *i.e.*, in the region of the gain and phase crossover. This tends to shift the gain crossover to lower frequencies (see the attenuation curve of Fig. 12-16), making possible an increase in over-all system gain which in turn reduces the velocity-lag error without sacrificing the necessary phase margin. Possibly the only

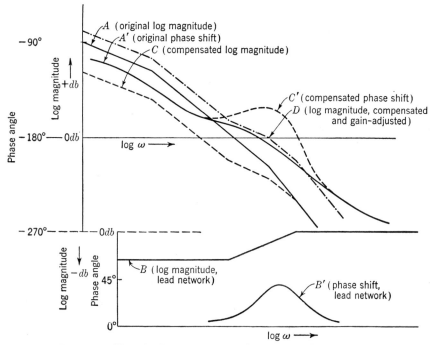

Fig. 12-15. Phase-lead compensation to improve transient response.

disadvantage of phase-lag compensation of such a system is the reduction of the system's natural frequency and attendant increase in acceleration errors and reduced speed of response. Naturally, some compromise in steady-state or transient performance must often be made, or else a corrective network having both phase-lead and -lag characteristics must be introduced.

Figure 12-16 illustrates the use of phase-lag compensation. Curves *A* and *A'* are the magnitude and phase loci of the same system represented in Fig. 12-15. The gain of the system has been raised to reduce the velocity-lag error to the desired minimum, and consequently the gain crossover is at a negative phase margin, indicating that the system is unstable. By introducing a phase-lag device with gain and phase characteristics as shown by curves B and B', the gain crossover is shifted to a lower frequency, and an acceptable positive phase margin is obtained as shown by the curves C and C' for the compensated system.

It may be seen from curve C of Fig. 12-16 that the transient performance has been considerably impaired by the phase-lag compensation. The initial slope of -6 db/octave has been kept at the same location; so extrapolation of this initial line produces the same intercept for

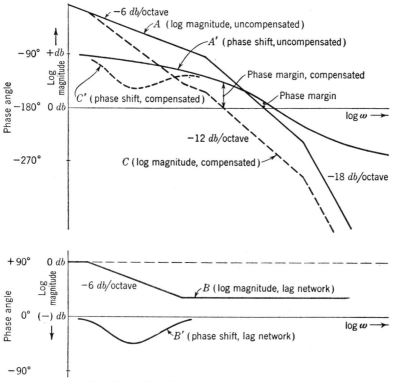

Fig. 12-16. Phase-lag compensation of system.

both the compensated and uncompensated systems. The steady-state velocity-lag error is therefore maintained at the desired value. However, in the compensated system that portion of the locus which has the first -12 db/octave slope has been moved to much lower frequencies and when extrapolated gives a low-frequency intercept. Since this intercept determines both the resonant frequency and the acceleration errors of the system, it is readily seen that the speed of response is decreased and the acceleration errors are increased.

12-16. Summary. Unstable systems may be stabilized through the use of either phase-lag or phase-lead compensation. Phase-lead networks accomplish this by shifting the phase crossover to a higher frequency and the gain crossover to a lower frequency. Phase-lag networks stabilize a system, normally, by shifting just the gain crossover to a lower frequency; the phase crossover of the system is not appreciably affected. For these reasons it may be seen that transient performance is improved but the expected steady-state errors are increased if a system, initially unstable, is stabilized by phase-lead compensation. On the other hand, if phase-lag compensation is employed, the steady-state performance can be noticeably improved by the allowable gain increases. The quality of transient performance (overshoot and speed of response) may be slightly reduced, however, in spite of these attendant gain increases.

Improvement in the transient performance of a stable system by phase-lead compensation is quite adequate. The acceleration errors are reduced and speed of response improved, and even some reduction in steady-state velocity lag error may be possible. But for appreciable reduction in the steady-state velocity-lag error of a stable system, phase-lag networks ordinarily are more suitable than phase-lead, provided the resultant transient performance is still acceptable.

12-17. Introduction to Log-magnitude vs. Phase-angle Plots. While manipulations on the log-magnitude vs. log ω plots permit adjustment of steady-state performance and give some indication of expected transient errors, more specific information is often desirable concerning the actual resonant frequency, ω_r, the associated resonance peak, M_p, and the range of frequencies in which compensation will be most effective. Most of this information was made available in polar-plot studies through the development and use of M-circle criteria. It is therefore logical to assume that if M circles can be transferred to the logarithmic plots, essentially the same principles of interpretation could be used for quantitative evaluation of servo performance. It has been found that M contours (logarithmic equivalents of the M circles) are most readily transferred to log-magnitude vs. phase-angle plots. This latter curve is a composite of the log-magnitude vs. log ω and phase-angle vs. log ω plots studied thus far. A system-response curve of this type is shown in Fig. 12-17.

Thus if a single curve is plotted of log magnitude vs. phase angle, with frequency, ω, as a parameter, the transient characteristics, frequency-response data, and proper system compensation will be more readily determined. It is convenient when the scale for the phase angle is set up to add a second scale of phase margin (also shown in Fig. 12-17). The phase margin may then be read directly from the intersection of the locus with the 0-db axis, and the gain margin may be read at the intersection of the locus with the zero-phase-margin axis.

12-18. Stability from Log-magnitude vs. Phase-angle Plot. Absolute stability may be determined directly from log-magnitude vs. phase-angle plots by noting the gain and phase margins existing for the given locus. In Fig. 12-18 are shown log-phase (abbreviated form of log of magnitude vs. phase angle to be used throughout remainder of chapter) plots of stable and unstable systems. Curve *a* depicts a stable system; curve *b* represents one that is unstable.

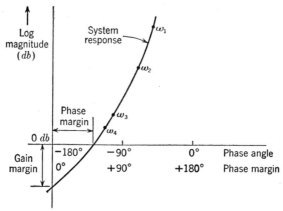

FIG. 12-17. Plot of log magnitude vs. phase angle.

If the definitions of gain and phase margin are reconsidered, as formulated for log-magnitude vs. log ω and phase-angle vs. log ω loci, a simple criterion for stability determination from log-phase plots can be established. Obviously, for curve *a*, the gain would have to be increased in order to move the gain crossover to -180 deg. Or considering the phase

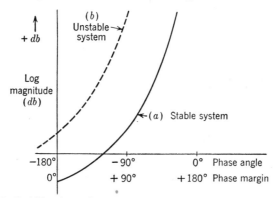

FIG. 12-18. Stability determination from log-magnitude vs. phase-angle locus.

angle, the phase crossover at unity gain is less than -180 deg, so that additional *negative* phase shift would be necessary to shift the locus to -180 deg. Therefore, since both the gain and phase margins are positive, the system corresponding to curve *a* is stable. For curve *b*, it is apparent that the converse is true: both the gain and phase margins are negative; therefore the system is unstable. If the log-phase curve passed through the intersection of the coordinate axis, a borderline stability condition would exist because the gain would be exactly unity at -180 deg phase shift. On a polar plot such a condition corresponds to the KG locus passing through the critical $-1 + j0$ point.

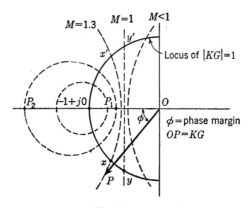

(a) M circles on polar plane

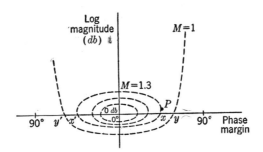

(b) M contours on log-magnitude vs.
phase-margin plot

FIG. 12-19. Comparison of M circles and M contours.

Briefly the stability criteria for log magnitude vs. phase angle or phase margin *curves* is this: A system is stable if its log-phase plot intersects the 0-db axis to the right of the zero-phase-margin axis.

12-19. Construction of M Contours. The procedures involved in transforming the M circles which are used on the polar plot into M contours on the log-phase plot are indicated in Fig. 12-19. The actual computation of M contours is best carried out from equations which will be derived subsequently; so Fig. 12-19 is used only for explanatory purposes. In Fig. 12-19 point P is selected on a given M circle. The vector OP is then KG. For the P selected, $|OP| = |KG| > 1$, so that

20 $\log_{10} |KG|$ is greater than 0 db and would be evaluated by taking an accurate measurement of the length OP. The angle between OP and the negative real axis is the phase margin, ϕ, and would be measured. These two values are then coordinates of the point P on the log-magnitude vs. phase-angle (or phase-margin) plot. The point P is located as in Fig. 12-19b as one point on the M contour. The point P is then allowed to assume a number of other locations on the same M circles, and other points on the M contour may be obtained by repeating the procedure.

A general idea of the shape and limited symmetry of the M contours may be obtained from further inspection of Fig. 12-19:

a. All M contours must cross the 0-db axis twice, since all points for which $|KG| = 1$ are at 0 db, and there are two such points on each M circle corresponding to intersections of $KG = 1$ radii and each M circle.

b. All points enclosed within the locus of $|KG| = 1$ have log values <0 db, and since relatively few of the points on the M circles are within this locus, only a minor portion of the M-contour plot is below 0 db.

c. For $M > 1$, every M contour crosses the zero-phase-margin axis twice. This may be seen from points P_1 and P_2 in Fig. 12-19a. On the other hand, for $M \leq 1$ the M contours cross the zero-phase-margin axis only once.

d. Since the M circles are not symmetrical with respect to the locus of $KG = 1$, the M contours are not symmetrical with respect to the 0-db axis. However, the M circles are symmetrical with respect to the negative real axis; so the M contours are symmetrical with respect to the zero-phase-margin axis.

The equations used to calculate the M contours may be derived as follows: Figure 12-20a shows an M circle with the location of the center and the radius expressed in terms of M. A point $P(x,y)$ is selected on the M circle so that $|OP| = |KG|$ and the angle ϕ between OP and the negative real axis is the phase margin. Then the equation of the circle in rectangular coordinates is

$$\left(\frac{M}{M^2 - 1}\right)^2 = \left(x + \frac{M^2}{M^2 - 1}\right)^2 + y^2 \qquad (12\text{-}28)$$

where
$$x = OP \cos \phi$$
$$y = OP \sin \phi \qquad (12\text{-}29)$$

Substituting,

$$\left(\frac{M}{M^2 - 1}\right)^2 = \left(OP \cos \phi + \frac{M^2}{M^2 - 1}\right)^2 + (OP \sin \phi)^2 \qquad (12\text{-}30)$$

and solving for OP gives

$$|KG| = |OP| = \frac{-M^2 \cos \phi}{M^2 - 1} \mp \sqrt{\frac{M^4 \cos^2 \phi}{(M^2 - 1)^2} - \frac{M^2}{M^2 - 1}} \qquad (12\text{-}31)$$

To plot the M contour, a value is chosen for M and substituted in Eq. 12-31; this expresses $|KG| = |OP|$ in terms of the phase margin ϕ. A series of values of ϕ are then substituted, and the resulting numbers are expressed in decibels and plotted against ϕ.

The M contours may be represented by the usual numbers applied on the polar diagram (that is, $M = 1.0, 1.1, 1.3$, etc.), but it is more common to express these on the logarithmic plot in terms of decibels. Thus the notation for $M = 1$ is 0 db, and for other values of M as shown in Table 12-1.

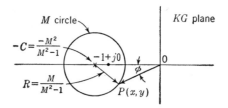

(a) M-circle relationships

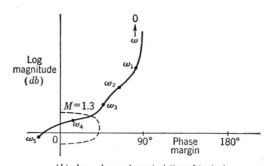

(b) Log-phase characteristics of typical
system showing M-contour application

Fig. 12-20. Derivation and application of M contours.

12-20. Use of M Contours—General. The M contours are used to determine the resonance peak of a given system by constructing a family of M contours on the log-phase plot of the system of interest and noting to which contour the log-phase characteristic is tangent. The frequency at the point of tangency is then the resonant frequency, ω_r, of the system. From this, some indication is given of the system speed of response. The frequency-response characteristics (θ_o/θ_i) may also be plotted by noting the frequencies at which the log-phase locus intersects the various M contours and plotting M vs. ω. M contours prove to be especially valuable in problems of synthesis where a system must be designed to satisfy definite transient and steady-state performance requirements. As an

TABLE 12-1

M rectangular	M, db	M, db	M rectangular
0.5	−6	−12	0.25
0.6	−4.7	−9	0.355
0.7	−3.1	−6	0.5
0.8	−1.9	−3	0.71
0.9	−0.9	0	1.0
1.0	0	3	1.41
1.1	0.83	6	2.0
1.2	1.6	9	2.82
1.3	2.3	12	4.0
1.5	3.5		
1.8	5.1		
2.0	6		
3.0	9.5		
4.0	12		

example of this, suppose that preliminary design of a servo system yields log-magnitude vs. log ω and phase-angle vs. log ω plots as curves A and A' in Fig. 12-14. Transferring these curves to log-phase coordinates would result in Fig. 12-20b. The M contour for the desired M_p (here assumed to be 1.3) may be added as shown.

It is immediately apparent that the system does not satisfy the specified M_p requirement; nor is the system even stable. Several procedures may be suggested for obtaining stability and also the desired resonance peak. Three possibilities are shown in Fig. 12-21. Each of the illustrated methods will be considered in detail. The influence of the various modes of system adjustment on over-all system performance is also discussed.

Before the methods illustrated are considered in detail and the influence of the various corrective modes on over-all system performance is discussed, some general features of each method may be pointed out. To facilitate this, arbitrary frequencies, ω_1 and ω_2, are singled out and the significant differences in corresponding compensated and uncompensated systems noted. Referring to curve a of Fig. 12-21, there is only a difference in magnitude between two loci throughout the entire frequency spectrum. No phase shift in the compensated locus is indicated as the M_p requirement is achieved through gain adjustment only. For the curves in Fig. 12-21b, apparently there are negligible phase shift and attenuation in the low-frequency range, for the compensated locus is nearly coincident with the original. However at the approximate resonant frequency, ω_{rb}, appreciable positive phase shift and *attenuation* are noted. Finally, a comparison of the original and compensated loci in Fig. 12-21c reveals appreciable negative phase shift at low frequencies with negligible decibel loss, while in the region of the system resonant frequency only attenuation is observed. A qualitative comparison can be made of the speed of response of the supposed system for the theoretical compensation methods chosen by noting the location of corresponding ω_r's. The speed of response of (b) is the most rapid.

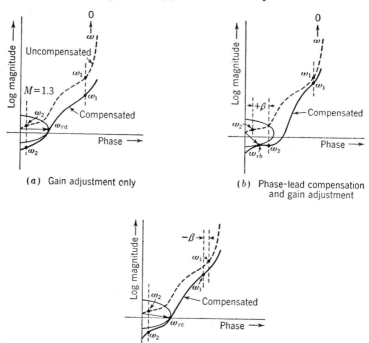

(a)   Gain adjustment only

(b)   Phase-lead compensation and gain adjustment

(c)   Phase-lag compensation and gain adjustment

Fig. 12-21. Procedures for obtaining a desired M_p for a specific system.

12-21. Use of M Contours—Effect of a Change in Gain. If the gain of the system is decreased, the entire locus of Fig. 12-20 is shifted downward as shown in Fig. 12-22. The resonant frequency is then ω_r, and the gain and phase margins are read from the scales as indicated. The resonance peak is, of course, $M_p = 1.3$ and occurs at frequency ω_r.

12-22. Use of M Contours—Effect of Phase-lead Compensation. The effect of the insertion of a phase-lead compensator for obtaining the desired M_p may easily be determined by plotting the log-phase characteristic of the selected network on the same axes as the uncompensated system. Curve b in Fig. 12-23 is an example of such a curve. The con-

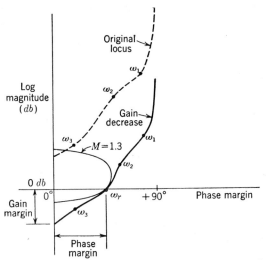

FIG. 12-22. Effect of gain adjustment on the log-phase plot.

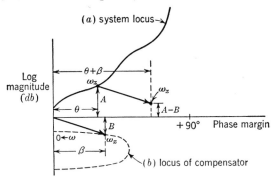

(a) Graphical procedure

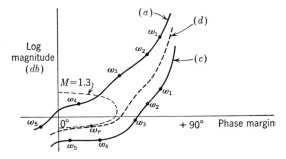

(b) Compensation and gain adjustment

FIG. 12-23. Compensation on log-magnitude vs. phase-angle plots.

struction of the compensated locus, c, is relatively simple: at the same angular frequency, the log magnitudes of the original loci and the compensator are added algebraically, and the phase angles of the two loci are added similarly. This graphical procedure is illustrated at a typical frequency ω_x. When repeated for many frequencies, locus c results (Fig. 12-23b).

The graphical procedure above can be greatly simplified if it is noted that construction of the compensated locus as shown is equivalent to laying off a vector such as A in Fig. 12-24 at a frequency ω_x. The vector is determined for the compensator locus and added to the system locus. This procedure is repeated at each frequency, and finally a curve is drawn through the loci traced by the tips of the arrows. Such procedures enable

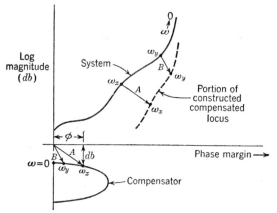

Fig. 12-24. Vector construction of compensated locus.

ready determination of the range of frequencies over which phase-shift and attenuation characteristics are most effective.

It is obvious from the resultant curve, c, in Fig. 12-23b that the phase-lead compensator has negligible effect on the system loci at low frequencies, appreciable effect on both phase-shift and attenuation in mid-frequency range, and a diminishing effect on the phase-shift characteristic at higher frequencies. The compensated locus can be raised by increasing the gain until it is tangent with the desired M_p circle as shown by curve d. The use of phase-lead compensation permits a larger gain than would be possible otherwise, leading to a higher resonant frequency and so improved speed of response.

12-23. Use of M Contours—Effect of Phase-lag Compensation. If, in addition to attaining the desired M_p, minimum steady-state error is specified, phase-lag compensation could be used. The somewhat slower speed of response which results must also be acceptable, however. Figure 12-25 shows the effect of phase-lag compensation: curve a is the original locus, curve b is the locus of a possible phase-lag device, and curve c shows the result of inserting the phase-lag device. (Graphical construction of compensated locus is essentially the same as for the phase-lead case previously cited.) The remaining curve d illustrates the compensated locus after final gain adjustment.

The compensator does not affect the lowest frequencies, causes both attenuation and phase lag in a range of frequencies somewhat above the lowest, and attenuates the high frequencies. This permits considerable gain increase, which would reduce the steady state-error, but results in a lowered ω_r, thus producing a more sluggish system. The selection of a suitable frequency range for either the phase-lag or the phase-lead compensator is primarily a matter of trial and error, with design experience

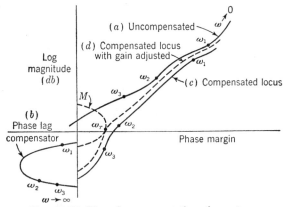

FIG. 12-25. Phase-lag compensation of a system.

being most helpful. Plotting of the log-phase characteristics of the compensator on the same axis as the system characteristics will prove to be helpful in determining the "effective" attenuation and phase-shift bands of each.

12-24. Multiloop Systems—Introduction. The logarithmic methods presented thus far have been limited to single-loop system performance and series compensation of such elementary systems. Extension of logarithmic procedures to multiloop systems and compensation by feedback is both possible and necessary. But, in general, it will be found that the work involved is materially more difficult than for single-loop systems.

In contrast with the ease of handling of feedback compensation and multiloop systems through inverse-function polar loci, the logarithmic approach requires that direct transfer functions be used; this would be expected, of course, because inverse transfer functions ordinarily contain additive terms, which do not lend themselves to logarithmic manipulations. In multiloop systems the general method of attack is to reduce subordinate loops to equivalent series elements, thus obtaining an over-all transfer function which is expressed as a product. Such computations may be carried out algebraically when the equations are available or may be handled as successive graphical manipulations. In general it seems preferable to use the graphical methods.

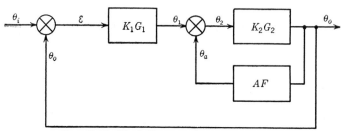

FIG. 12-26. Block diagram of a multiloop servo.

12-25. Graphical Procedures with Subordinate Loops. Consider the block diagram of Fig. 12-26, which represents a servo with a single sub-ordinate loop. The over-all transfer function is

$$\frac{\theta_o}{\varepsilon} = \frac{K_1 G_1 K_2 G_2}{1 + K_2 G_2 A F} \qquad (12\text{-}32)$$

which readily reduces to

$$\frac{\theta_o}{\varepsilon} = K_1 G_1 K_x G_x \qquad (12\text{-}33)$$

where $K_x G_x = K_2 G_2/(1 + K_2 G_2 A F)$, thus showing that the over-all transfer function may be expressed as a product.

If the transfer functions $K_1 G_1$, $K_2 G_2$, and $A F$ are known explicitly, the locus of θ_o/ε is readily computed and the performance may be analyzed with either a polar plot or logarithmic plots. However, if the analysis is to include a study of the effects of parameter variation, or if the problem is one of design, the successive computations and polar plots become quite laborious and graphical logarithmic methods are advantageous. The use of logarithmic methods is particularly valuable in setting the gain of the various units so as to obtain satisfactory over-all performance.

The first step in the manipulation of a multiloop system is to reduce the innermost subordinate loop to an equivalent series transfer function. This is done graphically as follows:

1. Plot the loop transfer function $(K_2 G_2 A F)$ on a log-magnitude vs. phase-margin plot.

2. Add M and N contours, determine the closed-loop frequency response, which will be $K_2 G_2 A F/(1 + K_2 G_2 A F)$, and plot on log-magnitude vs. log ω coordinates.

3. Determine the equivalent series transfer function, $K_x G_x = \theta_o/\theta_1$, by multiplying (on the log-magnitude vs. log ω plot) the result of step 2 by $1/AF$; that is,

$$\frac{\theta_o}{\theta_1} = \frac{K_2 G_2}{1 + K_2 G_2 AF} = \frac{1}{AF} \frac{K_2 G_2 AF}{1 + K_2 G_2 AF} \qquad (12\text{-}34)$$

If analysis is the primary consideration, any transfer functions in series with the innermost loop are then combined with the result of step 3. The entire procedure is repeated for each subordinate loop until log-phase loci representing the over-all transfer function are obtained.

When it is desired to design portions of the system or to adjust the system for better performance, additional manipulations are necessary. These manipulations may be outlined as follows and will be clarified by an example:

1. Each subordinate loop must be adjusted to some desired performance specification. To do this, the loop transfer function is plotted on

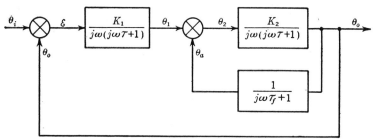

FIG. 12-27. Multiloop servomechanism.

log-magnitude vs. phase-margin coordinates, and the over-all gain is set for some chosen value of M. This value of M is frequently higher than is permissible for a complete system, and if necessary the loop may be made unstable.

2. The gain constants K_2 and A [Eq. (12-34)] must be selected. The product $K_2 A$ is, of course, set by step 1, but K_2 and A individually may have any desired value as long as the desired product is obtained. The choice of K_2 and A sets the equivalent gain of the subordinate loop considered as a series element in the main transmission path.

3. In each of the above steps the physical limitations of the components must be considered so as to avoid overloading.

4. If the inner loop is enclosed in a second subordinate loop, the above procedures are repeated but in adjusting the gain constants for the second loop there should be no change in the gains (K_2 and A) already determined for the inner loop.

12-26. Qualitative Illustration of Subordinate-loop Manipulation. If the transfer functions of the system shown in Fig. 12-26 are specified as in Fig. 12-27, the loop transfer function for the subordinate loop is

$$\frac{\theta_a}{\theta_2}(j\omega) = \frac{K_2}{j\omega(j\omega\tau + 1)(j\omega\tau_f + 1)} \qquad (12\text{-}35)$$

Assuming $\tau_f > \tau$, the log-magnitude vs. log ω plot is shown in Fig. 12-28a for $K_2 = 1$. It is apparent that an appreciable gain increase is possible.

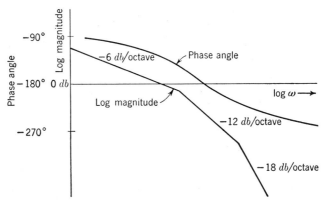

(a) Log magnitude and phase-angle locus

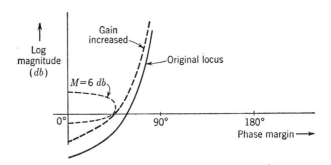

(b) Log magnitude vs. phase margin

FIG. 12-28. Logarithmic constructions for multiloop example.

Figure 12-28b shows the locus on log-magnitude vs. phase-margin coordinates and indicates the gain increase to give an M_p of 6 db. This gain increase is obtained by adjusting the product K_2A.

Theoretically either K_2 or A may be increased by the entire amount needed to set the loop gain K_2A, or both may be altered. Practically the adjustment of K_2 and A depends on the desired transfer function of the closed loop considered as a series element in the system. This transfer function is obtained [according to Eq. (12-34)] by determining the loop frequency response and multiplying by the reciprocal of the feedback transfer function. The loop frequency response and phase shift are obtained by adding M and N contours to Fig. 12-28b and reading off the intercepts of these contours with the loop transfer-function locus. The result is shown in Fig. 12-29, curves a and b.

When the loop is closed, the actual transfer of energy from input θ_1 to output θ_o is expressed by the over-all transfer function,

$$\frac{\theta_o}{\theta_1} = \frac{1}{AF}\frac{KGAF}{1 + KGAF} = \frac{K_2(j\omega\tau_f + 1)}{j\omega(j\omega\tau + 1)(j\omega\tau_f + 1) + K_2} \quad (12\text{-}36)$$

This is obtained from Fig. 12-29 as follows:

a. To the log-magnitude vs. log ω curve add the curve $20\log_{10}|1/AF|$, which in this case is $20\log_{10}|j\omega\tau_f + 1|$, obtaining the magnitude curve d in Fig. 12-29.

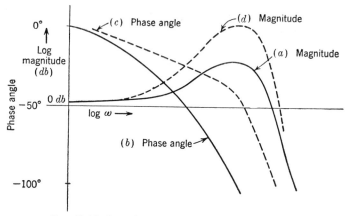

Fig. 12-29. Loop frequency response and phase shift.

b. To the phase-angle curve add the angle of $1/AF$, which in this case is $\tan^{-1} j\omega\tau_f$, obtaining curve c in Fig. 12-29.

The phase-angle curve thus obtained is fixed for all values of gain, as long as τ and τ_f are not altered. If K_2 and A are changed, provided the product K_2A is kept constant, the magnitude curve is merely raised or lowered on the decibel scale. Thus if $A < 1$, the magnitude curve is raised, indicating that the loop will provide increased gain from θ_1 to θ_o, while if $A > 1$, the magnitude curve is lowered, reducing the over-all gain. It may thus be seen that adjustment of the feedback gain, A, and main-path gain, K_2, can appreciably alter the performance of a subordinate loop. The choice of values for K_2 and A usually is determined from the performance specifications and the physical limitations of the components.

Procedures such as these are inherent in the analysis and design of multiloop systems when logarithmic methods are used. Simplifications may often be made in specific cases, but the procedures for such cases are not readily generalized.

PROBLEMS

12-1. Construct the logarithmic transfer-function curves for Probs. 6-1 and 6-2, using asymptotic approximations.

12-2. Repeat Probs. 6-5, to 6-7, using logarithmic plots.

12-3. Repeat Probs. 6-4 and 6-8, using logarithmic plots.

12-4. Repeat Prob. 9-1, substituting phase margins of 50, 40, and 30 deg for the specified M_p values, and determine ω_n instead of ω_r.

12-5. In Prob. 10-2, substitute a phase margin of 50 deg for the specified M_p, and solve, using logarithmic methods.

12-6. Repeat Prob. 10-4, using a phase-margin of 40 deg instead of $M_p = 2.0$ in part a, a phase margin of 50 deg instead of $M_p = 1.3$ in part c, and a phase margin of 60 deg instead of $M_p = 1.0$ in part e.

12-7. Plot log magnitude of KG vs. log ω and phase angle vs. log ω (using the procedures outlined in Chap. 12) for Prob. 4-1. Determine the phase margin. (Transfer functions of this problem and those succeeding have been assigned for determination in previous chapters.)

12-8. Repeat Prob. 12-7 for the parameter changes of the system of Prob. 4-2, and plot on the same axis with the results of Prob. 12-7.

12-9. Repeat Prob. 12-7 for the system of Prob. 4-3. Determine M_p and ω_r by using M contours.

12-10. Repeat Prob. 12-7 for the system of Prob. 4-5, and in addition determine the steady-state velocity-lag error that would exist for an input of 1 radian/sec.

12-11. Repeat Prob. 12-7 for the system of Prob. 4-6. Determine M_p and ω_r by using M contours.

12-12. For the derivative damping system of Prob. 4-14 repeat Prob. 12-7, plotting the various loci for the values of A on the same axis. In each case also determine the steady-state lag error for a constant-velocity input of 10 deg/sec.

12-13. Repeat Prob. 12-7 for the system described in Prob. 4-15, and calculate, by logarithmic methods, the steady-state lag error with a constant-velocity input of 10 deg/sec.

12-14. Repeat Prob. 12-7 for Probs. 4-16 and 4-17, plotting the curves on the same axis. What is the velocity-lag error for a velocity input of 1 radian/sec for each system?

12-15. Repeat Prob. 12-7 for the system of Prob. 4-20.

12-16. Repeat Prob. 12-7 for the system of Prob. 4-21.

12-17. Replot the curves of Prob. 12-12 on log-magnitude vs. phase-angle coordinates. Add M contours, and show the effect of the derivative damping on the resonance peak and the resonant frequency.

12-18. Replot the curves of Prob. 12-15 on log-magnitude vs. phase-angle coordinates, and investigate the effect of the phase-lag network on M_p and ω_r.

CHAPTER 13

RELAY SERVOMECHANISMS

13-1. Introduction.[1,33,51,70-73,*] The feature which distinguishes a servomechanism from other control systems is the presence of a feedback loop which compares the output and input of the system. This comparison provides a signal indicating the deviation or error, and in general this error signal (plus its approximate derivatives or integrals where desirable) is used to activate the power source which drives the output toward correspondence with the input. In the preceding chapters consideration has been given to those servomechanisms in which the amount of power applied to the output is proportional to the instantaneous error (plus its derivatives and/or integrals). In many applications it is desirable to activate the power source in a different manner; specifically, it is desirable to apply full power to the output whenever the error exceeds some given magnitude and to maintain full applied power until the error is reduced to an acceptable value. Such a servomechanism must include some switching device, and because electromagnetic relays are commonly used to accomplish the switching, systems of this type are commonly called *relay servomechanisms.*

Basically, then, the only difference between a relay servomechanism and a continuous-control servomechanism lies in the nature of the unit which applies the power (source) to the output member. The block diagrams of a relay servo and of a continuous-control servo may be identical, as many of the same components may be used in either type of system. However, since the physical natures of the controllers have little similarity, the mathematical expressions of the systems are quite different. Both the physical and mathematical differences are quite important in selecting either a relay servo or a continuous-control servo for a given control application.

The use of a relay-type controller normally results in a considerably simpler, smaller, and lighter control-system device, which frequently has greater mechanical strength than the more complex continuous controller. Usually, the relay-type system is considerably cheaper as well. The fac-

* Superior numbers, when they occur in the text proper, are the numbers of references given in the Bibliography.

tors of weight, space, and mechanical strength make relay servos particularly attractive in applications such as aircraft automatic control, guided missiles, etc., where such considerations are of primary importance.   The factors of relatively low cost and simplicity are particularly interesting in industrial uses since these considerations affect both capital investment and maintenance costs.   Yet it is true that, despite these desirable features, relatively few relay servomechanisms are used where accurate high-speed automatic control is desired, especially if the control problem is complex.   This apparent anomaly is due in part to the performance limitations of relay servos and in part to the mathematical difficulties encountered in their analysis and design.

It may be said in regard to general performance characteristics of a relay servo that it is impossible to obtain perfect steady-state stability

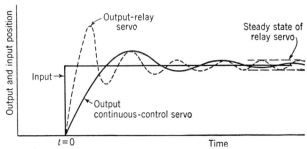

Fig. 13-1. Response characteristics of continuous-control and relay-control positional servos to a step-displacement input.

and absolute correspondence of output and input, even assuming ideal components.   For the continuous type of servomechanism, however, it *is* theoretically possible.   As will be shown, the relay servo inherently tends to oscillate, or hunt its steady state, if adjusted for perfect correspondence.   See Fig. 13-1 for a comparison of typical relay- and continuous-servo response to a step-input displacement.   This hunting may be eliminated, but only by sacrificing the possibility of perfect alignment.

The presence of hunting, or continuously oscillating response, may not be permissible in many applications, and where the best accuracy obtainable without hunting may not be good enough, a continuous-type servo must be used.   In many other applications (*i.e.*, turret control, guided missiles, pilotless aircraft, temperature control, etc.) relay servos can often meet specifications, and since they are very desirable for reasons already given, the relay type are used whenever a suitable design can be obtained.

The design of a relay servomechanism is quite difficult even for a relatively simple system and is extremely laborious if the system is at all complicated.   The reason for the difficulty lies in the nature of the switching process. Mathematically, the switching may be represented by a discontinuous (nonlinear) function. At present there are no simple mathematical methods for handling such functions; the methods which are available are rather difficult to apply and are also somewhat limited in the range of their application. It is usually possible to write the differential equations of the system, which will be nonlinear, and employ one of the several methods[1,33,71] available for solving such equations. It is also possible to transform the equation and use phase-plane[51,70,73] methods for analysis. Such methods are practically restricted to relatively simple cases because of the labor involved and even then are difficult to apply to design problems because they are basically analysis methods. More recently a method[72] for applying frequency-response principles has been developed which promises to be a more helpful tool in the design of relay servomechanisms.

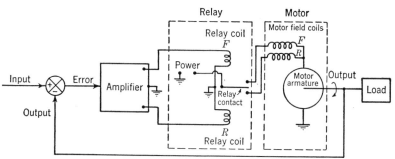

Fig. 13-2. Relay servomechanism.

Because the frequency-response method is practical for both analysis and design, it is the only method which is treated in detail in this text. However, in order to provide a physical concept of the nature and operation of relay servomechanisms a preliminary discussion is presented, including a very brief summary of the differential-equation methods.

13-2. Response of Relay Servomechanisms. Figure 13-2 gives a block diagram of a relay servomechanism with some portions shown schematically.

The operation of the system when used as a positioning device is as follows: If θ_o lags θ_i, the amplifier energizes relay winding F, moving the contact to position 1. The motor then drives the load in the forward direction to regain correspondence. If θ_o leads θ_i, the amplifier energizes relay winding R, moving the contact to position 2. The motor then reverses to regain correspondence. It should be apparent that the performance of the system is affected not only by the inertia and damping of motor and load but also by the speed of switching, the relay characteristics, and the magnitude of the power supplied to the load. A qualitative understanding of the performance of such a system may be obtained from a study of the following cases.

Case 1. Ideal Relay Servo with No Dead Zone. Figure 13-3 represents qualitatively the transient response of the relay servo of Fig. 13-2 when it is used for positioning. The following assumptions are made:

1. The system inertia and damping may be considered as lumped in the output.

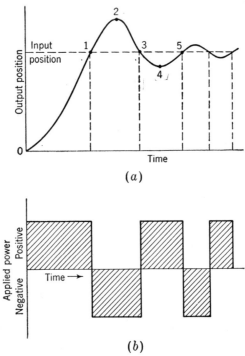

(a)

(b)

Fig. 13-3. (a) Transient response of a relay servo (with no dead zone) to a step-displacement input. (b) Power variation for relay servo with no dead zone.

2. The relay servo is ideal, *i.e.*, no time lags exist.

3. There is no "dead zone" in the relaying, *i.e.*, the application of power to restore correspondence is instantaneous with the appearance of error.

For the assumptions made, when a unit displacement is applied to the input, the relay immediately supplies power to the output member, which is then accelerated. The restoring power is applied continuously at full value from point 0 to point 1 (Fig. 13-3), at which point the error is reversed and the relay reverses the restoring power. The inertia of the system causes an overshoot but is opposed by the damping and the restoring power, bringing the system momentarily to rest at point 2.

However, the output and input are not in correspondence at point 2; so the restoring power accelerates the system from 2 to 3, after which the sequence of operations is repeated. The amplitude of the successive overshoots decreases if the damping is sufficient but can never be completely eliminated because the system always reaches the correspondence point with a finite amount of stored energy. The steady-state condition is therefore one of continuous hunting. If the damping present is either viscous friction or coulomb friction, it may be shown theoretically that (for the assumptions made) the hunting will be at infinite frequency and infinitesimal amplitude.

Case 2. Practical Servo, No Dead Zone. In any practical system it is impossible to realize the ideal conditions of no time lags and no dead zone, though both may be made small if so desired. The presence of a time lag delays the application or removal of the drive at the load. For example, in Fig. 13-2, if the relay contact is in position 2 and an error signal causes it to move to position 1, the circuit through position 2 and the reverse field winding cannot be broken instantaneously because of the field inductance and therefore power is applied to the load through the reverse field after the circuit is supposedly broken, *i.e.*, there is a time lag in the removal of power. Likewise, when the relay makes contact on position 1, power is not fully applied to the load instantaneously, *i.e.*, there is a time lag in the application of power.

Such time lags inherently make the system more oscillatory. If there is a time lag in the removal of power, then the system obtains undesired stored energy, which increases the amplitude of the subsequent overshoot. If there is a time lag in the application of power, then the system acquires substantial error before a restoring force is applied and a greater amplitude of overshoot results (see Fig. 13-4).

In Fig. 13-4 is shown the relay-servo response, still somewhat idealized, with existing time lag in power transferal and no dead zone. The dotted curve illustrates an ideal servo with no dead zone for qualitative comparison only.

Case 3. Ideal Servo with Dead Zone. Figure 13-5 illustrates the transient response of a relay servo with dead zone but no time lags. A dead zone is an error interval in which no power is applied to the output. Referring to Fig. 13-2, the relay shown may have a neutral position in which the contact arm would rest when neither coil is sufficiently energized to attract it. If it is assumed that a definite magnitude of current through the coil is required to pull in the contact, and if it is also assumed that the relay will drop out when the current decreases below that magnitude, then there will be a current range in which the relay is inoperative. This current range of course corresponds to an error interval for the system. If the input is subjected to a step displacement, then the output is

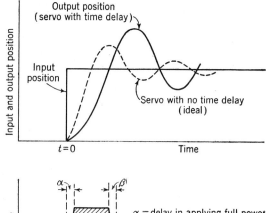

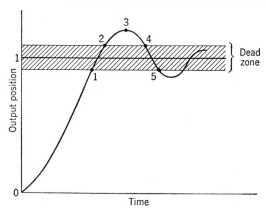

Fig. 13-4. Transient response of relay servo with time delay.

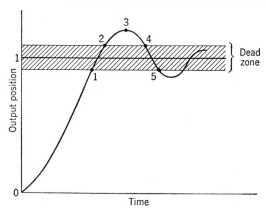

Fig. 13-5. Relay servo with dead zone.

accelerated from 0 to 1. At point 1 the forward contact drops out, and the output drifts through the dead zone with its velocity decreasing somewhat because of the damping. At point 2 the restoring torque is applied, and the system is momentarily stopped at point 3, then accelerated in the reverse direction to point 4, where the reverse contact drops out. The system then drifts through the dead zone to point 5, where the sequence of events is repeated. If there is sufficient damping, the output may come to rest within the dead zone but the position correspondence between input and output cannot be specified more closely than plus or minus one-half of the dead-zone width. The accuracy may be increased by reducing the dead zone, but this in general makes the system more oscillatory and, depending on the damping, may result in continuous hunting.

The illustrative curves of Figs. 13-3 and 13-5 are greatly idealized, of course, and in practical cases the presence of both dead zone and time lag is to be expected. In addition most relays have a type of hysteresis, in that they pull in at one value of current but do not drop out until the current is reduced to some lower value. Thus, during one cycle of operation of a practical relay servo the operating conditions are changed a number of times, and the analysis of system performance is correspondingly quite complicated.

The qualitative response characteristics of idealized relay servos have been discussed in some detail, but in practical relay-servo applications more quantitative information is necessary than just the approximate mode of variation. The response characteristics of relay servos with time lags, dead zones, and relay hysteretic effects can be determined in a number of ways, with varying accuracy. An obvious and accurate mathematical approach for determining the desired characteristics is to write the necessary number of differential equations, substitute the appropriate boundary conditions in each equation, and obtain solutions.[1] This method is quite laborious for even simple systems and is not at all practical when the differential equation is of high order, third or above; furthermore the method is not useful in design problems. A second approach[51,70,73] (which considerably reduces the labor involved) consists in applying phase-plane (output position–output velocity) plots to obtain graphical solutions of system performance. This method, however, seems restricted to systems of relatively simple dynamics and is not readily applied to design. A third method[71] applies Laplace-transform theory to the differential equation and obtains a solution in the form of a series of terms. Each of these terms involves the system response to a relay switching operation (step function). The transient response of the system may be formed by graphic addition of terms provided proper precautions are taken to consider initial conditions. Further manipulation permits expression of the system velocity in terms of the time interval between successive changes in operating conditions. Curves may be drawn and interpreted in terms of stability, transient performance, and steady-state performance. This method involves less labor than the preceding two and may be extended to systems of greater complexity. However, the method is primarily intended for analysis and has not yet been extended to include design.

13-3. Frequency-response Method—General. Recent investigations[72] have developed a means for applying frequency-response methods to the analysis and synthesis of relay servos. All the advantages of the transfer-function method as applied to linear systems are retained, *i.e.*, simple representation of components, algebraic methods of manipulation, analysis of performance from graphical plots, and ready insertion of compensating devices. The results obtained should be sufficiently accurate for most engineering purposes but cannot be expected to duplicate the accuracy of similar methods applied to linear systems because of certain approximations which must be made in obtaining a transfer function for the relay unit.

The transfer-function approach to the analysis and design of relay servomechanisms is essentially the same as for the continuous-type servo. The treatment here is limited to elementary single-loop systems, with no element in the feedback path, as extensions to more complex contactor servomechanisms still bear investigation.

The usual transfer functions of all components except the relay, of a system such as that of Fig. 13-2, are available and in general will not differ from those derived in preceding chapters. These may be combined to give a partial system transfer function, $KG(j\omega)$. Because of the nonlinear nature of the relay-controller response, only an approximate transfer function, KG_R, can be written. The relay approximate transfer function is found to be a function not of ω but rather of the error-signal magnitude; this greatly complicates the graphical manipulations of the polar plots which are used in performance studies.

To summarize the frequency-response approach, curves are ordinarily plotted of the partial system transfer function $KG(j\omega)$ and the approximate relay transfer function KG_R, the latter for various error-signal magnitudes. A modified version of the Nyquist stability criteria is then applied to determine necessary stability information. Transient and steady-state performance may be found by constructing M circles, but special interpretations are required. Due consideration is finally given to the effect of relay characteristics and system compensation on over-all servo performance.

13-4. Approximate Relay Transfer Function. The determination of the transfer function of the relay in Fig. 13-2 is difficult because of its discontinuous response characteristics. When a sinusoidal signal is applied to the relay input, the output of the relay is a series of rectangular pulses of alternating polarity; and thus the relay cannot be represented by a true transfer function in the sense which has previously been attached to that term. However, an approximate transfer function can be derived which may be used in analysis and design of relay servos with sufficient engineering accuracy.

The approximate transfer function is formed by replacing the rectangular pulse by just the fundamental frequency component of its equivalent Fourier series; the higher frequency components are ignored. Justification for neglecting the higher frequency terms in the Fourier series of the rectangular pulse is as follows:

1. In a normal rectangular repeating wave the amplitude of the fundamental is considerably greater than the amplitude of any higher harmonic.

2. The output stages of most servomechanisms are effectively low-pass filters, so that the amplitudes of the higher harmonics in the rectangular wave are appreciably attenuated before reaching the output.

There are circumstances under which the above statements are not completely valid, *i.e.*, if the output pulse is of very short duration compared with the spacing between pulses, the amplitudes of certain harmonics increase; also, some systems may have a resonance peak near one of the higher harmonics so that its effect may not be negligible. In general, however, the above statements are substantially correct, and reasonably accurate results may be expected.

In general, the relay produces one rectangular pulse for each half wave of its sinusoidal input, so that under steady-state conditions the Fourier series representing the relay output has a fundamental, or lowest, frequency which is of the same frequency as the sinusoidal input though probably different in amplitude and phase. It is then possible to form an approximate transfer function for the relay which may be defined as the vector ratio of this fundamental Fourier component of the output contactor wave to the sinusoidal input signal.

13-5. Determination of Relay Transfer Function. In order to determine the transfer function of the relay unit, certain characteristics of the relay must be known; these are the pull-in and drop-out currents (or voltages). Any delay time such as might be introduced by the inductance of the relay winding is better handled in the transfer function of a preceding component. The use of the pull-in and drop-out values is applied as shown in Fig. 13-6. For simplicity, assume that the pull-in and drop-out voltages are the same; then Fig. 13-6 illustrates the relationship between the input and output. If the input is a pure sine wave with its zero axis centered at the relay null position, then as the input attains a positive value a the relay closes and the output delivers full voltage (assuming output is a voltage). The relay stays locked in until the input reaches the drop-out point b; then the relay opens and the output voltage drops to zero. As the input goes from b to c, there is no output, but at c the relay closes on the opposite polarity, producing full output in the negative direction. This output is maintained until the input signal reaches point d, after which the sequence of events is repeated.

If the pull-in and drop-out currents of the relays are equal in magnitude, and if they are the same for both polarities, then the lowest frequency term in the Fourier representation of the output will be in time

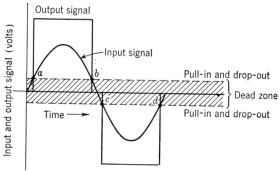

FIG. 13-6. Relay input and output waves when pull-in = drop-out.

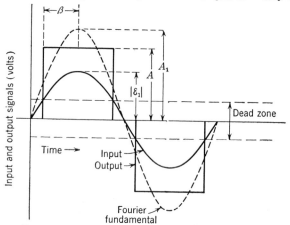

FIG. 13-7. Sinusoidal approximation of relay output.

phase* with the input signal. Figure 13-7 shows the simple graphical relationships, and the approximate transfer function of the relay is then

$$KG_R = \frac{\bar{A}_1}{\bar{\varepsilon}_1} = \frac{4A \sin \beta}{\pi |\varepsilon_1|} \underline{/0^\circ} \tag{13-1}$$

where A = amplitude of pulse
A_1 = amplitude of Fourier fundamental
β = one-half duration of pulse, deg
$|\varepsilon_1|$ = amplitude of input signal

* The center line of the rectangular pulse coincides with the center line of the input wave; hence the fundamental Fourier component will be maximum at the same time as the input wave and there is no "phase" displacement. In general, where pull-in and drop-out currents are unequal, there will be a phase angle between the approximating Fourier fundamental and the input wave.

It should be noted that the transfer function stated in Eq. (13-1) is an approximation and is valid only for the specified conditions and only for one amplitude of the input signal. The effects of variations in input-signal amplitude and of variations in relay characteristics are discussed in the following paragraphs.

13-6. Effect of Input-signal Variation on Relay Transfer Function. When the amplitude of the input signal, $\mathcal{E}$, is varied, the gain constant of the transfer function is changed but the phase angle remains the same (for equal pull-in and drop-out values). This is shown in Fig. 13-8. Three different input signals, $\mathcal{E}_1$, $\mathcal{E}_2$, $\mathcal{E}_3$, are shown. As the amplitude is

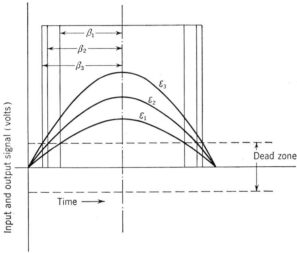

Fig. 13-8. Effect of input-signal amplitude on relay output.

increased, the duration of the output pulse is increased so that the angles corresponding to half of the negative pulses are β_1, β_2, β_3, respectively. The amplitudes of the corresponding lowest Fourier frequencies for $\mathcal{E}_1$ would be

$$|A_1| = \frac{4A \sin \beta_1}{\pi}$$

for $\mathcal{E}_2$,

$$|A_2| = \frac{4A \sin \beta_2}{\pi} \qquad (13\text{-}2)$$

and for $\mathcal{E}_3$,

$$|A_3| = \frac{4A \sin \beta_3}{\pi}$$

It may be seen by inspection that no phase angle is introduced by increasing the input-signal amplitude, but at the same time the amplitude of the output fundamental is not proportional to the input amplitude.

13-7. Effect of Relay Characteristics on Relay Transfer Function.
When the pull-in and drop-out conditions of the relay system are different but are, respectively, equal for positive and negative signals, then in
general the center line of the pulse output lags the center line of the
assumed sinusoidal input and the relay transfer function has a constant
phase lag associated with it.   Figure 13-9 illustrates this.   If the input
sine wave starts at zero when the relay is in the neutral position, the
relay does not close until the signal reaches a.   Full forward power is
applied until the input decreases to the drop-out value at b.   A similar
sequence is repeated on the negative half cycle.   It may be seen that
for forward operation the effective dead zone is from the negative drop-

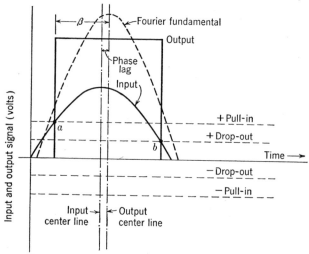

Fig. 13-9. Effect of unequal pull-in and drop-out values.

out point to the positive pull-in point, whereas for reverse operation the
dead zone is from the positive drop-out point to the negative pull-in point.
The positive and negative output pulses will have equal durations, but
their center lines are delayed in time with respect to the input-sine-wave
maximum.   This phase lag then appears in the Fourier fundamental-
frequency component.

When the forward and reverse output pulses have the same amplitude
and duration, the amplitude of the Fourier fundamental is determined as
in the preceding case and is still dependent on the amplitude of the input
signal.   The phase angle is calculated as follows from Fig. 13-10:

$$2\beta = \pi - \sin^{-1}\frac{P_1}{|\mathcal{E}_1|} - \sin^{-1}\frac{P_2}{|\mathcal{E}_1|} \tag{13-3}$$

and

$$\beta = \frac{1}{2}\left(\pi - \sin^{-1}\frac{P_1}{|\mathcal{E}_1|} - \sin^{-1}\frac{P_2}{|\mathcal{E}_1|}\right) \tag{13-4}$$

where $\mathcal{E}_1$ = amplitude of input signal
P_1 = pull-in amplitude
P_2 = drop-out amplitude

The center line of the output pulse is delayed with respect to the origin by an amount

$$\alpha = \beta + \sin^{-1} \frac{P_1}{|\mathcal{E}_1|}$$

$$= \frac{1}{2}\left(\pi - \sin^{-1}\frac{P_1}{|\mathcal{E}_1|} - \sin\frac{P_2}{|\mathcal{E}_1|}\right) + \sin^{-1}\frac{P_1}{|\mathcal{E}_1|} \tag{13-5}$$

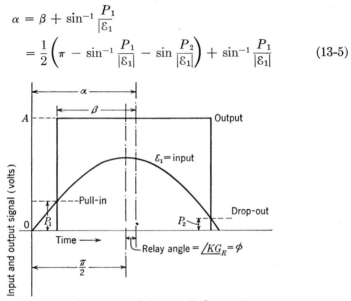

Fig. 13-10. Calculation of phase angle due to relay.

and the delay between the center line of the input signal and the center line of the pulse (which is also the center line of the Fourier fundamental) is given by

$$\phi = \underline{/KG_R} = \alpha - \frac{\pi}{2}$$

$$= \frac{\pi}{2} - \frac{1}{2}\sin^{-1}\frac{P_1}{|\mathcal{E}_1|} - \frac{1}{2}\sin^{-1}\frac{P_2}{|\mathcal{E}_1|} + \sin^{-1}\frac{P_1}{|\mathcal{E}_1|} - \frac{\pi}{2}$$

$$= \frac{1}{2}\left(\sin^{-1}\frac{P_1}{|\mathcal{E}_1|} - \sin^{-1}\frac{P_2}{|\mathcal{E}_1|}\right) \tag{13-6}$$

The transfer function of the relay system is then

$$KG_R = \frac{\bar{A}_1}{\bar{\mathcal{E}}_1} = \frac{4A\sin\beta}{\pi|\mathcal{E}_1|}\underline{/\phi} \tag{13-7}$$

The above transfer functions for the relay are in general a good approximation when the servomechanism is used as a positioning system, because the positive and negative pulses (if any) are then of the same duration

under steady-state conditions.   If the system is to be used with a constant-velocity input or a constant-load torque, then in general the positive
and negative pulses are not of the same duration and the preceding transfer functions are not valid.   The derivation of transfer functions to fit
such conditions may be handled by methods similar to those used here if
the effect of the velocity input or load torque is represented by a zero-
frequency component[72] in the input signal, $\mathcal{E}$, that is, if the axis of the
input sine wave is displaced from the relay neutral position by an amount
indicative of the input velocity or load torque.   Further discussion of
this topic is beyond the scope of this text.

13-8. Graphical Manipulations and Interpretations.   Once the relay
portion of the system has been expressed as a transfer function, normal
graphical means may be used to represent the locus.   However, special
interpretation of plots is required because the relay transfer function

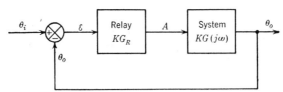

Fig. 13-11. Block diagram of a single-loop relay servo.

depends on the amplitude of the signal input to the relay, and this automatically changes during normal operation.   In general, the graphical
representations should permit determination of

1. Absolute stability
2. Steady-state performance
3. Transient performance

Consideration will first be given to stability data.

13-9. Absolute-stability Determination.   Several methods may be
employed to determine the stability and degree of stability of relay servos.
The method developed presently is satisfactory for limited interpretation
only, but it serves well to introduce a second, more versatile means of
determining stability.

Consider a simple relay servo, which may be represented by the block
diagram of Fig. 13-11.   The transfer function of the system is simply

$$\frac{\theta_o}{\mathcal{E}}(j\omega) = KG_R KG(j\omega) \qquad (13\text{-}8)$$

where KG_R is a function of the error signal and the relay characteristic
and $KG(j\omega)$ is a function of the frequency and the system gain.

The simplified Nyquist stability criteria can be employed if Eq. (13-8)
is plotted on the familiar $KG(j\omega)$ plane.   For a given error-signal ampli-
tude, $|\mathcal{E}_1|$, the relay function may be symbolized as K_1G_R and is a constant.

The polar plot of the complete transfer function might then be curve a in Fig. 13-12. The system obviously is stable. Curve a, however, repre-

sents only one error-signal amplitude, and since this amplitude
changes during normal operation, a
family of curves is required to determine complete stability data. For
other error-signal amplitudes the
transfer-function locus might appear as in curves b and c. It is seen
that curve c represents an unstable
condition.

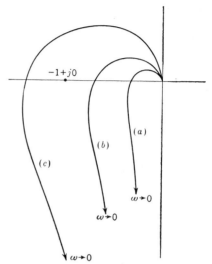

If a family of curves is plotted
for a system, as in Fig. 13-12, three
conditions are possible depending
on the specific system:

1. None of the curves enclose
the $-1 + j0$ point, in which case
the system is absolutely stable
and will not hunt its steady-state
condition.

FIG. 13-12. Polar loci for Eq. (13-8).

2. All of the curves enclose the $-1 + j0$ point, so that the system is completely unstable.

3. Only a few of the curves enclose the $-1 + j0$ point. Such cases require more detailed analysis. (Enough curves must be plotted to cover the possible range of error signals before system stability can be adequately determined.)

A more convenient means of determining the stability of a relay servo-mechanism is to plot a locus of stability points, one corresponding to each error amplitude. By doing this the need for a family of curves, as in Fig. 13-12, is eliminated. Furthermore, the use of such a stability locus lends itself readily to the modification and design of a relay servo. The following paragraphs develop the graphical representation of sta-bility loci.

Instability results when the over-all system transfer function passes through or encloses the $-1 + j0$ point (or stability point). Mathe-matically this may be stated as follows:

$$KG(j\omega)KG_R \geqq -1 + j0 \qquad (13\text{-}9)$$

If the above equation is rewritten, then the location of the stability point for each error signal may be defined as:

$$\text{Stability point} = \frac{1\underline{/180°}}{|KG_R|\underline{/\phi}} \qquad (13\text{-}10)$$

Thus, for a single-loop system, a locus of stability points may be drawn by assuming different error signals and joining the tips of the vectors described by

$$|KG_R{}^{-1}|/180° - \phi$$

The following illustrations are intended to clarify the general application of the stability criterion used with these stability loci: First, consider the ideal case of a relay servo in which the relay pull-in and drop-out points are identical. Then the angle of the relay transfer function is $/KG_R = \phi = 0$ for all amplitudes, and all stability points are located on the negative real axis. Assume also that $KG_R \to \infty$ as $\mathcal{E} \to 0$ and

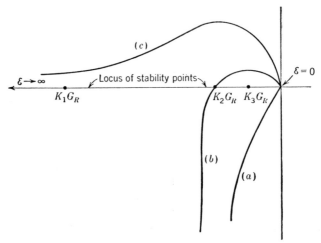

Fig. 13-13. A locus of stability points.

$KG_R \to 0$ as $\mathcal{E} \to \infty$. As $KG_R \to \infty$, then the stability point approaches the origin of the plot, whereas when $KG_R \to 0$, the stability point approaches minus infinity. Thus, for the conditions of equal relay pull-in and drop-out points, and temporarily assuming no limits on the magnitude of KG_R, the locus of stability points is the entire negative real axis. Figure 13-13 shows such a locus of stability points with three possible $KG(j\omega)$ loci.

Figure 13-13, curve a, represents an inherently stable system since the $KG(j\omega)$ locus does not enclose any point on the stability locus except the origin. If such a system is disturbed, each succeeding overshoot decreases in amplitude. Curve c, on the other hand, is inherently unstable since it encloses the entire stability locus. Any disturbance causes oscillations of increasing amplitude. Curve b represents a conditionally stable system, since part of the stability locus is enclosed by the transfer-function locus. For small disturbance the system is unstable

$(KG_R \rightarrow \infty$ and $KG_R^{-1} \rightarrow 0)$, and the oscillations build up in amplitude. For large disturbances the system is stable, and the oscillatory amplitude decreases. The steady-state condition therefore corresponds to continuous hunting at an amplitude and frequency determined by the inter-

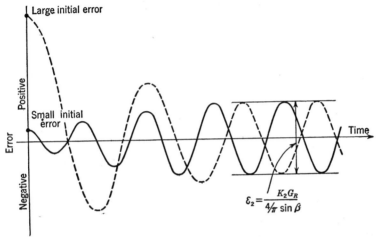

FIG. 13-14. Error variation for system corresponding to curve b in Fig. 13-13.

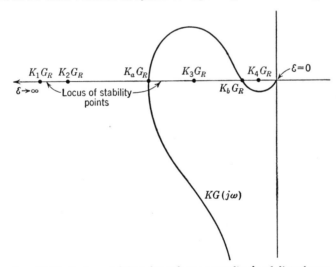

FIG. 13-15. System stability dependent on amplitude of disturbance.

section of the transfer-function locus with the stability locus. See Fig. 13-14 for possible response curves.

Somewhat more complicated conditions may exist for systems with higher-order transfer functions. Figure 13-15 illustrates a possible case (for the same stability locus). For the system shown, the stability is dependent on the disturbance amplitude. For large disturbances such as K_1G_R or K_2G_R the system is stable, and the amplitude decreases to a value corresponding to point K_aG_R, which is the final steady state which the system will hunt, because any decrease in amplitude would make the system absolutely unstable and the amplitude would increase again. For disturbances smaller than K_aG_R but greater than K_bG_R, such as K_3G_R, the system is unstable, and steady state is once more a condition of hunting at K_aG_R. In either case the frequency of oscillation in steady state is approximately the frequency on the transfer-function locus which coincides with the point at K_aG_R. For disturbances smaller than K_bG_R, such as K_4G_R, the system is stable, and the oscillations decrease in amplitude.

13-10. Practical Stability Loci. The preceding paragraphs have discussed stability with the aid of a theoretical stability locus which is seldom realized in a practical relay servomechanism. This approach was taken for the sake of continuity and simplicity. Before further discussion is possible, the various cases of practical stability loci must be considered.

The general equation for the relay transfer function* may be obtained by expanding Eq. (13-7) and is

$$KG_R = \left\{ \frac{4A \sin [\tfrac{1}{2}(\pi - \sin^{-1} P_1/|\mathcal{E}_1| - \sin^{-1} P_2/|\mathcal{E}_1|)]}{\pi|\mathcal{E}_1|} \right\} \bigg/ \frac{1}{2}\left(\sin^{-1} \frac{P_1}{|\mathcal{E}_1|} - \sin^{-1} \frac{P_2}{|\mathcal{E}_1|} \right) \quad (13\text{-}11)$$

From this, the stability-locus equation is

$$\text{Stability locus} = \frac{\pi|\mathcal{E}_1|}{4A \sin [\tfrac{1}{2}(\pi - \sin^{-1} P_1/|\mathcal{E}_1| - \sin^{-1} P_2/|\mathcal{E}_1|)]} \bigg/ \pi - \frac{1}{2}\left(\sin^{-1} \frac{P_1}{|\mathcal{E}_1|} - \sin^{-1} \frac{P_2}{|\mathcal{E}_1|} \right) \quad (13\text{-}12)$$

The practical variables in this equation, in addition to the error-signal amplitude, are the amplitude of the relay output, A; the pull-in signal, P_1; and the drop-out signal, P_2. The practical restrictions on these quantities are:

1. A must be finite and greater than zero.
2. P_1 must be finite but must be equal to or greater than P_2. P_1 may approach zero as a limit.
3. P_2 must be finite. It may be equal to or less than P_1 and might conceivably be zero or slightly negative (though a relay with zero or negative drop-out characteristic probably would not be used).

---

* For a positioning system without load torques.

The amplitude A is effectively a gain constant in Eq. (13-11) and therefore contributes to the over-all system gain. An increase in A with all other conditions unchanged results in a stiffer, or more oscillatory, system, as is known from the theory of linear systems. The effect of changes in A on the stability locus is readily seen from the equation and needs no comment. The effect of other variables on the stability locus will now be investigated, assuming A to be finite and constant. The cases to be considered are

(a) $\qquad\qquad\qquad P_1 = P_2 = 0$
(b) $\qquad\qquad\qquad P_1 = P_2 > 0$
(c) $\qquad\qquad\qquad P_1 > P_2 > 0$

Case (a). $P_1 = P_2 = 0$ *(no dead zone)*
1. The phase angle ϕ of the relay transfer function is zero, from Eq. (13-11); so all points on the stability locus lie on the negative real axis, regardless of error-signal amplitude.
2. If $\varepsilon_1 = 0$, then $KG_R = \infty$ and $KG_R^{-1} = 0$, so that the end of the stability locus corresponding to zero error-signal amplitude lies at the origin of the plot.
3. As ε_1 increases, KG_R decreases and KG_R^{-1} increases and approaches infinity. Thus the stability locus includes the entire negative real axis, with small error-signal amplitudes represented by points approaching minus infinity.
This is now seen to be the case which was previously used for illustration and needs no further comment.
Case (b). $P_1 = P_2 > 0$
1. The phase angle is zero, from Eq. (13-11); so all points on the stability locus are on the negative real axis. This is true regardless of the magnitude of P_1 and P_2.
2. For error-signal amplitudes $|\varepsilon_1| < P_1$, the relay does not close, and the system is inoperative, or "cut off." Under such conditions the relay transfer function has no meaning.
3. For $|\varepsilon_1| = P_1 = P_2$ the term $\sin\left[\frac{1}{2}(\pi - \sin^{-1} P_1/|\varepsilon_1| - \sin^{-1} P_2/|\varepsilon_1|)\right]$ is equal to zero; so $KG_R = 0$, and $|KG_R^{-1}| = \infty$.
4. For values of $|\varepsilon_1|$ slightly greater than P_1, $|KG_R^{-1}|$ is larger because the sine term remains small.
5. As $|\varepsilon_1|$ increases, the sine term approaches unity. KG_R increases to a maximum, then decreases to zero as $|\varepsilon_1| \to \infty$. The points on the stability locus therefore decrease (as $|\varepsilon_1|$ increases), go through a minimum value, and then recede to minus infinity.
Figure 13-16 illustrates a stability locus of the type described in case (b). To clarify the picture, the locus is shown as two lines parallel to the axis, though actually both coincide with the axis. Curves a and b in

Fig. 13-16 represent inherently stable systems, and their output would come to rest within the dead zone for any amplitude of disturbance. Curve *c*, however, encloses part of the stability locus and is conditionally stable. For small disturbances, less than the value required at point 3, the system is stable, and the output would come to rest in the dead zone. For larger disturbances, the system would reach equilibrium with steady hunting at an amplitude and frequency corresponding to point 4.

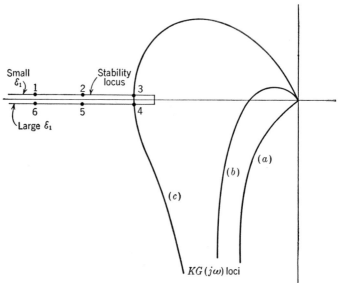

FIG. 13-16. Stability locus for $P_1 = P_2 > 0$ (*i.e.*, finite dead zone; equal pull-in and drop-out points).

Case (*c*). $P_1 > P_2 > 0$.   In this case the phase angle ϕ is not zero and is a function of the error-signal amplitude. It is convenient to study both the magnitude and phase effects simultaneously.

1. The relay is inoperative for $|\mathcal{E}_1| < P_1$.

2. For $|\mathcal{E}_1| = P_1$ the relay closes and holds until the value of $\mathcal{E}_1$ has dropped to P_2. Thus ϕ has a finite positive value [see Eq. (13-11)], and in general this is the maximum value of ϕ. The term $\sin \beta$ [see Eq. (13-2)] has a finite value, which is its smallest value. Thus the magnitude of the relay transfer function has a finite value.

3. The above condition locates one point on the stability locus corresponding to the smallest activating error signal. This point lies in the second quadrant at a position determined by the magnitudes of A, $|\mathcal{E}_1|$, P_1, P_2.

4. As $|\mathcal{E}_1|$ increases, ϕ decreases but KG_R may increase or decrease depending on the relative magnitudes of the terms involved. As $|\mathcal{E}_1|$

becomes very large, $\phi \to 0$ and $|KG_R| \to 0$ so that the stability locus $|KG_R^{-1}|/\pi - \phi$ approaches $-\infty$ as $|\mathcal{E}_1| \to +\infty$.

Figure 13-17 shows a stability locus of the type discussed under case (c). Curves a and b represent inherently stable systems. Curve c is conditionally stable; for disturbances less than indicated at point 2 it is stable, but for larger disturbances it would hunt at point 3. Curve d represents a system which hunts its steady state regardless of disturbance amplitude. Since the locus encloses the cutoff point, any small disturbance is unstable and the amplitude increases to the value required at point 4. For larger disturbances the amplitude decreases to this value.

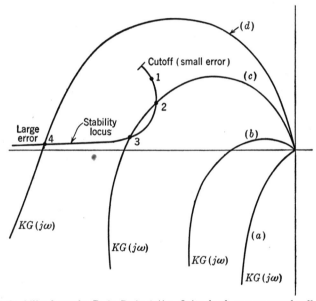

FIG. 13-17. Stability locus for $P_1 > P_2 > 0$ (i.e., finite dead zone; unequal pull-in and drop-out points).

13-11. Effect of Dead Zone and of the Difference between Pull-in and Drop-out Points on the System Stability. In general the presence of a dead zone improves system stability, and increasing the size of the dead zone further improves stability. This may be seen qualitatively by comparing curves b in Figs. 13-13 and 13-16. These curves are essentially the same; yet for zero dead zone the system hunts with finite amplitude, while for a finite dead zone there is no hunting. Quantitatively it may be seen from Eq. (13-11) that increasing the dead zone $(P_1 + P_2)$ requires that $|\mathcal{E}_1|$ be increased for KG_R to become a maximum. But for a fixed A the magnitude of this maximum is decreased. This moves the stability locus farther from the origin of the plot and thus provides greater stability for a given system. There is, of course, a corresponding disadvantage in the fact that increasing the dead zone decreases the accuracy. The exact location of the output position is not known when the system is at rest except that it is within the dead zone. Thus, it may not be possible to meet specifications of both accuracy and stability by merely adjusting the dead zone.

The effect on stability of a difference between relay pull-in and drop-out may be seen from Eq. (13-11). The analysis is itemized below:

1. If pull-in and drop-out are equal $(P_1 = P_2)$, $\sin \beta$ starts at zero for $|\mathcal{E}_1| = P_1$. Then $\sin \beta$ must traverse the entire range of values $0 \leq \sin \beta \leq 1$ as the signal $\mathcal{E}_1$ increases.

2. If P_2 is decreased so that $P_1 > P_2$, then $\sin \beta > 0$ for $|\mathcal{E}_1| = P_1$. Thus $\sin \beta$ does not have to traverse the entire range of values from zero to unity and will approach the value unity for some error signal $|\mathcal{E}_1'|$, which is less than the value required when $P_1 = P_2$.

3. Since the magnitude of the relay transfer function is

$$KG_R = 4A \sin \beta / \pi |\mathcal{E}_1|$$

and since it may be seen from steps 1 and 2 that the ratio of $\sin \beta / |\mathcal{E}_1|$ for any value of $|\mathcal{E}_1|$ is greater if $P_1 > P_2$, then in general $|KG_R|$ is larger when $P_1 > P_2$ than when $P_1 = P_2$.

4. This effectively moves the stability locus closer to the origin of the plot and thus decreases stability.

13-12. Steady-state Performance of Relay Servos. The salient features of the steady-state performance of positional relay servomechanisms have already been indicated in the discussion on stability. They will merely be summarized in this section and compared as far as possible with the performance of linear servos.

Linear servomechanisms in general have only two possible steady-state operating conditions; they are either stable or unstable, and in either case this condition is inherent in the system and not dependent on signal amplitude if the system is truly linear. If stable, the accuracy depends on the type system and the system gain. Relay servos have at least four possible steady-state operating conditions:

1. Stable
2. Unstable
3. Oscillatory (but stable)
4. Conditionally stable

The stable and unstable conditions have essentially the same meaning as for linear systems. However, when a relay servo is stable, the accuracy depends primarily on the magnitude of the dead zone. The term "oscillatory" as used here means that the system hunts its steady-state position regardless of the magnitude of the disturbance. The accuracy, of course, depends on the amplitude of the oscillation. A conditionally stable system is one which is stable for small disturbances but may be unstable or oscillatory for large disturbances. In such cases the accuracy is obviously a function of the disturbance amplitude as well as the other factors. It is also possible to have system loci $[KG(j\omega)]$ which intersect the stability locus at a number of points; in such cases there may be several possible oscillatory steady-state conditions.

When linear systems are analyzed, it is possible to predict the effect of constant-velocity input or of load torque on the steady-state performance. In the case of relay servos, however, constant-velocity input or constant load torque changes the relay transfer function (KG_R) and thus alters the stability locus. In order to discuss steady-state performance, an analysis of the relay transfer function under these conditions must be undertaken. Such investigation is beyond the scope of this text.

13-13. Transient Performance of Relay Servomechanisms. The transient performance of a servomechanism is not directly obtainable from the transfer-function plot of the system; the system differential equations must be solved for accurate results. For linear systems the magnitude loci or M circles provide a convenient and reasonably accurate indication of the transient performance when combined with certain figures of merit which are based on experience. For relay servomechanisms the M circles may be used in similar fashion if *proper* precautions are taken. They may be used with any relay servo system which is stable, and with conditionally stable systems for disturbances which result in a stable steady-state performance. They are not readily interpreted when the steady-state performance is oscillatory.

Consider the $KG(j\omega)$ locus and the stability locus of Fig. 13-18. The system represented is inherently stable. It must be remembered that each point on the stability locus represents a $-1 + j0$ point for a given amplitude of error signal. Then, if a disturbance corresponds to point c the value of M_p for this amplitude may be determined as follows:

1. Draw a straight line (ocx) from the origin through point c. This is the negative real axis for an error amplitude corresponding to point c.

2. Mark off a scale on line ocx, using the distance oc as unity.

3. Use line ocx as a negative real axis, and draw M circles to determine M_p and ω_r.

4. Repeat above procedure for other points on the stability locus, and obtain values of M_p and ω_r.

Since the system is known to be stable, the amplitude of successive oscillations must decrease; therefore if the initial disturbance locates point c on the stability locus, a point indicative of system operation must move along the stability locus from c toward cutoff at e. This general knowledge may be coordinated with the results of the indicated M_p and ω_r studies as follows:

1. Values of M_p are in general inversely related to the damping; *i.e.*, for a large M_p there is little damping, and for a small M_p considerable damping is expected.

2. Values of ω_r are roughly the same as the transient oscillating frequency.

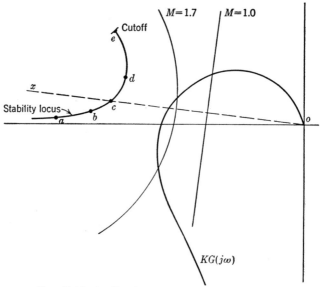

FIG. 13-18. Application of M circles to relay servos.

3. If a table is prepared from the M-circle studies showing values of M_p and ω_r as functions of the disturbing amplitude (curves may be desirable), expected variations in damping and oscillatory frequency may be seen qualitatively.

TABLE 13-1

M_p	ω_r	ε_1, deg
1.6	6	10
1.5	8	8
1.3	9	6
1.1	9.5	5
1.1	9.7	4

For example, assume that the values in Table 13-1 have been obtained from an M-circle study. For a large disturbance the system would be somewhat underdamped ($M_p = 1.6$) but relatively sluggish ($\omega_r = 6$). As the system approaches cutoff, the damping increases (M_p decreases) and the system becomes faster (ω_r increases). From such data a very well damped system is to be expected.

Analysis of such data must be based largely on experience, especially since variations in M_p and ω_r may not be as simple as in Table 13-1. For a large initial disturbance M_p and ω_r might well go through a maximum value before reaching cutoff, or M_p might increase continuously. Kochenburger states that a satisfactory criterion is that of $M_p = 1.3$ for large amplitudes and $M_p = 2.0$ for near cutoff.

13-14. Compensation of Relay Servos. Little need be said concerning the compensation of relay servos. It is apparent that the need for compensation is primarily a matter of adjusting transient performance, since the steady-state performance is affected only by reshaping the locus to eliminate hunting, and not in the sense of increasing steady-state accuracy. Therefore, reshaping of the $KG(j\omega)$ locus is required in the high-frequency portion only, and phase-lead devices are most likely to be effective. The design of such devices for relay servos involves trial-and-error methods because stability is determined as a locus rather than an isolated point; thus the design of phase-lead compensators may be considerably more difficult than for linear systems. Other adjustments which can improve performance but are not generally called compensation are:

1. Variations in the amplitude of the drive source, A.
2. Adjustment of system gain.
3. Adjustment of relay characteristics P_1 and P_2.

PROBLEMS

13-1. Calculate and plot the transfer function of a pair of relays having a pull-in current of 8 ma and a drop-out current of 5 ma.

13-2. If the time constant of the motor and load in Fig. 13-1 is $\tau = 0.1$, determine the system characteristics by a polar-locus study, using the relays of Problem 13-1 and assuming a relay-winding time constant of $\tau = 0.01$. List all assumptions made.

13-3. Repeat Probs. 13-1 and 13-2 for relays with equal pull-in and drop-out currents of 8 ma.

13-4. To the system of Fig. 4P-2 add an error detector, and insert a relay unit between the amplifier and the generator field with a supply voltage of 200 volts. Prepare polar-loci studies for the system for relay characteristics as in Probs. 13-1 and 13-3.

CHAPTER 14

THE ROOT-LOCUS METHOD

14-1. Introduction. The problem facing the designer of a servo-mechanism is twofold: he must be able to analyze a system so as to predict its performance, and he must be able to adjust or compensate the system should the response fall short of specifications. It has been shown, previously, that deriving the differential equations which describe the dynamical system and solving these equations to obtain their roots does give the system performance, accurately and completely. But carrying out a transient analysis, as this approach is called, is not feasible for other than greatly idealized systems. Moreover the information obtained is not of great help in adjusting or compensating the system, if the performance is not as desired. In other words, though the roots are of primary importance to the designer, for they do determine the system performance, knowledge of the roots alone does not point out a practical or direct method of accomplishing changes which may be required to bring the system response within specifications.

If the designer chooses to study the system response by means of the transfer-function analysis, the roots of the system equation are not obtained but information indicative of system performance is provided through proper interpretation of familiar transfer-function loci. Though an exactly quantitative prediction of system performance is not reached, the information obtained here is more readily interpreted in terms of practical system adjustment and compensation, which may be needed.

The root-locus method,[75],* which is now discussed, will be seen to utilize the more desirable features of both the transfer-function and transient analysis. Graphical procedures (somewhat akin to those used in the transfer-function approach) are provided which lead to a clear indication of the effect of gain adjustment or compensation upon system performance. This is accomplished with minimum labor because of the graphical nature of the approach. The root-locus method extends somewhat along the lines of the transient analysis because ultimately the roots of the differential equations are obtained, which means that complete and accurate transient and steady-state data may be determined. Appli-

* Superior numbers, when they appear in the text proper, are the numbers of references given in the Bibliography.

cation of this approach to best advantage, particularly in compensation design, depends considerably on experience. The principles and practices of this method as applied to servomechanism* systems, set forth in this chapter, must be restricted to rather simple cases because of space limitations.

14-2. Root-locus Method—Outline of Procedure. The procedures involved in obtaining graphical plots and using them will first be outlined. In subsequent paragraphs the details of these procedures are supplied, and, where necessary, mathematical justifications are given.

1. Obtain the open-loop transfer function of the system, and arrange it in factored form.

2. Determine the poles and zeros of the transfer function by inspection.

3. Plot the poles and zeros of the transfer function on the $s = \sigma + j\omega$ plane.

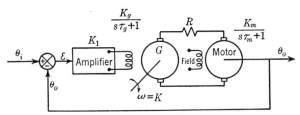

Fig. 14-1. Simple closed-loop system.

4. Use graphical computation combined with inspection to determine the loci on which the roots of the closed-loop system must fall. The previously plotted poles and zeros determine these loci.

5. Graphically locate the exact position of the roots by considering the gain of the open-loop transfer function.

6. Write the equation for system performance, using the roots thus determined.

7. If the problem is one of design or adjustment, analyze the root-locus plot to determine the desired shape of the root locus. Select (from experience, etc.) an adjustment or a compensation device to produce the desired change.

14-3. Open-loop Transfer Function. In finding the open-loop transfer function of a system, for use in the root-locus method, the transfer functions of components are determined and combined in the usual fashion, but it is desirable to maintain the s notation because the transfer function is to be used as a complex variable equation. If the simple closed-loop system of Fig. 14-1 is chosen as an example, the direct trans-

* The root-locus method is not limited to servomechanism systems but has a much wider field of application.

fer function is

$$\frac{\theta_o}{\varepsilon} = KG(s) = \frac{K_1 K_g K_m}{s(s\tau_g + 1)(s\tau_m + 1)} \tag{14-1}$$

Of course in a single-loop servo, where the feedback is unity, the open-loop transfer function is identical with the direct transfer function.

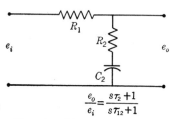

Should the feedback loop contain a network or other device, then the open-loop transfer function would be the product of $KG(s)$, given in Eq. (14-1), and the feedback-network transfer function.

$$\frac{e_0}{e_i} = \frac{s\tau_2 + 1}{s\tau_{12} + 1}$$

Fig. 14-2. Phase-lag network.

14-4. Poles and Zeros of Transfer Function. When the usual methods are used to obtain the transfer function, it is normally in factored form as seen from Eq. (14-1). The poles and zeros are then readily obtained by inspection. In Eq. (14-1) there are no zeros, since no value of s (except $s = \infty$) makes the transfer function zero. On the other hand, there are three poles; *i.e.*, the transfer function becomes infinite for $s = 0$, $s = -1/\tau_g$, $s = -1/\tau_m$.

Ordinarily both poles and zeros can be expected to exist, but the example cited here has been purposely simplified. If, for example, a series-compensating device, as shown in Fig. 14-2, had been incorporated in the system, an additional pole and a zero would be added to the open-loop transfer function. The simple phase-lag network produces a zero at $s = -1/\tau_2$ and a pole at $s = -1/\tau_{12}$ resulting in an open-loop transfer function,

$$KG(s) = \frac{K_1 K_g K_m (s\tau_2 + 1)}{s(s\tau_g + 1)(s\tau_m + 1)(s\tau_{12} + 1)} \tag{14-2}$$

It is obviously possible to have many poles and zeros depending on the complexity of the system. Often the elements introduced produce poles and zeros which are complex.

14-5. Use of Transfer-function Poles and Zeros. The poles and zeros of the open-loop transfer function may then be plotted on the $s = \sigma + j\omega$ plane as illustrated in Fig. 14-3. The poles plotted are those taken from Eq. (14-1). If additional complex poles existed (perhaps due to an additional term in the equation), they might appear on the plot as points A and A'. Such complex poles are normally conjugates.

When the poles and zeros of the *open-loop* transfer function have been plotted, they may be used to determine the loci of the roots of the *closed-loop* frequency-response function. The graphical manipulations are based on a vector interpretation of the frequency-response equation so that some discussion is provided before presenting the details.

The frequency-response equation is

$$\frac{\theta_o}{\theta_i}(s) = \frac{KG(s)}{1 + KG(s)AF(s)} \tag{14-3}$$

The roots of this equation are those values of s which make θ_o/θ_i approach

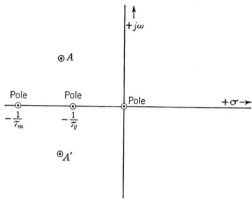

Fɪɢ 14-3. Plotting the poles and zeros of the open-loop transfer function.

zero or infinity. Therefore, by inspection, any zero of $KG(s)$ or any pole of $AF(s)$ automatically becomes a zero of the frequency response.

The poles of the frequency response, then, are those values of s which make

$$KG(s)AF(s) = -1 \tag{14-4}$$

since these values make the denominator zero and thus make θ_o/θ_i infinite. These specific s values normally cannot be seen by mere inspection of the equation but can be calculated by graphical manipulations on a complex plane such as Fig. 14-4.

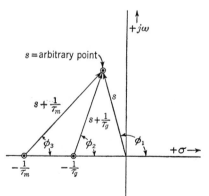

Fɪɢ. 14-4. Vector representation of terms in the frequency-response equation.

In finding, by graphical means, those values of s which make

$$KG(s)AF(s) = -1,$$

it must be remembered that

$$KG(s)AF(s)$$

is a complex quantity and so must be interpreted by vector methods. Thus the vector which has a value of -1 is $KG(s)AF(s) = 1/\underline{180°}$. The term $KG(s)AF(s)$ has some net phase angle, ϕ, corresponding to each value of s, but only those values of s which make $\phi = 180$ deg need be considered as roots. Furthermore, though many values of s may result in $\phi = 180$ deg, only certain of these values, the ones which make $|KG(s)AF(s)| = 1$, are actually roots. The procedure in finding the roots is then to find the locus or loci of points which produce a net angle, $\phi = 180$ deg. Such a plot of possible roots is called the root-locus plot. The next step is to locate the specific points on the root locus which satisfy the magnitude requirement.

The graphical manipulations necessary to determine the root locus will be outlined for the servo system of Fig. 14-1. The open-loop transfer function can be written as

$$KG(s)AF(s) = \frac{K_1 K_g K_m}{\tau_g \tau_m} \frac{1}{s(s + 1/\tau_g)(s + 1/\tau_m)} \tag{14-5}$$

so that

$$\frac{\theta_o}{\theta_i}(s) = \frac{\dfrac{K_1 K_g K_m}{\tau_g \tau_m} \dfrac{1}{s(s + 1/\tau_g)(s + 1/\tau_m)}}{1 + \dfrac{K_1 K_g K_m}{\tau_g \tau_m} \dfrac{1}{s(s + 1/\tau_g)(s + 1/\tau_m)}} \tag{14-6}$$

or

$$\frac{\theta_o}{\theta_i}(s) = \frac{K_1 K_g K_m/\tau_g \tau_m}{s(s + 1/\tau_g)(s + 1/\tau_m) + K_1 K_g K_m/\tau_g \tau_m} \tag{14-7}$$

It can be shown first that the variable terms in Eq. (14-7) can be represented as vectors on the s plane. This is done by selecting an arbitrary point on the plane and constructing vectors from each pole and zero to that point as in Fig. 14-4. The vectors constructed in Fig. 14-4 correspond to the variable terms in the θ_o/θ_i equation. The phase angles assigned to the terms for the arbitrary value of s are ϕ_1, ϕ_2, and ϕ_3.

The various portions of the root-locus plot may now be drawn roughly by inspection of the s plane, on which the poles and zeros of the open-loop transfer function are already plotted. An exact plot may be obtained by simple graphical calculations.

The evaluation of the angle of $KG(s)AF(s)$ may be shown by inspection of Eq. (14-6) or a study of Fig. 14-4. Inspection of the equation shows that the $KG(s)AF(s)$ term has three factors which contribute to the net phase angle. All three terms are in the denominator of $KG(s)AF(s)$ so that the net angle (which is the algebraic sum of the angles of the factors) is negative. Of course, if there were similar terms in the numerator, the net angle of $KG(s)AF(s)$ would be the difference between the angles of the numerator and of the denominator. Figure 14-4 shows the three angles, and the net angle of $KG(s)AF(s)$ would be

$$\phi = -(\phi_1 + \phi_2 + \phi_3)$$

The root locus is then the locus of all points for which this sum is 180 deg.

The root-locus plot for Eq. (14-7) is shown in Fig. 14-5.   If the variable point, s, is located along the negative real axis between 0 and $-1/\tau_g$,
it can be shown that the phase angle of $KG(s)AF(s)$ is -180 deg and so
that portion constitutes a part of the root locus.   For this section the
angles are $\phi_1 = 180$ deg and $\phi_2 = \phi_3 = 0$ so that $\phi(\text{net}) = 180$ deg.   A
second part of the root locus may be shown to exist between $-1/\tau_m$ and
$-\infty$; here $\phi_1 = \phi_2 = \phi_3 = 180$ deg, so $\phi(\text{net}) = 540$ deg, for which the
resulting vector is in the desired direction.   The existence of the curved,
and final, portion of the root locus may be justified as follows: If a point,

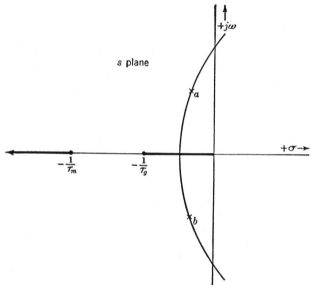

FIG. 14-5. Root locus for the single-loop servo of Fig. 14-1.

such as a, is selected slightly above the 0 to $-1/\tau_g$ region, then $\phi_1 < 180$
deg but $\phi_2 > \phi_3 > 0$ deg.   It is then obvious that proper selection of the
point can make the decrease in ϕ_1 equal to the increase in $\phi_2 + \phi_3$, so
that the total angle, ϕ, is still 180 deg.   If a point such as b is chosen,
the same reasoning would justify the existence of the negative curved
portion.
   Obtaining the complete curved root locus can be quite tedious if
point-by-point calculations are made, but in general a reasonably accurate locus may be obtained by locating several "key" points (intersections
of the root locus with horizontal and vertical axes) and calculating appropriate asymptotes.   The general procedure for obtaining such specific
information is outlined below because of the frequency of occurrence of
similar curved loci.

14-6. Determination of Asymptotes. From Fig. 14-5 it may be seen that the curved locus must extend into the first and fourth quadrants. At large distances from the origin the three poles are essentially located at a point, and so the three angles ϕ_1, ϕ_2, and ϕ_3 must be approximately equal; hence the asymptotes to the locus would be drawn at ± 60 deg to the real axis with intercept at $\sigma = \frac{1}{3}(-1/\tau_g - 1/\tau_m)$. Similar reasoning may be applied to various combinations of poles and zeros.

14-7. Intercepts with the Vertical. Again considering the curved locus of Fig. 14-5, it obviously crosses the vertical axis. At the point of crossing $\phi_1 = 90$ deg, and for ϕ to be 180 deg, it is necessary that $\phi_2 + \phi_3 = 90$ deg. A point on the vertical axis satisfying this condition is thus readily located after a few trials with a protractor. For loci which do not cross the vertical axis, a vertical line may be extended

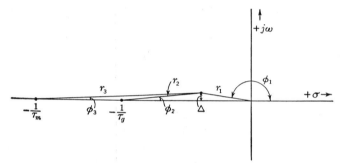

Fig. 14-6. Location of intercept with the horizontal.

through the pole around which the locus curves. At the point of intersection between the locus and such a line $\phi_p = 90$ deg, then the requirement for the point to be on the locus is that the sum of the other angles must be $n(180°) - 90°$, where n is an odd integer. Another way of stating this is that

$$\sum_{0}^{n} (180° - \phi_i) = 90° \qquad (14\text{-}8)$$

14-8. Intercepts with the Horizontal. To locate points on the root locus very near to the horizontal, or real, axis and to locate the horizontal intercepts, much the same procedure may be followed as in Sec. 14.7, except that the use of a protractor is obviously not very accurate. Such points, however, may be located rather simply by measuring lengths.

Select a point, s, close to the horizontal axis and above (or below) the region where the intercept is expected (see Fig. 14-6). If the displacement from the horizontal is Δ and this is intentionally made very small, then

$$\sin (180° - \phi_1) = \frac{\Delta}{r_1} \cong 180° - \phi$$

$$\sin \phi_2 = \frac{\Delta}{r_2} \cong \phi_2 \qquad (14\text{-}9)$$

$$\sin \phi_3 = \frac{\Delta}{r_3} \cong \phi_3$$

To satisfy the condition that $\phi = \phi_1 + \phi_2 + \phi_3 = 180$ deg, it is necessary that

$$180° - \phi_1 = \phi_2 + \phi_3 \qquad (14\text{-}10)$$

or

$$\frac{\Delta}{r_1} = \frac{\Delta}{r_2} + \frac{\Delta}{r_3} \qquad (14\text{-}11)$$

or

$$\frac{1}{r_1} = \frac{1}{r_2} + \frac{1}{r_3} \qquad (14\text{-}12)$$

Thus the intercept may be determined as a point such that the equality indicated in Eq. (14-12) exists.

Generally speaking, the ease of determination of these horizontal and vertical intercepts and also the asymptotes will be largely dependent upon both the designer's experience and the order of system.

14-9. Location of Roots on the Root-locus Plot. The root locus, thus determined, is simply a locus of possible roots, *i.e.*, the roots of the equation must lie on the locus, but the magnitude requirement must be satisfied before their actual location can be determined. For the system represented by Eq. (14-7) and Fig. 14-5, there are three roots, since the equation is of the third order. These roots may occur as three real roots or one real and two complex roots. Their location on the root-locus plot is determined by the relationship of Eq. (14-13).

$$\left| s \left(s + \frac{1}{\tau_g} \right) \left(s + \frac{1}{\tau_m} \right) \right| = \frac{K_1 K_g K_m}{\tau_g \tau_m} \qquad (14\text{-}13)$$

This condition must be met if the denominator of Eq. (14-6) is to be zero. The procedure for establishing the location of the roots is then:

1. Evaluate the magnitude of $K_1 K_g K_m / \tau_g \tau_m$.
2. Arbitrarily select a point anywhere on the root locus.
3. Lay off vectors s, $s + 1/\tau_g$, $s + 1/\tau_m$, which are the lengths from the base points to the selected point on the locus.
4. Measure the lengths of these vectors, and multiply them. Check the numerical result to see whether or not Eq. (14-13) is satisfied.
5. If Eq. (14-13) is not satisfied, shift the selected point along the locus, and repeat.

6. Repeat the above process until the required number of roots are located; then read off the numerical values of the roots.

A simple scalar multiplication is sufficient for step 4 because only the magnitude of the result is of interest. Also, if any zeros exist for the open-loop transfer function, then the vector lengths measured from these zeros must be *divided* into the product of the lengths from the poles.

It may be convenient to measure the lengths of the vectors with a logarithmic scale marked in decibels so that the final multiplication reduces to a simple addition or subtraction. This is justified in Eq. (14-14).

$$20 \log_{10} s + 20 \log_{10} \left(s + \frac{1}{\tau_g} \right) + 20 \log_{10} \left(s + \frac{1}{\tau_m} \right)$$
$$= 20 \log_{10} \left(\frac{K_1 K_g K_m}{\tau_g \tau_m} \right) \quad (14\text{-}14)$$

The trial-and-error process indicated in steps 5 and 6 normally is not laborious. Two or three tries should suffice to locate each root with sufficient accuracy.

14-10. Transient Response of the System. The roots of the denominator having been determined from the root-locus plot, the frequency-response equation may be written as

$$\frac{\theta_o}{\theta_i} (s) = \frac{KG(s)}{1 + KG(s)AF(s)} = \frac{KG(s)}{(s - r_1)(s - r_2) \cdots (s - r_n)} \quad (14\text{-}15)$$

In other words, the denominator is replaced by a product of terms of the form $(s - r_i)$. Note that Eq. (14-15) should not be interpreted too literally; *i.e.*, the initial equation for the frequency response is usually manipulated algebraically before setting up the base points for the root-locus plot, and the numerator may not be explicitly $KG(s)$ after such manipulation, but the final manipulated form of the numerator is used in applying Eq. (14-15). For example, Eq. (14-6) is an initial form of the frequency response but is manipulated to Eq. (14-7) before setting up the root-locus plot. After finding the roots, the numerator of Eq. (14-7) would be used in applying Eq. (14-15); the final result would be

$$\frac{\theta_o}{\theta_i} (s) = \frac{K_1 K_g K_m / \tau_g \tau_m}{(s - r_1)(s - r_2)(s - r_3)} \quad (14\text{-}16)$$

The time response is then obtained by substituting the proper initial conditions for θ_i (step function, ramp function, etc.) and taking the inverse transform.

When the output response is plotted on the same axis as the input, then it is fairly simple to note how system performance compares with specifications. Maximum overshoots are readily picked off such a plot.

Response time and steady-state performance ordinarily can be determined directly from the inverse transform of Eq. (14-16) without the labor of plotting the curve (assuming that representative initial conditions are inserted).

In most instances a first design is found not wholly satisfactory because of the failure of the system to meet some of the specifications. It is then necessary to modify or alter the system by gain-adjustment or compensation procedures. Again it will be found that the root-locus method lends itself well to these procedures.

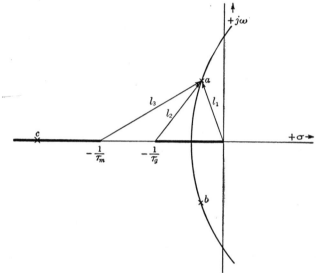

FIG. 14-7. Effect of gain on root location.

14-11. Gain Adjustment and Stability Determination. The topics of gain adjustment and stability are so closely related in the root-locus method that they are more readily studied together. Since it is known that increasing the gain of a closed-loop system makes the system more oscillatory and may even lead to instability, it is obvious that gain-adjustment procedures on the root-locus plots must change the location of all the roots on the s plane. No change will be made in the root-locus plots themselves.

If the location of the system roots for a specific gain is a, b, c in Fig. 14-7, then the system is stable because the real parts of all roots are negative (see Chap. 7). However, the system response is oscillatory because of the existence of complex roots. Since the open-loop gain is the scalar product of three vectors of the type l_1, l_2, l_3, that is, vectors from the base points to one of the roots, if the gain is decreased, this product must decrease so that in general the vector lengths decrease, and the location of the root must change in such a direction as to permit this decrease in the vector lengths. Conversely, any gain increase requires an increase in the vector lengths, and the roots must move correspondingly.

Considering, first, the root a in Fig. 14-7; if the gain is increased, this root must move along the locus toward the vertical (or $j\omega$) axis. Therefore its real part decreases while its imaginary part increases so that any oscillations set up in the system will be at an increased frequency, indicating that relative damping is lessened. If the gain is still further increased so that the root falls on the $j\omega$ axis, then there is no damping ($\sigma = 0$) and the system hunts continuously. Thus a simple stability criterion may be set up for the root-locus method by noting that the $j\omega$ axis on the root-locus plot corresponds to the $-1 + j0$ point on the Nyquist diagram. If any root lies to the right of the $j\omega$ axis, it has a positive real part and so the system is inherently unstable.

The limitations on gain adjustment are readily seen from the root-locus plot, and the maximum permissible gain for a given system may easily be established from the specifications for its transient performance. If the maximum permissible gain is not large enough to meet other specifications such as speed of response or steady-state error, then the root-locus plot must be reshaped by compensation to permit the use of additional gain, without moving the roots into an unstable region. As pointed out before, the compensating device generally introduces poles and zeros in the open-loop transfer function, and of course this reshapes the root locus. An illustration or example of compensation by root-locus methods will be given later in this chapter.

14-12. Frequency Response from the Root-locus Plot. In many applications the frequency response of a servomechanism is dictated by circumstances outside the system itself. The presence of noise in the incoming signal or at any point in the loop or mechanical vibration which may introduce extraneous signals in certain components often requires that the design of the system compensate for such effects. The usual procedure is to design the system frequency response so that the servo is not sensitive to the frequencies expected from such disturbances. In such situations it is therefore necessary to investigate the system frequency response in addition to determining its transient response, since a satisfactory transient response would not necessarily indicate the proper frequency response. Fortunately the system frequency response may also be obtained directly from the root-locus plot by graphical calculations.

Equation (14-16) gives the output-input response equation of a simple servomechanism. This may be transformed into the system-frequency-response equation merely by substituting $j\omega$ for s. Thus

$$\frac{\theta_o}{\theta_i}(j\omega) = \frac{K_1 K_g K_m / \tau_g \tau_m}{(j\omega - r_1)(j\omega - r_2)(j\omega - r_3)} \qquad (14\text{-}17)$$

If the numerator of this equation (*i.e.*, the system gain) is known, the denominator is readily determined from the root-locus plot. Assume that the root-locus plot is as shown in Fig. 14-8, with roots r_1, r_2, r_3. On the complex plane the vertical axis is the locus of values of $j\omega$. Therefore if a point $j\omega_1$ is selected, the vectors $(j\omega_1 - r_1)$, $(j\omega_1 - r_2)$, and $(j\omega_1 - r_3)$ are as shown and their product is readily evaluated. By dividing the product into the numerator one point is determined on the frequency-response curve of the system (both in magnitude and in phase). Any desired number of frequencies may be investigated, and curves plotted, by repeating the procedure for additional values of $j\omega$.

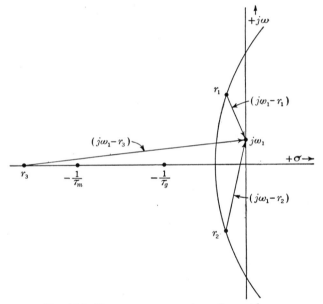

Fig. 14-8. Frequency response from the root locus.

14-13. A Single-loop Servo. In order to provide a comparison of the root-locus approach to system-performance determination with other methods, and to allow comparison of the results obtained by each, the following illustrative example utilizes a greatly simplified servo system. Detailed calculations are presented in all cases. Special consideration is given later to compensation procedures by the root-locus method.

In the servo system of Fig. 14-9 it is assumed that the d-c motor field is supplied from a constant-current source, that the motor armature inductance is negligible, and that there is no friction loading of the motor. Assume that it is desired to find the system performance as a positional servo by the differential-equation method, the transfer-function analysis, and the root-locus method.

14-14. Analysis from the Differential Equation. The differential equation of the system in Fig. 14-9 is derived as follows:

a. The output torque is

$$T_o = J\frac{d^2\theta_o}{dt^2} = K_t I_a \tag{14-18}$$

where J = inertia of load and motor
K_t = motor torque constant
I_a = motor armature current

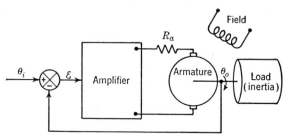

FIG. 14-9. A simple servo system.

b. The armature current is found from

$$K\mathcal{E} = I_a R_a + K_v\frac{d\theta_o}{dt} \tag{14-19}$$

$$I_a = \frac{K\mathcal{E} - K_v\dfrac{d\theta_o}{dt}}{R_a} \tag{14-20}$$

c. The equation for the torque equilibrium is

$$T_o = J\frac{d^2\theta_o}{dt^2} = \frac{K_t K\mathcal{E}}{R_a} - \frac{K_t K_v}{R_a}\frac{d\theta_o}{dt} \tag{14-21}$$

d. Rearranging and substituting $\mathcal{E} = \theta_i - \theta_o$ gives

$$\frac{JR_a}{K_t K_v}\frac{d^2\theta_o}{dt^2} + \frac{d\theta_o}{dt} + \frac{K}{K_v}\theta_o = \frac{K}{K_v}\theta_i \tag{14-22}$$

where K = amplifier gain constant
K_v = motor back-emf constant

e. In order to facilitate comparison with the equations derived later by transfer-function methods, it is convenient to define

$$\frac{JR_a}{K_t K_v} = \tau_m = \text{motor time constant}$$

$$\frac{K}{K_v} = K_1 = \text{system gain}$$

Thus

$$\tau_m \frac{d^2\theta_o}{dt^2} + \frac{d\theta_o}{dt} + K_1\theta_o = K_1\theta_i \qquad (14\text{-}23)$$

Let $\tau_m = 0.5, K_1 = 10$. Then the differential equation of the system is

$$0.5 \frac{d^2\theta_o}{dt^2} + \frac{d\theta_o}{dt} + 10\theta_o = 10\theta_i \qquad (14\text{-}24)$$

Solving by normal methods, the roots of this equation are

$$r_1, r_2 = -1 \mp j\sqrt{19} \qquad (14\text{-}25)$$

and the solution for a unit step input is then of the form

$$\theta_o = 1 + A e^{(-1+j\sqrt{19})t} + B e^{(-1-j\sqrt{19})t} \qquad (14\text{-}26)$$

Inserting boundary conditions allows evaluation of A and B as

$$A = \frac{-1 - j\sqrt{19}}{j2\sqrt{19}}$$
$$B = \frac{+1 - j\sqrt{19}}{j2\sqrt{19}} \qquad (14\text{-}27)$$

From these

$$\theta_o = 1 + \frac{-1 - j\sqrt{19}}{j2\sqrt{19}} e^{(-1+j\sqrt{19})t} - \frac{1 - j\sqrt{19}}{j2\sqrt{19}} e^{(-1-j\sqrt{19})t}$$
$$= 1 - 1.025 e^{-t} \cos(\sqrt{19}\, t - 13°) \qquad (14\text{-}28)$$

from which $\omega_r \cong \sqrt{19}$ radians/sec and the output peak is approximately 1.49 as shown in Table 14-1.

TABLE 14-1

t, sec	θ_o
0	0
0.3	0.652
0.6	1.408
0.7	1.472
0.8	1.445
1.0	1.2
1.1	1.0+
1.2	0.913
1.3	0.815
1.4	0.773
1.5	0.777
1.75	0.921
1.9	1.03
2.0	1.081
2.1	1.107
2.2	1.11

14-15. Analysis by the Root-locus Method. The open-loop transfer function of the system of Fig. 14-9 is seen by inspection to be

$$KG(s) = \frac{K/K_v}{s(s\tau_m + 1)} \tag{14-29}$$

The output-input function is then

$$\frac{\theta_o}{\theta_i}(s) = \frac{\dfrac{K/K_v}{s(s\tau_m + 1)}}{1 + \dfrac{K/K_v}{s(s\tau_m + 1)}}$$

$$= \frac{K_1/\tau_m}{s(s + 1/\tau_m) + K_1/\tau_m} \tag{14-30}$$

The base points for the root-locus plot are then at 0 and $-1/\tau_m$ (since these make θ_o/θ_i infinite) as in Fig. 14-10. The root loci are readily seen

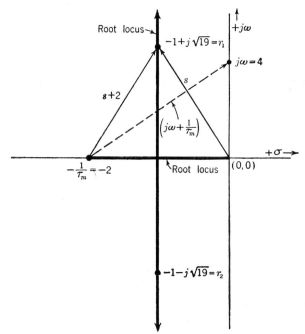

Fig. 14-10. Root-locus plot for the system of Fig. 14-9.

to be the section of the negative real axis between 0 and $-1/\tau_m$ and a straight line parallel to the $j\omega$ axis at $-1/2\tau_m$. The second of the above loci is readily derived by application of Eq. (14-12).

The exact location of the roots is obtained by applying Eq. (14-13), which gives

$$\left| s \left(s + \frac{1}{\tau_m} \right) \right| = \frac{K_1}{\tau_m}$$
$$|s(s + 2)| = 20 \qquad (14\text{-}31)$$

Normal procedure would be to select a point on the locus and measure $|s|$ and $|s + 2|$, but in this case inspection of Fig. 14-10 shows that

$$|s| = |s + 2| = \sqrt{20} \qquad (14\text{-}32)$$

There are two roots, and since the gain requirement does not permit location on the negative real axis, they must be complex conjugates.

Again from Fig. 14-10 the roots are

$$r_1 = -1 + j\sqrt{19}$$
$$r_2 = -1 - j\sqrt{19} \qquad (14\text{-}33)$$

which agrees with the differential-equation solution. The output-input response equation then becomes

$$\frac{\theta_o}{\theta_i}(s) = \frac{20}{[s - (-1 + j\sqrt{19})][s - (-1 - j\sqrt{19})]} \qquad (14\text{-}34)$$

Solving for $\theta_o(s)$ for a unit step-input displacement gives

$$\theta_o(s) = \frac{20}{s(s + 1 - j\sqrt{19})(s + 1 + j\sqrt{19})} \qquad (14\text{-}35)$$

The solution of this equation in the time domain is known to be of the form

$$\theta_o(t) = 1 + Xe^{r_1 t} + Ye^{r_2 t} \qquad (14\text{-}36)$$

The coefficients are evaluated in the usual fashion, and thus

$$\theta_o(t) = 1 + \frac{-1 - j\sqrt{19}}{2j\sqrt{19}} e^{(-1+j\sqrt{19})t} + \frac{1 - j\sqrt{19}}{2j\sqrt{19}} e^{(-1-j\sqrt{19})t} \qquad (14\text{-}37)$$

which is identical with Eq. (14-28). The reduction in labor is apparent.

The transfer-function locus of the system may also be calculated from Fig. 14-10. This is not done here, but a single point at $j\omega = 4$ is calculated for comparison with the results of the transfer-function method which is to follow. Locate the point $j\omega = +4$ on the vertical axis, and draw a line from $-1/\tau_m$ to this point. Measure the length of this line; then

$$j\omega = 4 \underline{/+90°}$$
$$j\omega + \frac{1}{\tau_m} = 4.45 \underline{/+63°} \qquad (14\text{-}38)$$

Then

$$KG(j4) = \frac{K_1/\tau_m}{j\omega(j\omega + 1/\tau_m)} = \frac{10/0.5}{(4\underline{/90°})(4.45\underline{/63°})} = 1.12\underline{/-153°} \quad (14\text{-}39)$$

14-16. Analysis by the Transfer-function Method. The transfer-function equation of the system of Fig. 14-9 in terms of frequency is

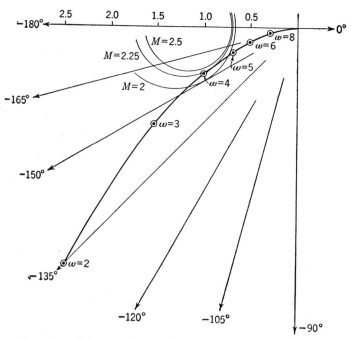

Fɪɢ. 14-11. Polar-transfer-function plot for the system of Fig. 14-9.

obtained by substituting $j\omega$ for s in Eq. (14-29), which gives

$$KG(j\omega) = \frac{K/K_v}{j\omega(j\omega\tau_m + 1)} = \frac{10}{j\omega(0.5j\omega + 1)} \quad (14\text{-}40)$$

The transfer-function plot is shown in Fig. 14-11, and the data from which it is plotted are shown in Table 14-2.

Adding M circles to Fig. 14-11 shows that the resonance peak of the closed-loop system occurs at $\omega = 4.3$ and has a magnitude $M_p = 2.2$. Interpreting these values on the basis of the methods presented in previous chapters, it is seen that the system is considerably underdamped, i.e., has a large transient overshoot and hunts at low frequency for a considerable time before reaching steady state. This information certainly is obtained with less labor than is required by the root-locus method, but the information is only semiquantitative.

TABLE 14-2

$|KG|$	ω	$\underline{/KG}$
8.93	1	$-116°34'$
3.58	2	$-135°$
1.85	3	$-146°19'$
1.12	4	$-153°26'$
0.74	5	$-158°12'$
0.53	6	$-161°34'$
0.303	8	$-165°58'$
0.197	10	$-168°41'$

14-17. Comparison of Methods. The preceding simple example probably is not too fair a basis for comparison of the three methods because the system is oversimplified. However, certain general remarks seem to be in order. First it is seen that the root-locus method gives the same answer as the differential equation and (for the one value calculated) gives an accurate calculation for points on the transfer-function locus. Second there seems to be some saving in labor in finding the differential-equation solution when the root-locus method is used. Third the labor involved in calculating the transfer function is about the same for either method. Thus one obvious advantage of the root-locus method is that it makes available both the solution of the differential equation of the system and the transfer-function plot of the system from the same basic equation without excessive labor.

14-18. Compensation by the Root-locus Method—General Discussion. The compensation procedures discussed here are outlined for the simple positioning system considered in the previous section. Though a specific example is studied, little generality in approach is lost, while the presentation of necessary detailed procedures is simplified.

When Eq. (14-37) is graphed and the plot inspected, the conclusions obtained are essentially those found from the transfer-function analysis. To improve system performance, it is necessary to increase the magnitude of the real part of the complex roots in order to damp the response. In terms of the root-locus plot this means reshaping of the locus. To do this, a compensating device must be added which will introduce the additional base points (this inherently introduces additional roots) necessary to alter the root locus.

The general effect of additional base points may be observed, for the simple servo, in Fig. 14-12. In Fig. 14-12a the original uncompensated locus is shown with base points 0 and $-1/\tau_m$, and the original roots r_1 and r_2. The introduction of an additional pole, $1/\tau_p$, as shown in Fig. 14-12b, introduces one additional root which must necessarily be a real root. Following the procedures outlined before, a new locus of complex roots results which curves into the first and fourth quadrants as indicated.

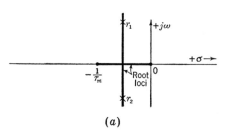

(a)

Because the real parts of the complex roots tend to become positive, the system is made less stable. The introduction of a zero, $-1/\tau_0$, on the other hand, makes the locus of complex roots curve toward $-\infty$ since the angle of the vector at the zero subtracts from the angles at the poles, i.e.,

$$\phi_1 + \phi_2 - \phi_3 = 180° \quad (14\text{-}41)$$

This is shown in Fig. 14-12c. Thus in the illustrative example, where performance is not as desired, the required change in root-locus shape may be accomplished by adding a network or device which produces a zero in the open-loop transfer function.

A choice of series or parallel connection of the compensator to produce the desired zero would suit the individual design problem. Assuming here that series compensation is selected, the necessary zero may be produced by a phase-lead device. Such devices, in their simplest practical form, have a transfer function,

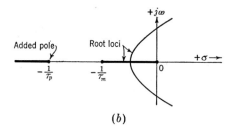

(b)

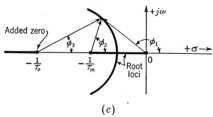

(c)

Fig. 14-12. Root loci for uncompensated and compensated servos. (a) Uncompensated system; (b) effect of introducing an additional pole; (c) effect of introducing an additional zero.

$$KG(s) = \frac{\tau_p}{\tau_0} \frac{s\tau_0 + 1}{s\tau_p + 1} = \frac{s + 1/\tau_0}{s + 1/\tau_p} \quad (14\text{-}42)$$

where $\tau_0 > \tau_p$

The device therefore introduces both a zero and a pole, with the zero closer to the origin than the pole, yielding a net phase-lead characteristic. Some attention to gain adjustment is necessary because of the attenuation caused by the compensator; but ordinarily gain-adjustment procedures are delayed until proper reshaping of the locus is attained.

With the addition of a series phase-lead network, the open-loop transfer function equation becomes

$$KG(s) = \frac{K}{K_v\tau_m} \frac{1}{s(s + 1/\tau_m)} \frac{s + 1/\tau_0}{s + 1/\tau_p} \quad (14\text{-}43)$$

and the output-input function is then

$$\frac{\theta_o}{\theta_i}(s) = \frac{K}{K_v \tau_m} \frac{s + 1/\tau_0}{s(s + 1/\tau_m)(s + 1/\tau_p) + K(s + 1/\tau_0)/K_v \tau_m} \quad (14\text{-}44)$$

The denominator of this equation is of the third order; therefore three roots will be obtained rather than two, at least one of which must be real. Since it is desired only to alter the system performance to meet specifications, then it may be assumed that two of the roots are still complex and that they are merely relocated so as to have negative real parts of larger magnitude. Only if the compensation is exceedingly great is it possible for all three of the roots to be real. Such circumstances are not likely to exist since the system response would be comparatively sluggish.

Assuming two complex and one real root exist for the system of Eq. (14-44), the time solution for the output variation after a unit step displacement will be of the form

$$\theta_o = 1 + A e^{\sigma_1 t} + B e^{\sigma_2 t} \sin(\omega t \mp \phi) \quad (14\text{-}45)$$

where σ_1 is the real root and σ_2 is the real part of the conjugate complex roots.

Many factors must be considered in quantitatively determining the roots necessary to achieve the desired compensation. The root $r_1 = \sigma_1 + j0$ should, of course, be made as large as possible without creating excessive power losses. But, generally speaking, the root $r_2 = \sigma_2 + j\omega_2$ is of primary importance as it indicates the damping of the oscillatory component of the response. Because excessive overshoots may overload equipment or cause control operation to be completely unsatisfactory, it is necessary that r_2 be carefully selected. Let it suffice to say that r_2 should have a relatively large negative real part, to provide adequate damping ($0.4 < \zeta < 1.0$). The imaginary part of the root is of equal importance, for it normally corresponds to the fundamental frequency of the oscillatory response. This frequency should be made as high as possible without approaching the frequency of any possible forcing functions to ensure rapid response and freedom from extraneous mechanical disturbances. Obviously, the phase-lead network parameters must be so chosen as to cause the above variation in roots.

Strictly trial-and-error methods could be used to determine the network parameters, but it can be shown that a first approximate setting of the complex root, r_2, may be chosen by noting the ratio of the real and imaginary components of the root, σ_2/ω, since the ratio will correspond to the approximate system damping factor ζ. This may be combined with information already obtained from the transfer-function analysis to facilitate more rapid network determination.

In Chap. 4, it was shown that the real part of a complex root may be expressed in terms of a damping factor and the undamped natural frequency of the system.   Thus if the real part of a complex root is σ_2, then

$$\sigma_2 = \zeta\omega_n \qquad (14\text{-}46)$$

The entire complex root is

$$r_2 = \sigma_2 + j\omega \qquad (14\text{-}47)$$

where

$$\omega = \sqrt{1 - \zeta^2}\,\omega_n$$

$$\omega_n = \frac{\omega}{\sqrt{1 - \zeta^2}} \qquad (14\text{-}48)$$

$$\sigma_2 = \frac{\zeta\omega}{\sqrt{1 - \zeta^2}} \qquad (14\text{-}49)$$

$$\frac{\sigma_2}{\omega} = \frac{\zeta}{\sqrt{1 - \zeta^2}} \qquad (14\text{-}50)$$

Thus if the designer is given the approximate damping desired or can, from experience, interpret the specifications in terms of the damping factor, ζ, an approximate setting of the roots may immediately be established.   Of course, the relationship stated in Eq. (14-50) does not necessarily apply to all servo systems, but it is still convenient and sufficiently accurate to use as a figure of merit for the compensation of complex systems.   Graphical procedures are used, where possible, to simplify the amount of work which is entailed in arriving at the proper degree of compensation.   These procedures are carried out in considerable detail in the following example.

14-19. Compensation of an Elementary Servo, Using Root-locus Method.   The root-locus plot and the roots obtained for Eq. (14-30) are shown in Fig. 14-13.   The damping already has been found insufficient, but this may be reiterated by noting that when σ/ω_n is calculated for the roots r_1 and r_2, $\zeta = 0.22$.   It may be assumed then that $\sigma/\omega = 0.5$ ($\zeta = 0.446$) would result in the desired performance.   A locus of possible roots having $\sigma/\omega = 0.5$ can be drawn on the same axis as the original uncompensated system root locus.   Such loci are indicated by the dotted lines on Fig. 14-13.

The intersection of the $\sigma/\omega = 0.5$ line and the uncompensated root-locus line fixes the location of the desired root.   Decreasing the gain could move the roots to the intersection, but this would make the system response sluggish.   Therefore the root locus should be reshaped by a phase-lead network so as to maintain the gain setting at a high level while obtaining a desirable value for the roots.

In this instance it is supposed that the transfer function of Eq. (14-42) describes the network selected for reshaping of the locus.   Since both a pole and zero are introduced and the locations of the network pole and zero influence the root-locus shape, the positions of these on the complex

plane are very important.   Their optimum positions are not readily predicted so that trial-and-error procedures must still be used.   However,
on the basis of information obtained from transfer-function analysis, it is
generally true that τ_0 is not the largest time constant in the system, so
that $\tau_m > \tau_0$ is a probable condition.   Also $\tau_p < \tau_0$, and (for networks of
the type chosen) τ_0/τ_p is usually between 3 and 10.   On the basis of this,
the phase-lead network parameters may be assumed, corresponding poles
and zeros calculated, and a new root locus constructed.   Assuming, here,
that $\tau_0 = 0.125$ and $\tau_p = 0.031$, a preliminary sketch of the root locus
may be prepared as in Fig. 14-14.

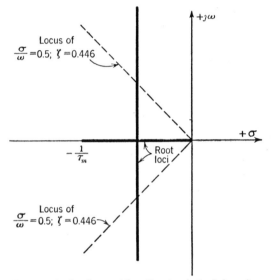

Fɪɢ. 14-13. Setting root location for desired damping.

It is readily seen that the portions of the negative real axis between
0 and $-1/\tau_m$ and between $-1/\tau_0$ and $-1/\tau_p$ are root loci.   No locus of
complex roots can exist for the section between $-1/\tau_0$ and $-1/\tau_p$, but
such a complex locus can emerge from the 0 to $-1/\tau_m$ section.   A few
measurements with a protractor establish several points on this locus,
which may then be sketched in (only one-half of this locus shown in
Fig. 14-14).   It is not necessary to construct an accurate locus in this
case because it has been predetermined that the complex root is to have
$\sigma/\omega = 0.5$, and the only points of real interest are the intersections of
the complex root locus with the $\sigma/\omega = 0.5$ line.   Therefore, after sketch-
ing the locus, a more careful investigation is made in the region of apparent intersection with the $\sigma/\omega = 0.5$ line.   This establishes the fact that
the locus is tangent at $s = 2 + j4$ and that complex roots with $\sigma/\omega = 0.5$

exist at $s = -2 \mp j4$. If no intersection had existed, the values of τ_0 and τ_p would have to be adjusted, whereas if two intersections existed, the one farthest from the origin would probably be used because it would permit higher over-all gain and lead to higher speed of response.

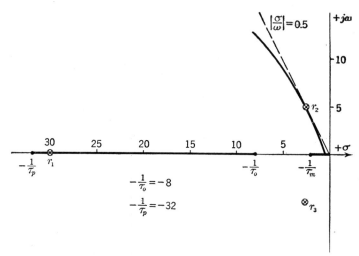

FIG. 14-14. Relocation of roots with phase-lead compensator.

The desired complex root having been located, the over-all system gain can be established by calculation from the plot. To evaluate the gain, the denominator of Eq. (14-44) may be rewritten as

$$ s\left(s + \frac{1}{\tau_m}\right)\left(s + \frac{1}{\tau_p}\right) + \left(\frac{K}{K_v \tau_m}\right)\left(s + \frac{1}{\tau_0}\right) = 0 \qquad (14\text{-}51) $$

This equation must hold for all values of s so that if the complex root $s = -2 + j4$ is inserted in (14-51), the gain K/K_v can be found directly. Since the root is known to satisfy the angular requirement of the complex numbers, only the magnitudes need be considered. The various vector lengths may be measured directly from the graph, and if a logarithmic scale is used for the measurements, Eq. (14-51) becomes

$$ |s| \text{ db} + \left|s + \frac{1}{\tau_m}\right| \text{ db} + \left|s + \frac{1}{\tau_p}\right| \text{ db} = -20 \log_{10} \frac{K}{K_v \tau_m} - \left|s + \frac{1}{\tau_0}\right| \text{ db} $$

$$ (14\text{-}52) $$

The vector lengths are measured from the base points to the complex root $s = -2 + j4$. If the indicated operation is performed, it is found that $K/K_v = 37.6 = K_1$, so that the compensated system has much higher gain than the original system, for which $K_1 = 10$.

The remaining real root must be on that portion of the negative real axis which is also the root locus. It must have a value $s = \sigma_R + j0$ which satisfies Eq. (14-51) or (14-52) when $K/K_v = 37.6$. The location of this root can be found by graphical methods, $i.e.$, scaling off the vectors of Eq. (14-51) until the magnitude requirement is met; or direct mathematical substitution in the equations can be made until the magnitude requirement is satisfied. Using the latter scheme, the values in Table 14-3 are found. Therefore assume $s = -30.1 + j0$ as the location of the real root. This root, as expected, falls between $-1/\tau_0$ and $-1/\tau_p$.

TABLE 14-3

s	K/K_v
$-10 + j0$	440
$-20 + j0$	180
$-30 + j0$	38.2
$-30.5 + j0$	29.0

To obtain the transient solution, Eq. (14-44) is rewritten as

$$\frac{\theta_o}{\theta_i}(s) = \frac{(s + 1/\tau_0)37.6/\tau_m}{(s - r_1)(s - r_2)(s - r_3)}$$
$$= \frac{75.2(s + 8)}{(s + 30.1)(s + 2 - j4)(s + 2 + j4)} \qquad (14\text{-}53)$$

So for a unit step-displacement input the solution of this equation is of the form

$$\theta_o = A + Be^{-30.1t} + Ce^{(-2+j4)t} + De^{(-2-j4)t} \qquad (14\text{-}54)$$

The coefficients are evaluated by the usual methods, and

$A = +1.0 \qquad B = +0.069 \qquad C = -0.535 + j0.0097$
$$D = -0.535 - j0.0097$$

Then

$$\theta_o = 1.0 + 0.069e^{-30.1t} + (-0.535 + j0.0097)e^{(-2+j4)t}$$
$$+ (-0.535 - j0.0097)e^{(-2-j4)t}$$
$$= 1.0 + 0.069e^{-30.1t} - 2e^{-2t}\cos\left(4t - \tan^{-1}\frac{0.0097}{0.535}\right)$$
$$= 1.0 + 0.069e^{-30.1t} - 2e^{-2t}\cos 4t \qquad (14\text{-}55)$$

from which $\omega_r = 4$ and the output peak is approximately 1.47, as seen in Table 14-4. The transient responses of the uncompensated system [Eq. (14-28) and Table 14-1] and of the compensated system (Table 14-4) are plotted in Fig. 14-15. It is seen that the compensation damps out the oscillation much more rapidly but the initial overshoot is essentially the same.

TABLE 14-4

t	θ_o
0.3	0.603
0.4	1.026
0.5	1.306
0.6	1.452
0.7	1.467
0.8	1.404
0.9	1.298
1.0	1.176
1.1	1.067
1.2	0.984
1.3	0.923
1.4	0.904
1.6	0.919
1.8	0.968
2.0	1.005

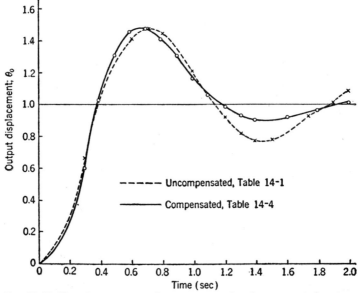

FIG. 14-15. Transient response of uncompensated and compensated systems.

If the result is still unsatisfactory, changes in the location of the roots may be accomplished by further gain adjustment. Where this does not suffice, changes must be made in the compensation device and the procedure repeated.

In conclusion it may be noted that a phase-lead device could be designed for the preceding system, using transfer-function methods already discussed. However, some saving in time results from the employment of the root-locus method if the designer is sufficiently familiar with its use. But the principal advantage of this method is that the transient response is obtained directly, and so all performance data are known.

14-20. Summary of Compensation Procedures.

1. Plot the root locus of the uncompensated system.

2. On the same coordinate axis plot a line corresponding to the approximate degree of damping consistent with specifications. Note the intersection of the line and the complex root locus.

3. Select the type of network or device to produce the phase lead or lag necessary to move the roots to the desired location.

4. Assume parameters for the selected type of compensator, and calculate the poles and zeros produced.

5. Plot the additional base points on the same coordinate axes used for the uncompensated system locus.

6. Construct the approximate new root locus, using the open-loop transfer function of the compensated system. Attention need be given only to the portion of the s plane in the neighborhood of the desired complex roots.

7. Detailed calculations should be made in the vicinity of the desired roots to find the new complex root.

8. Substitute the complex root thus determined in the denominator of the θ_o/θ_i equation, and evaluate the gain.

9. Determine the real root by substitution in the same equation as in (8) with proper gain constants.

10. Obtain the inverse transformation, substituting appropriate initial conditions. Plot $\theta_o(t)$.

11. Compare $\theta_o(t)$ with specifications. If the result is not as desired, alter the gain or the compensation.

The procedure is essentially the same for higher-order systems, except that the work involved is somewhat increased.

14-21. Multiple-loop Systems.

In applying the root-locus method to multiple-loop systems, the procedure is fundamentally the same as is used with the transfer-function method. The innermost loop is treated first and is reduced to an equivalent series element; then all series elements are combined and the next loop closed, etc.

As a qualitative illustration consider the relatively simple system of Fig. 14-16. The inner loop is the system of Fig. 14-9, and its output-input function is given by Eq. (14-30). To analyze the system, the roots of the inner loop would be found as in Fig. 14-10, and the output-input function would then be given by Eq. (14-34). This equation, (14-34), is the transfer function of the system as far as the external loops are concerned, and the roots determined for this inner loop become base points (poles) in finding the roots for the entire system.

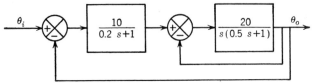

FIG. 14-16. Simple multiloop system.

Thus the open-loop transfer function for the outer loop of the system of Fig. 14-16 is

$$KG(s) = \frac{10}{0.2s + 1} \frac{20}{(s + 1 - j\sqrt{19})(s + 1 + j\sqrt{19})} \qquad (14\text{-}56)$$

The base points for the root-locus plot are shown in Fig. 14-17, and the root locus may be sketched in. The location of the specific roots is then determined in the manner previously discussed. The general procedure may be repeated for any number of subordinate loops.

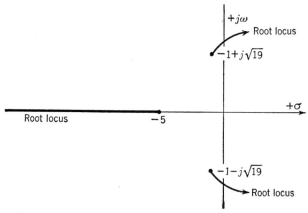

FIG. 14-17. Approximate root locus for system of Fig. 14-16.

14-22. Use with Experimental Data. In practice the characteristics of a component or a group of components may be available only in the form of experimental data. These data may be a frequency response or a transient response, depending on the equipment available for measurement, the accuracy desired, and the physical nature of the component. In order to represent the component mathematically for use with the root-locus method, it is necessary to determine its poles and zeros. These are not too difficult to determine if the frequency response is known but are rather obscure in the transient curves.

It has been shown in a previous chapter that the transfer function of a unit over a given frequency range may be represented by logarithmic magnitude and phase curves. The magnitude curves may be approximated by asymptotes, and the break points in the curve occur at frequencies corresponding to the time constants. Since, in general, the negative reciprocal of each time constant represents a pole or zero, most of the poles and zeros are readily determined. When the frequency response contains a peak, indicative of a complex pole (quadratic term), it is also necessary to determine the damping factor, ζ. This might be done by comparison with standard curves or by conformal mapping techniques.[74,76]

When the characteristics are given as transient curves, the poles and zeros are not as readily obtained and accurate evaluation depends largely on experience. If the envelope of a transient oscillation can be drawn, the value of the real part of the complex roots may be determined and the frequency of oscillation gives an indication of the imaginary part of the root. If several pairs of complex roots are present, their determination is naturally more difficult. Real negative roots indicate their presence largely by producing a "dead time," or time of negligible change in output response near $t = 0$. Other factors which may be helpful in estimating the roots are the maximum slope of the initial build-up, the magnitude of the initial overshoot, and the time for the system to come to steady state. All of these factors are obviously difficult to interpret in terms of numerical roots unless the user has considerable familiarity with transient curves.

14-23. Summary and Conclusions. The root-locus method is another useful tool for the analysis and synthesis of servomechanisms. It is not independent of the differential-equation and transfer-function methods but uses them as a foundation for its practical application. Time and effort are reduced by using the root-locus method, at least in so far as it makes both the transient response and the frequency response available from a single graphical plot. Its chief drawback seems to lie in the fact that the concepts of poles, zeros, and roots are not familiar tools to most engineers, so that complete understanding and appreciation are not readily attained, nor are the results of experience easily interpreted in terms of the required concepts. The authors feel that the root-locus method should prove very valuable in the analysis and design of servomechanisms.

APPENDIX A

TABLE 1

LAPLACE TRANSFORMS

$f(t)$	$F(s) = \mathcal{L}[f(t)]$
1. A (a constant)	$\dfrac{A}{s}$
2. $1 = u(t)$	$\dfrac{1}{s}$
3. $e^{-\alpha t}$	$\dfrac{1}{s + \alpha}$
4. $\dfrac{1}{\tau} e^{-t/\tau}$	$\dfrac{1}{s\tau + 1}$
5. $Ae^{-\alpha t}$	$\dfrac{A}{s + \alpha}$
6. $\sin \beta t$	$\dfrac{\beta}{s^2 + \beta^2}$
7. $\cos \beta t$	$\dfrac{s}{s^2 + \beta^2}$
8. $\dfrac{1}{\beta} e^{-\alpha t} \sin \beta t$	$\dfrac{1}{s^2 + 2\alpha s + \alpha^2 + \beta^2}$
9. $\dfrac{e^{-\alpha t}}{\beta - \alpha} - \dfrac{e^{-\beta t}}{\beta - \alpha}$	$\dfrac{1}{(s + \alpha)(s + \beta)}$

10. $\dfrac{Ae^{-\alpha t} - Be^{-\beta t}}{C}$ $\dfrac{s + a}{(s + \alpha)(s + \beta)}$

where $A = a - \alpha$, $B = a - \beta$, $C = \beta - \alpha$

11. $\dfrac{e^{-\alpha t}}{A} + \dfrac{e^{-\beta t}}{B} + \dfrac{e^{-\delta t}}{C}$ $\dfrac{1}{(s + \alpha)(s + \beta)(s + \delta)}$

where $A = (\beta - \alpha)(\delta - \alpha)$, $B = (\alpha - \beta)(\delta - \beta)$, $C = (\alpha - \delta)(\beta - \delta)$

$f(t)$	$F(s) = \mathcal{L}[f(t)]$
12. t	$\dfrac{1}{s^2}$
13. t^2	$\dfrac{2}{s^3}$
14. t^n	$\dfrac{n!}{s^{n+1}}$
15. $\dfrac{d}{dt} f(t)$	$sF(s) - f(0+)$
16. $\dfrac{d^2}{dt^2} f(t)$	$s^2F(s) - sf(0+) - \dfrac{df}{dt}(0+)$
17. $\dfrac{d^3}{dt^3} f(t)$	$s^3F(s) - s^2f(0+) - s\dfrac{df(0+)}{dt}$

$$- \dfrac{d^2f(0+)}{dt^2}$$

18. $\int f(t)\,dt$ $\qquad\qquad\qquad\qquad \dfrac{1}{s}\left[F(s) + \int f(t)\,dt\Big|_{0_+} \right]$

19. $\dfrac{1}{\alpha}\sinh \alpha t$ $\qquad\qquad\qquad\qquad\qquad \dfrac{1}{s^2 - \alpha^2}$

20. $\cosh \alpha t$ $\qquad\qquad\qquad\qquad\qquad\quad \dfrac{s}{s^2 - \alpha^2}$

TABLE 2
M LOCI FOR POLAR PLOTS

M	Center (x-coordinate)	Radius	$\psi = \sin^{-1} 1/M$, deg
0.5	+0.333	0.67	
0.6	+0.562	0.94	
0.7	+0.960	1.37	
0.8	+1.777	2.22	
0.9	+4.26	4.74	
1.0	∞	∞	90
1.1	−5.77	5.24	65.2
1.2	−3.27	2.73	56.5
1.3	−2.45	1.88	50.2
1.4	−2.04	1.46	45.6
1.5	−1.80	1.20	41.8
1.6	−1.64	1.03	38.7
1.7	−1.53	0.9	36
1.8	−1.47	0.84	33.7
1.9	−1.38	0.73	31.7
2.0	−1.33	0.666	30.0
2.2	−1.26	0.573	27.0
2.4	−1.21	0.505	24.6
2.5	−1.19	0.476	23.6
2.6	−1.17	0.451	22.6
2.8	−1.15	0.41	20.9
3.0	−1.12	0.375	19.5
3.5	−1.10	0.34	16.6
4.0	−1.07	0.266	14.5
4.5	−1.05	0.234	12.8
5.0	−1.04	0.208	11.5

TABLE 3
N LOCI FOR POLAR PLOTS*

$/\theta_o/\theta_i$, deg	Center (y coordinate)	Radius
0	∞	∞
-5	-5.73	5.75
-10	-2.84	2.88
-15	-1.84	1.90
-20	-1.37	1.46
-25	-1.07	1.17
-30	-0.866	1.00
-35	-0.714	0.872
-40	-0.596	0.775
-45	-0.5	0.707
-50	-0.42	0.656
-55	-0.35	0.61
-60	-0.29	0.577
-65	-0.223	0.548
-70	-0.18	0.531
-75	-0.134	0.518
-80	-0.087	0.506
-90	000	0.500

* The centers of all circles are at $x = -\frac{1}{2}$.

TABLE 4
CONVERSION FOR RATIO AND DECIBELS

Ratio	Decibels	Ratio	Decibels	Ratio	Decibels
5.0	14	1.8	5.1	0.9	-0.906
4.5	13	1.7	4.6	0.8	-1.938
4.0	12	1.6	4.08	0.7	-3.10
3.5	10.85	1.5	3.52	0.6	-4.44
3.0	9.51	1.4	2.91	0.5	-6.0
2.5	7.93	1.3	2.28	0.4	-7.93
2.0	$+6.0$	1.2	1.58	0.3	-10.44
1.9	5.57	1.0	0.00	0.2	-14
				0.1	-20
				0.05	-26

Decibels	Ratio	Decibels	Ratio	Decibels	Ratio	Decibels	Ratio
$+20$	10	6	2.0	-0.5	0.945	-8	0.398
18	7.94	5	1.78	-1.0	0.894	-9	0.354
15	5.62	4	1.59	-2	0.795	-10	0.316
12	3.99	3	1.41	-3	0.707	-12	0.251
10	3.16	2	1.26	-4	0.63	-15	0.178
9	2.82	1	1.12	-5	0.562	-18	0.125
8	2.51	0.5	1.06	-6	0.50	-20	0.100
7	2.24	0	1.00	-7	0.447		

TABLE 5
M-CONTOUR DATA

$M = 2$ db		$M = 3$ db		$M = 4$ db		$M = 5$ db	
ϕ, deg	db	ϕ, deg	db	ϕ, deg	db	ϕ, deg	db
−180	13.7	−180	10.7	−180	8.6	−180	7.0
−170	13.5	−170	10.4	−170	8.3	−170	6.8
−160	13.0	−160	9.7	−160	7.8	−160	6.0
−150	12.0	−150	8.3	−150	6.3	−155	5.3
−140	10.5	−145	7.7	−145	5.0	−150	4.0
−130	7.2	−140	6.6	−141	2.2	−147	1.2
−128	4.5	−135	3.0	−145	−0.6	−150	−0.7
−130	1.5	−140	−0.6	−150	−2.0	−155	−2.2
−140	−1.8	−145	−1.9	−160	−3.3	−160	−2.7
−150	−3.4	−150	−2.7	−170	−3.9	−170	−3.5
−160	−4.3	−160	−4.0	−180	−4.2	−180	−3.9
−170	−4.8	−170	−4.4				
−180	−5.1	−180	−4.8				

$M = 6$ db		$M = 9$ db		$M = 12$ db	
ϕ, deg	db	ϕ, deg	db	ϕ, deg	db
−180	6.0	−180	3.8	−180	2.5
−170	5.7	−175	3.7	−175	2.3
−160	4.8	−170	3.5	−170	1.9
−155	3.9	−165	2.8	−166	0.2
−150	1.0	−160	1.5	−170	−1.2
−155	−1.5	−159	0.8	−175	−1.8
−160	−2.3	−160	−0.2	−180	−1.9
−170	−3.4	−165	−1.6		
−180	−3.7	−170	−2.2		
		−175	−2.4		
		−180	−2.5		

APPENDIX B

ERROR DETECTORS

B-1. Introduction. Closed-loop automatic-control systems are used to maintain some functional relationship between an input quantity and an output quantity. In order to accomplish this purpose, it is necessary to measure the output quantity, or controlled variable, determine the deviation of the output from the desired value, and apply power to reduce this deviation. Thus, an error detector is any device or combination of devices used to determine the deviation of the output from the desired value.

In order to compare the output with the input or the reference quantity, the error-detector system must be capable of accepting signals of different physical natures and often must be able to convert them to a common physical quantity in order to effect the comparison. The output of the error detector, which is the difference between the two signals compared, must be of the proper physical nature to actuate the controller of the power supply that drives the output, or affects the controlled variable. With the existing variety of control problems and the numerous ways of solving each, a large number of error detectors are available. Some are separate units, while others are merely a part of a complete controller. This appendix attempts to illustrate a reasonable number of the types of available error detectors, with emphasis placed on the principle of operation.

The discussion here presented is divided into three general classifications, electrical, mechanical, and fluid error detectors, since the great majority of applications use detectors which may be conveniently grouped under these headings. Furthermore, the quantities most commonly controlled are position and velocity; thus each of the major classifications will be so subdivided, with an additional subclassification of miscellaneous types which do not fit in the position or velocity classes.

SECTION I. ELECTRICAL ERROR DETECTORS

CLASS A. POSITION ERRORS

B-2. Potentiometer Bridge. If two potentiometers are connected to a single voltage source, E, as in Fig. B-1, the variable tap on one connected to the reference quantity (desired position), and the variable tap on the other connected to the output (controlled position), then there is zero

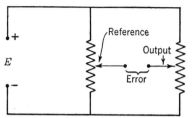

voltage between the taps when reference and output are in correspondence. If the movable arms are not in correspondence, then a net voltage exists between the taps and the output tap is positive with respect to the reference if the output is electrically above the reference, and vice versa. The magnitude of the voltage is proportional to

FIG. B-1. Potentiometer bridge.

the error if the potentiometers are linear, and the direction of the error is indicated by the polarity of the voltage between the taps.

Example. An elementary illustration of the use of a potentiometer bridge is shown in Fig. B-2. If it is desired to control the level of liquid in a tank, the arrangement shown may be used. If the level is too low, the error voltage closes the solenoid valve, reduces the outgoing flow, and permits the level to rise. For too high a liquid level, the solenoid valve

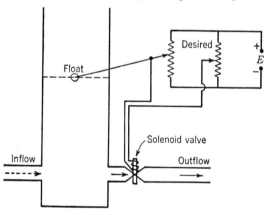

FIG. B-2. Liquid-level control.

is opened and the drainage increased. Additional circuitry might be required to obtain satisfactory performance under various conditions, but the principle involved is clearly shown.

Rotational potentiometers would normally be used with systems involving rotary motion and may be obtained with helical windings if several revolutions are desired. The accuracy of the system depends on the mechanical construction of the potentiometers, including such factors as wire size, winding pitch, brush width, bearing friction, etc., as well as any backlash or play introduced by linkage mechanisms or gearing which may be needed to properly couple the potentiometers to respective input and output members.

If translational motions are involved, some type of gearing may be employed or a straight-line potentiometer may be used.

B-3. E Transformer. When small position errors are to be measured and corrected in systems where limits or stops are used to avoid excessive errors, a device known as an E transformer may be used. Figure B-3 illustrates a type for translational motion and a type for rotational motion. The structural parts, A and B, are of magnetic material and form a closed magnetic circuit. One of these, B, might be attached to the output, either directly or through some type of linkage, while part A is suitably connected to the reference.

The magnetic circuit is excited with an alternating voltage, E, applied to the center coil. The secondary coils (which must have identical characteristics) are connected in series opposing, with the free ends used to produce an error signal. When output and reference are in correspondence, the magnetic circuit is balanced, the voltages induced in the secondary coils are equal, and they cancel each other owing to the series connection, thus producing no error voltage. When correspondence does not exist, part A is displaced with respect to B, thus increasing the reluctance of one of the magnetic paths. The induced voltages are not equal, and a net error signal is produced. The magnitude of the error signal is proportional to the position error (over a limited displacement range), and

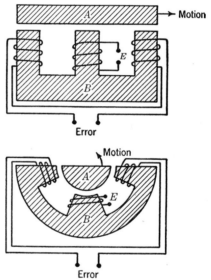

Fig. B-3. E transformers.

the direction of the error is indicated by a 180-deg phase shift as the error goes through zero.

The accuracy of the E transformer is limited by both its mechanical and electrical characteristics. For accurate indications the air gap should be small and uniform. This introduces problems in machining and in alignment. The inductance of the windings tends to introduce some phase shift which affects the net error signal. The fringing flux produced at the air gap also tends to limit the accuracy.

The rotational type of E transformer is sometimes used in gyro pickups. No simple illustration is available for use in this appendix.

B-4. Synchro Systems—General and Definitions. *Synchro* is a generic term used to describe a rotary inductor similar to an induction regulator, in which variable coupling is obtained by changing the relative orientation of the primary windings. The primary windings, from one to three in number, are normally wound upon a rotor of laminated magnetic material. The rotor may have only limited rotation, in which case the connections to the primary windings are brought out on flexible leads, but usually it is free to rotate continuously, and the connections are brought out by slip rings and brushes.

All standardized units are known as synchros, but manufacturers have designated their particular units by trade names, such as Selsyn for the General Electric Company, Autosyn for the Bendix Aviation Corporation, Teletorque for the Kollsman Instrument Division of Square D Company, and Diehlsyn for the Diehl Manufacturing Company. The most common use of synchros is the transmission of angular data or torque by the use of two such units back to back or in conjunction with a servo system.

Before a consideration of the theory and construction of units and a complete synchro generator-motor system is presented, a few definitions will be given.

Synchro generator. A unit the rotor of which is mechanically driven, for generating or transmitting electrical signals corresponding to the angular position of the rotor.

Synchro motor. A unit the rotor of which is free to turn in accordance with the electrical signals received.

Synchro differential generator. A unit the rotor of which is mechanically driven, for modifying a received signal and transmitting an electrical signal corresponding to the sum or difference of the impressed and modifying signals.

Synchro differential motor. A unit the rotor of which is free to turn in accordance with the sum or difference of electrical signals received from two sources.

Synchro control transformer. A unit which is normally used to produce a single-phase voltage whose magnitude is proportional to the sine of the angle of rotation of its rotor with respect to the magnetic field of its stator.

Synchro capacitor. A unit whose function is to counteract the lagging component of the exciting current drawn by a differential unit or a control transformer, thereby reducing the heating of the rotors of the synchro generator and also improving the stiffness of the system.

B-5. Synchro Systems—Theory and Construction of Units. The structure of most synchros is similar to that of a conventional three-phase fractional-horsepower alternator. The stator of a synchro is a cylindrical slotted laminated magnetic structure, usually bearing a three-phase Y-connected winding which is (with the exception of differentials and control transformers) the secondary of the synchro. In most cases the stator laminations are skewed one slot pitch to eliminate slot lock and the resulting angular errors. In units in which the stator laminations are not skewed, the rotor laminations are skewed instead.

The stator winding is not three-phase in the usual meaning of the term since all induced voltages are in time phase. The three legs of the stator winding are spatially displaced 120 deg from each other.

The standard types of synchros are of two-pole rotor construction. The salient-pole rotor is the most common type of synchro rotor. This is also known as the *dumbbell* or H type and is used in both synchro generators and motors. It bears a machine-wound single-phase spool winding which serves as the primary, or excitation winding, of the synchro. Only two slip rings are required for this unit. The rings have full excitation voltage impressed upon them at all times. The other rotors used are the umbrella rotor and the wound rotor. The wound rotors are laminated and slotted structures carrying either a single-phase winding with two collector rings for control transformers or a Y-connected three-phase winding with three collector rings for differential units.

B-6. Synchro Generators. In the conventional synchro generator, single-phase a-c excitation is applied to the winding of a dumbbell rotor. The exciting current flowing in this primary winding produces a flux which links each of the three stator (secondary) windings to a greater or lesser degree depending upon the angular position of the rotor with respect to the several stator windings. Figure B-4 shows the induced secondary line voltages for three different positions of the rotor. These induced voltages may be represented as $V \sin \alpha$, $V \sin (\alpha - 120°)$, and $V \sin (\alpha - 240°)$, where V is the rated secondary voltage and α is the angular displacement of the rotor from its electrical zero position. A plot of these voltages as functions of α is shown in Fig. B-4b.

For a given distribution and polarity of stator voltages, there is but one corresponding position of the rotor; conversely, for any position of the rotor, there is but one secondary-voltage condition. Thus the stator voltages constitute an electrical indication of the rotor position.

B-7. Synchro Motors. Electrically, a synchro motor is identical with a synchro generator, and the preceding discussion applies. The distinguishing feature of a synchro motor is that near one end of the rotor shaft there is an oscillation damper, a flywheel with about the same moment of inertia as that of the rotor itself, which is free to rotate on the shaft. A friction coupling between the rotor and the shaft provides a means for transferring energy from the rotor to the disk, and "stops" limit to about 45 deg the free rotation of the flywheel relative to the shaft. This friction coupling dissipates energy when the rotor oscillates, as it does when coming into the synchronous position. (Two synchros are in synchronism when their unbalanced voltages are minimized by placing their rotors in corresponding positions.)   The added inertia furnished by the oscillation damper prevents the motor from "running away," an inherent danger in either synchro motors or differentials.

Running away of a synchro motor is not the same phenomenon as that associated with the high speed attained by a series motor on removal of its load but arises from the similarity of a synchro unit to a single-phase induction motor.   The currents in the stator are approximately in the same time phase and so produce a magnetic field constant in direction.

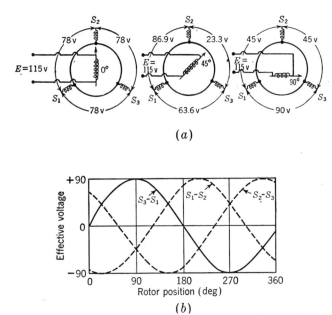

(a)

(b)

Fig. B-4. (a) Induced voltages in synchro generator rotor (for various rotor angles); (b) synchro stator voltages for various rotor positions.

There is, also, a primary magnetic field due to the rotor current.   This is the same situation that exists in the single-phase induction motor, and, like this induction motor, the synchro unit has no starting torque.   When the synchro generator drives a synchro motor or a differential at low angular velocities, the motor torque developed is not great enough to overcome the synchronizing torque and the units remain in step.   If, however, the angular velocity becomes large, the motor torque becomes sufficiently great to overcome the synchronizing torque and the synchro generator no longer has control.   The effect of the inertia and the dissipation added by the damping flywheel is to prevent momentary oscillatory velocities greater than the critical value.

A synchro motor can be used as a synchro generator, but the converse is not true for 60-cps units.   Synchro motors designed for 400-cps application generally have little tendency to run away and so are not provided with dampers.

B-8. Differential Units.   Differential machines are wound with three-phase Y-connected windings on both rotor and stator.   The rotor is a slotted cylindrical structure.

A 60-cps differential machine is usually connected between two salient-pole synchros.   The stator winding is the primary and derives its magnetizing current from the stator of a connected synchro generator.   The three line voltages of the synchro generator give rise to proportional currents in the three-phase stator windings of the differential machine.   The resultant magnetic flux produced by these currents in the differential stator is in the same position with respect to its stator winding.   Thus, there is produced in the differential machine a flux whose position corresponds to the position of the synchro-generator rotor.

As was the case with the synchro generator, this flux induces in the secondary windings of the differential, voltages whose magnitudes are dependent upon the relative positions of the windings and the flux.   The distribution and polarity of the voltages induced in the secondary of the differential machine represent the algebraic sum of the rotations of the rotors of the synchro generator and the differential with respect to their stators.

The differential generator obtains its excitation from the other units of the system to which it is connected.   Since it has losses, it is evident that to have 90-volt primary (stator) windings supply 90 volts on the secondary (rotor) windings, the units cannot be wound on a 1:1 turn ratio, but on a 1:1 plus ratio.   For this reason the stator is always considered the primary and should be connected to the stator windings of its associated synchro generator.

This machine can be used either as a differential generator for superimposing a correction on the signal from a synchro generator or as a differential motor for indicating the sum or difference of rotation of two separate synchro generators.   In the latter case, it is equipped with a mechanical damper, as was explained in the discussion on Synchro Motors.

B-9. Synchro Control Transformers.   The control transformer is equipped with a single-phase winding on a cylindrical rotor.   The stator constitutes the primary winding and receives its excitation from a synchro generator.   The exciting currents produce a resultant flux in the machine, the position of which, with respect to the stator, corresponds to the angle represented by the applied stator voltages.   This flux induces in the rotor winding a voltage whose magnitude is dependent upon the position of the rotor with respect to the flux. If the rotor is in such a position as to link a maximum of the flux, the voltage induced is a maximum; a 90-deg displacement will place the rotor coil across the flux, and the voltage induced will be zero. The latter position, often called the *null* position, is the normal condition of operation of a control transformer.

It is apparent that there are two null positions of the rotor. A slight rotation of the rotor in the clockwise direction, for example, will produce a small voltage whose polarity depends upon which of the two null positions is chosen. Thus, if means are provided for recognizing polarity, there is but one correspondence position of a control transformer for a given distribution of existing voltages.

The impedances of the stator and rotor windings of a control transformer are considerably higher than those of an equivalent-sized synchro

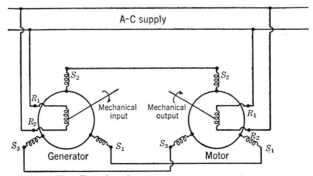

Fig. B-5. Synchro motor-generator system.

generator or motor, and a control transformer should never be used to feed a low-impedance load. High impedance of the stator winding reduces the excitation current drawn from the system by the addition of the control transformer, and high impedance of the rotor winding gives a higher and more useful output-voltage gradient.

B-10. Synchro Generator and Motor. It has been shown that for a given position of a synchro-generator rotor there is a given distribution of single-phase voltages between the three stator leads; the same holds true for a synchro motor. If the two stators are interconnected, as shown in Fig. B-5, and if the rotors are in identical positions, the stator voltages will balance and no current will flow in the stator windings. However, if the rotors are displaced with respect to each other, then the stator voltages will not be matched and the net unbalanced voltages will cause current to flow in the stator windings. These currents will create torques in both machines, and the motor rotor, being unrestrained, will move to a position of synchronism with the generator. It is interesting to note that the synchro motor is not a "motor" in the usual sense of the word: the mechanical work done by the synchro motor is derived from the work done on the synchro generator; electricity serves only as the means for transmitting this work from the synchro generator to the synchro motor.

The uses of this synchro generator-motor combination are many. If the rotor of the generator is turned manually or automatically to represent the position of a gyro compass, a water-level float, a valve, etc., then the attached synchro motor, wherever it may be located, will indicate the position of the controlled member. Furthermore, one synchro generator can control several synchro motors so that the desired position can be indicated at a number of different locations. The synchro generator and motor combination is thus seen to provide a means of remote indication, but not automatic control. This combination is an open-loop system and thus is not a servomechanism.

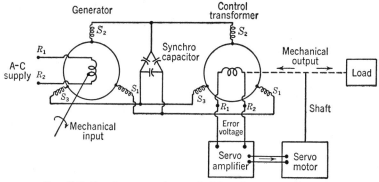

Fig. B-6. Synchro generator–control transformer servo system.

B-11. Synchro Generator and Control Transformer. A control transformer is used when it is desired to position a load of any sort by a synchro-servo system. When connected to a transmitting synchro system as shown in Fig. B-6, the rotor of a control transformer furnishes an a-c voltage the magnitude of which is an indication of the size of the angular error between the control-transformer rotor and the transmitting-element rotor, while its polarity or phase is an indication of the direction of the error. This voltage may be fed to a visual-reading meter and the position of the control-transformer rotor adjusted manually until the meter reads zero, or it may be fed into an amplifier of some sort and used to control a motor that automatically positions the rotor. All automatic controls have antihunt features incorporated in their systems to prevent overtravel and oscillation at coincidence and to improve accuracy and speed of response. The system may be more complex depending on the power and degree of precision required as well as upon other special control features. The use of a synchro differentials is frequently required in more complex systems, particularly multiloop systems. Their application is not discussed here.

CLASS B. VELOCITY ERRORS

B-12. Use of Position-error Detectors. When an automatic-control system is used to duplicate a velocity or to produce a velocity proportional to some input signal, it is frequently possible to use a position-type detector as an error-sensing device. A synchro-generator and synchro-transformer combination are readily used when both input and output are rotational velocities, whereas the potentiometer bridge may be employed provided the number of revolutions involved is reasonably

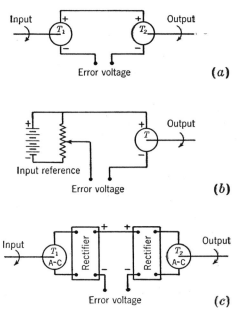

FIG. B-7. Tachometers as velocity-error detectors. (a) D-C tachometer bridge; (b) comparison of output velocity with input reference; (c) A-C tachometer bridge.

limited. Either type may prove satisfactory in control of linear velocities if suitable gearing or similar conversion mechanisms are available.

In general, when position-type error detectors are used, the output velocity exactly duplicates the input; *i.e.*, there is no velocity error. This is due to the fact that the error detector compares the position of a point on the output with that of a reference point and endeavors to reduce any displacement error. Mathematically this corresponds to an integration, *i.e.*, systems using position-error detectors are inherently class 1 or higher, since the system equation must have at least one integration.

B-13. Tachometer Bridge. In many applications involving velocity as an output quantity, the exact duplication of an input velocity is not required, and the use of position-type error detectors with associated equipment is not economically justified. Under such conditions tachometers which convert the velocity to voltage are frequently used as error detectors, by connecting them back to back through suitable filters and rectifiers.

Figure B-7a shows the use of two d-c tachometers in what is commonly called a tachometer bridge. The output voltage of each tachometer is proportional to the velocity, and they are connected electrically in opposition so that any difference in velocity appears as a voltage at the error terminals. The polarity of the voltage indicates the direction of the error (output velocity too high or too low) while the magnitude of the error voltage is proportional to the difference in velocity.

Figure B-7b shows a common application in which the desired output velocity is specified by a command signal which is not in itself a velocity, but a voltage derived from a standard source. Quite often, where d-c tachometers are used, filtering units must be added to minimize noise caused by commutation.

Alternating-current tachometers are also used as velocity-measuring devices and therefore may be used as error detectors. They have some inherent advantages over d-c tachometers, such as higher voltage output per rpm, less required maintenance, absence of commutator ripple, etc. When used in a tachometer bridge, as in Fig. B-7c, rectifiers are required, since phase relationships affect the addition of a-c voltages.

CLASS C. MISCELLANEOUS

There are many other electrical devices which are used as error detectors. They are too numerous to list exhaustively, since any measuring device is potentially an error detector and may be used as such if the quantity which it measures is to be controlled. But as a large number of the remaining electrical devices are essentially bridge-type detectors, brief consideration is given to a few such typical arrangements.

In bridge-type detectors, the measured variable may be converted directly to an electrical voltage or current for comparison with a similar reference quantity to yield an error signal; or the measured variable may cause a change in a resistance or inductance element in the bridge circuit, producing a disturbance of the bridge balance, and so indirectly may make available an electrical signal corresponding to the error.

B-14. Temperature Errors. Figure B-8 illustrates two common methods for detecting error in temperature-control systems. The resistance thermometer in Fig. B-8a is placed in a medium or fluid whose temperature is to be controlled. The reference resistor is so adjusted that when the medium temperature is at the desired point, no voltage appears between taps A and B. Any departure in the medium temperature will be reflected by a change in the resistance of the thermometric element, which forms one leg of the bridge. The unbalance causes a voltage to appear across the terminals AB which is a function of both the magnitude and sense of the temperature deviation.

In Fig. B-8b, measurement of the controlled variable is obtained by a thermocouple which converts the temperature to a voltage directly. Obviously it is necessary only to set the reference, or input, arm so that the thermocouple emf is balanced out at the desired temperature. No error voltage appears, then, until there is some deviation of the thermocouple emf, indicating a temperature change. An auxiliary compensation

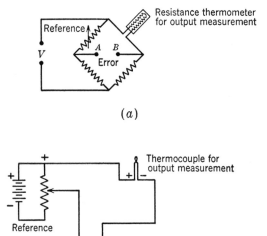

(a)

(b)

Fig. B-8. Error detectors for temperature control. (a) Resistance thermometer in Wheatstone bridge; (b) thermocouple bridge.

device must usually be incorporated into the error detector to keep current flow in the reference loop constant. Otherwise, a spurious error signal may be developed any time the d-c voltage source changes. The magnitude and polarity of the voltage at the error terminals is indicative of the extent and sense of any temperature error.

Some slight modification of the thermocouple-type bridge is necessitated in many applications because of the limited temperature range of the thermocouple, its relatively sluggish speed of response, or the difficulty in properly locating a thermocouple to obtain the desired measurement. In these cases radiation-type measuring devices may be substituted for the thermocouple. The error-sensing properties of the bridge remain the same.

B-15. Pressure Errors. Though the operation of pneumatic-type error detectors is discussed in a later section, some discussion of bridge-type pressure-measuring and error-detecting devices is given here. In Fig. B-9a is shown the usual bridge arrangement for this means of detecting pressure errors. A differential-bellows and strain-gage combination as shown in Fig. B-9b is used as a measuring device. When reference and measured pressures are identical, the active gage resistance is constant and resistor R_1 is adjusted so that no error voltage appears at the terminals. When the measured pressure varies above or below the reference, the strain-gage resistance changes, unbalancing the bridge, and so providing an error signal whose magnitude and direction are functions of the resistance variation.

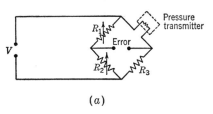

(a)

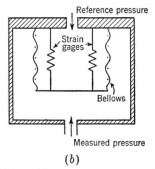

(b)

Fig. B-9. Bridge-type pressure-error detector. (a) Bridge; (b) pressure transmitter.

B-16. pH Concentration Errors. Control of hydrogen-ion, or pH, concentration (control of acidity or alkalinity) is extremely important in process industries where uniformity and quality of the product are a prime requirement. A common means of measuring and detecting pH concentration is by the insertion of two special unlike electrodes in the process to be controlled. The process material serves as an electrolyte for the cell formed by the electrodes. The function of the electrodes may be considered as similar to

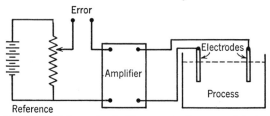

Fig. B-10. Schematic of pH-concentration-error detector.

that of the ordinary thermocouple (used for detecting temperature variations) except that here the voltage generated by the cell is dependent upon the pH concentration. In Fig. B-10 is shown the manner of comparing this weak generated voltage with some reference to determine the error. The amplifier is necessary because of the extremely low voltage generated by the cell. As the pH concentration varies, an error voltage will be developed, indicating the deviation from the selected reference.

SECTION II.   MECHANICAL ERROR DETECTORS

CLASS A.   POSITION ERRORS

B-17. Lever Systems.   Possibly the simplest type of mechanical position-error detector is a simple lever device as indicated schematically in

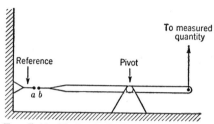

Fig. B-11.   The output quantity is connected to one end of the lever either directly or through some system of linkages, while the other end is compared with a reference quantity.   Any error then appears as a displacement of point *b* (Fig. B-11) relative to point *a*.

Fig. B-11. Mechanical error detector, lever type.

For practical use in a control system, point *b* would normally be connected to some activating device.   It might be used to open or close contacts in an electrical circuit, to displace a valve in a hydraulic or pneumatic circuit, etc.

B-18. Mechanical Differential.   To determine position errors in rotational systems where input and output are not remotely located, a mechanical differential may be used.   A schematic drawing of an elementary mechanical differential is shown in Fig. B-12.   The input and output shafts are free to rotate in the frame, thus turning their respec-

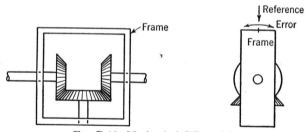

Fig. B-12. Mechanical differential.

tive bevel gears.   A third gear is anchored to the frame but is free to rotate.   If the output shaft rotates with respect to the input shaft, the intermediate gear rolls on the input-shaft gear and displaces the frame, thus indicating an error.   As for the lever system, some activating device must be connected to the frame if the error is to control the system output.

When desirable, the motion of the frame (which is a mechanical indication of the error) is readily converted to an electrical error signal by some such means as indicated in Fig. B-13.   A spur (or bevel) gear is fastened to the frame with adequate spacing for free rotation of the input shaft provided.   A second matching gear is needed whose shaft is connected to the movable arm of the potentiometer as shown. A d-c error signal is thus provided by frame rotation.

B-19. Position Gyroscopes. Physical bodies which are given large rotational momentum tend to maintain a fixed axial alignment in three-dimensional space. This alignment is not affected by translational motion, but if a torque is applied, a reaction is set up perpendicular to the axis of the applied torque. Practical application of this principle is found in modern gyroscopes, which are used in automatic pilots on aircraft, in the gyrocompass, to stabilize guns in tanks, etc.

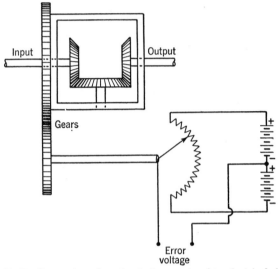

Fig. B-13. Conversion of mechanical error signal to electrical signal.

Figure B-14 shows a simplified diagram of the basic components of a gyroscope. The rotor with shaft pivoted in frame, or gimbal, B, is free to spin along axis 1. The entire mounting ring, or gimbal B, is pivot-connected to gimbal A and is free to revolve about axis 3. The rotor in the center is driven at high velocity to obtain the required angular momentum. The system as shown tends to maintain a fixed relationship in space* between the direction of its axis and the axis of any arbitrarily chosen coordinate axis, and this relationship is not affected by translation of the gyro. However, if a torque is applied to axis 2, reaction will cause gimbal B to rotate about axis 3; this is called precession. Thus, if axis 2 is fastened to an output shaft which is to be positioned at a fixed angular location, any rotation of this shaft causes an angular displacement of frame B about axis 3, thus indicating the

---

* In practical gyros, bearing friction and windage tend to cause some drift, or change in axis alignment. There are several ways to overcome this.

error.   An E transformer or a potentiometer is usually used to convert this mechanical displacement to an electrical signal.

In the gyros in use at present, the spinning members are essentially induction motors, which are normally operated from a 400-cycle supply to obtain the high speeds required to attain large angular momentum.

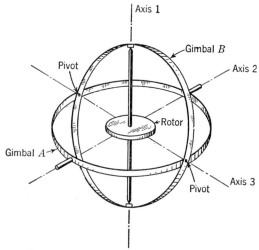

FIG. B-14. Schematic diagram of gyroscope.

Speeds vary from 10,000 to 20,000 rpm, depending on the size of the gyro. Constructional features vary somewhat with the manufacturer, and the accuracy depends largely upon the mechanical tolerances in machining and assembly.

CLASS B.   VELOCITY ERRORS

B-20. Spring-loaded Lever System.   If a pointer is mounted on some

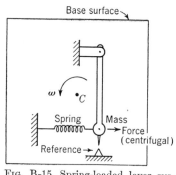

FIG. B-15. Spring-loaded lever system.

convenient base surface and is pivoted so that it is free to move, and if the base surface is then rotated at a velocity, ω, about some center, C (see Fig. B-15), the pointer attempts to swing outward and align itself radially to C.   If a mass, M, is attached to the pointer and if all dimensions and masses are known, the centrifugal force acting on M may be calculated for any desired pointer location at any given velocity.   A spring may then be designed to counterbalance this force so that the pointer balances at the reference position when the system rotates at the desired velocity. For lower velocities the spring pulls the pointer to the left, and at higher velocities the centrifugal force moves the pointer to the right for assumed counterclockwise rotation. Thus the displacement of the pointer with respect to the reference is a measure of the velocity error. In such a type of error detector the spring tension is normally made adjustable so that the velocity reference can be changed, and one of the methods discussed before could be used to convert the mechanical error signal to an electrical signal if so desired.

B-21. Mechanical Differential. A mechanical differential, such as is shown in Fig. B-12, may be used to measure velocity errors. The output and input of the system must both be available as rotational velocities and must be connected to the differential so that the input and output measuring shafts rotate in opposite directions. Then, if the two velocities are identical, the intermediate, or idler, gear merely spins, and the frame is not displaced. If the input and output velocities differ, the frame rotates at a speed proportional to the difference between the velocities and in a direction determined by the sense of the error.

B-22. Rate Gyroscopes. Referring to Fig. B-14, if gimbal A is locked to some reference structure and if axis 2 is collinear with the axis around which rotation is expected, then the gyro will precess around axis 3 when the expected rotational velocity occurs. Furthermore, if gimbal B is restrained by some elastic medium, such as spring loading, it can be shown that the angular displacement due to the precession force is a function of the rotational velocity. By proper design the displacement is made proportional to the rotational velocity, *i.e.*, the gyro measures the rate at which the assembly is rotating round the designated axis. Thus the rate gyroscope can be used to determine velocity errors.

Rate gyros are used principally in aircraft instrumentation, as, for example, turn-and-bank indicators, in automatic pilots for rate-of-turn compensation, in rockets and guided missiles for control and stabilization. In addition they are used for gun stabilization in tanks, in certain types of gun sights, and in other fire-control applications. Rate gyros use various methods to produce usable error signals, including the E transformer, variable-inductance devices, and potentiometers. They are available from several manufacturers, with a considerable range of accuracies and various response speeds. In general the rate gyro itself must be damped, and the damping provided varies considerably with the manufacturer and model.

CLASS C. MISCELLANEOUS

B-23. Bimetallic Strip for Temperature Errors. A simple method for detecting variation in temperature, *i.e.*, temperature errors, utilizes the well-known fact that different metals have different coefficients of expansion. If two properly selected different metals have nearly identical dimensions at a given temperature and are fastened together in strip form as shown in Fig. B-16, they effectively form a single straight strip and the position of the free end corresponds to a reference temperature. If the temperature decreases, both metals contract, but M_2 contracts more than M_1, and so the combination bends to the right, displacing the free end from the reference position. For temperature increases, M_2 expands more than M_1, and displacement is to the left. Thus the displacement of the free end is a function of the temperature error and may be transformed into various types of error signal as required by the control system.

B-24. Mercury-column Thermometer. A very simple device to measure temperature errors is obtained by inserting wires through the

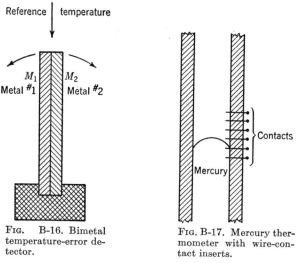

FIG. B-16. Bimetal temperature-error detector.

FIG. B-17. Mercury thermometer with wire-contact inserts.

wall of a mercury thermometer. When the mercury column contacts two or more wires, a conducting path is provided. The external terminals of the wires may be connected to various types of electrical circuits which provide a signal indicative of the direction and magnitude of the error. (See Fig. B-17.)

B-25. Linear Accelerometer. In some applications it is desired to control the linear acceleration of a system or component. Figure B-18 shows a simple device for measuring acceleration. The spring holds the lever arm against one limit stop when the system is stationary, moving at constant velocity, or moving with acceleration below a predetermined value. For acceleration above this value, the reaction force moves the lever-arm pointer counterclockwise until the increased spring force brings the system to equilibrium. The displacement of the lever-arm point is then an indication of the acceleration. This indication can be converted to an error signal by use of an E transformer, potentiometer, differential transformer, etc. Well-designed linear accelerometers are available commercially.

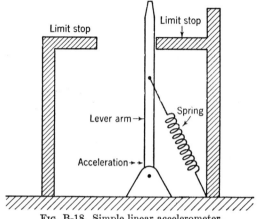

Fig. B-18. Simple linear accelerometer.

SECTION III. FLUID ERROR DETECTORS

In applications where fluid flow (velocity) or fluid pressure (position) are the controlled variables, pneumatic and hydraulic error-detecting devices are ordinarily used. This is also true in the many instances where the controlled variable might be humidity, or temperature, or fuel ratio, etc., and where fluid flow or pressure are the control agents.* The basic principles used in the design of error detectors are the same for all fluids, though the physical device is, of course, adapted to the specific fluid involved.

The selection of the proper device for detection of flow errors requires consideration of a large number of factors, and so the manufacturer's literature should be consulted. A partial list of the items which should be considered in making a selection are type of fluid, presence of suspended material in fluid, fluid velocity, pipe sizes, ease of maintenance and adjustment, allowable line losses, and, of course, accuracy and speed of response. Though it is often found convenient to modify such devices to allow conversion of the error signal to an electrical signal, the following discussion will not include such extensions.

CLASS A. PRESSURE ERRORS

B-26. Spring-loaded Pistons.   Possibly the simplest type of pressure-measuring device is a simple spring-loaded piston as shown in Fig. B-19a. The fluid forces the piston up the cylinder until the spring force balances

---

* For nearly every control operation may be reduced to one of controlling flow rate.

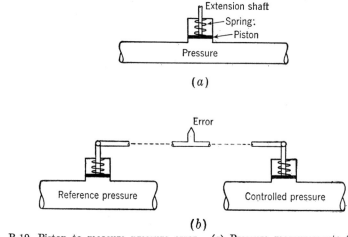

(a)

Error

(b)

Fɪɢ. B-19. Piston to measure pressure error. (a) Pressure measurement; (b) pressure error.

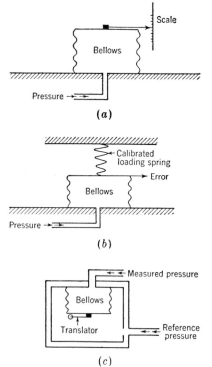

(a)

(b)

(c)

Fɪɢ. B-20. Metal bellows. (a) Metallic bellows for pressure measurement; (b) bellows to determine pressure error; (c) differential pressure bellows.

the fluid pressure. The displacement of the extension shaft is a measure of the fluid pressure. Two such devices, one applied to a reference pressure and the other to the controlled pressure, may be coupled together through a mechanical linkage as shown in Fig. B-19b. Then the displacement of a reference point on the linkage is a function of the pressure difference, or error.

B-27. Metal Bellows. Figure B-20a shows a simplified schematic drawing of a metallic bellows which measures pressure. Its action is very similar to that of the spring-loaded piston in that the pressure displaces the upper surface of the bellows; the magnitude of this displacement is proportional to the pressure. The force opposing the displacement is supplied by bending stresses in the bellows web.

To measure pressure error, the bellows may be used with a calibrated spring as shown in Fig. B-20b. When the pressure is at the desired point, or value, the external reference point is at a predetermined location. Changes in pressure cause a displacement from this location; thus the displacement is then a measure of the pressure error.

B-28. Differential-pressure Bellows. Instead of using a spring loading to effect a comparison of measured and desired pressure level, a differential-pressure scheme as shown in Fig. B-20c is often used. The bellows is enclosed in a sealed housing with the reference and measured pressures fed in as shown. A mechanical link fastened to the bottom of the bellows translates the displacement of the bellows into a mechanical error signal whenever a difference exists between the reference and measured pressures.

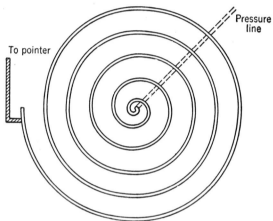

FIG. B-21. Bourdon gage.

B-29. Bourdon Gages. If a hollow metal tube is bent into a spiral as shown in Fig. B-21, with the outer end sealed and a pointer or lever attached, it may be used to measure pressure and is called a Bourdon gage. When pressure is applied to the inner end of the tube, the tube tries to unwind and the motion of the pointer tip is along a circular arc (for limited travel). The displacement of the pointer is proportional to the pressure. Such a device may be used in conjunction with various mechanisms to measure pressure deviations and errors. Bourdon gages are commonly used in pneumatic indicating instruments, recording meters, and automatic process controllers, in conjunction with metallic bellows.

CLASS B. FLOW ERRORS

B-30. Venturi Meters, Flow Nozzles, Orifices. When a fluid flows through a constriction in a pipe, the velocity increases and the pressure decreases. Since there is a relationship between the pressure drop and the velocity of flow, when a constriction is placed in the pipe and a pressure difference measured the velocity may be determined. The basic types of constriction in general use are shown in Fig. B-22a, b, and c. A number of design variations for each basic type are in common use. For use as an error detector, the differential pressure $P_1 - P_2$ would be

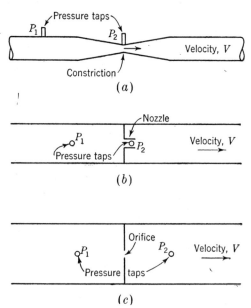

Fig. B-22. Basic types of flow meters. (a) Venturi flowmeter, $P_1 - P_2 \propto V$; (b) Flow nozzle, $P_1 - P_2 \propto V$; (c) Orifice plate, $P_1 - P_2 \propto V$.

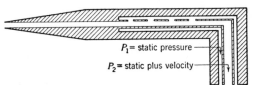

Fig. B-23. Pitot tube. (Note: Two concentric tubes, inner measures $P_2 = P_1 + dV^4/2g$, outer measures static pressure P_1.)

compared with a reference quantity, either directly or by means of a pressure transmitter.

B-31. Pitot Tubes. If a bent tube is inserted in a flowing fluid so that the tube opening (at the tip of the bent section) is pointed into the flow as shown in Fig. B-23, then the pressure transferred to the tube depends not only on the static pressure but on the velocity of flow and is

$$P_2 = P_1 + \frac{1}{2g}\, dV^2$$

where P = static head, or pressure

V = velocity of fluid flow

g = acceleration of gravity

d = density of fluid

Thus, if the static pressure is measured at P_1, the velocity depends on the pressure differential $P_2 - P_1$, and this may be compared with a reference to determine any velocity error.

APPENDIX C

CONTROLLERS

C-1. Introduction. Servomechanisms control the performance of a given load by controlling the application or flow of power to that load. The power source which is controlled is, of course, external to the system, as shown in Fig. C-1, in order to provide the system with ultimate sensitivity. Figure C-1 is a block diagram of a typical servo system. The individual blocks are functional, rather than physical, *i.e.*, in specific systems it may not be possible to separate the controller from the error detector or the motor in terms of components, or the motor function may not be separable from the power source.

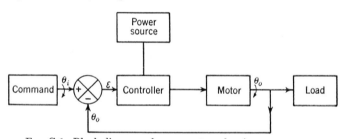

Fɪɢ. C-1. Block diagram of servo system showing power source.

The controller may then be defined as that combination of components which utilizes the error signal to determine the flow of power to the motoring device. The controller may be a very simple device consisting of one or two basic components, or it may be a complex device including electronic, electrical, mechanical, and fluid devices in various combinations. The natures of the error signal, the power source, and the output signal to the motor all influence the controller complexity. Few controllers are purely electrical, mechanical, or fluid devices, and therefore no attempt is made to classify them. The following pages consider many of the different types of controllers utilized in the automatic-control field.

C-2. Contactors; Relay Controllers. Mechanical or electromagnetic contactors are potentially the simplest type of controller, since in many applications they can apply power directly to the load or to the motor device and frequently need little auxiliary apparatus to provide acceptable operation.   Because maintenance is low, operation is simple, and cost is relatively small, varied forms of relay controllers are most widely used in process-control industries.   In general the contactors are light and compact and so are widely used in many air-borne applications.   In the examples now considered, the relay controllers are assumed to govern the flow of electrical power, though, of course, slight modification of the systems described would permit control of fluid flow, or pressure, or temperature as desired.

C-3. Mechanically Operated Contactor.   If the error in the system is detected mechanically, *i.e.*, appears as a mechanical rotation or displace-

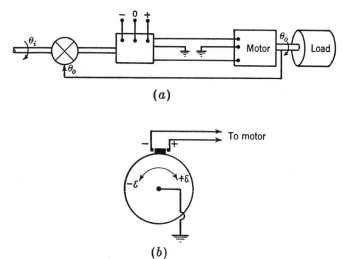

(a)

(b)

Fig. C-2. Mechanically operated contactor. (*a*) Schematic of contactor servo; (*b*) contactor mechanism.

ment, this motion can be used to close electrical contacts connecting the power source directly to the motor device as in Fig. C-2.   The controller thus consists of the electrical contacts only, though the mechanical member which indicates the error may be considered part of the controller.   Such devices are on-off controllers and usually result in system performance which is considerably underdamped.

The on-off nature of this type of controller can be modified somewhat to give smoother output control (less oscillatory response) by using multiple-contact arrangements which provide for only a small portion of the total power available to be applied to the motor device when errors are small.   When errors are large, correspondingly larger parts of the full capacity of the power source would be applied.   Often, too, a mechanical interrupter-timer is introduced between the motor and the contacts so that power is applied to the motor only when an error exists and for as long a period as the interrupter may be set. This will cause the response to be more damped than for a simple on-off controller.

C-4. Silverstat. Another method for controlling and applying an electrical signal through a mechanical displacement utilizes a device known as a silverstat. The silverstat is shown schematically in Fig. C-3.

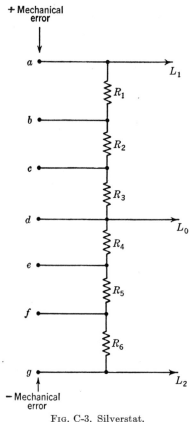

Fig. C-3. Silverstat.

A mechanical displacement due to the error signal closes contacts a, b, c, etc., consecutively, thus shorting out resistors R_1, R_2, etc. The electrical connections L_1, L_2, L_0 may be connected through the main power supply so that the resistors are in series with the motor device and thus limit the power delivered. If such an arrangement is practical, then the silverstat is the controller. On the other hand, the three terminals may be used in a bridge circuit to convert the mechanical error signal to an electrical signal. In this case the silverstat is only one component in the controller, and a variety of voltage or power amplifiers may be used as other controller components.

C-5. Electromagnetic Relays. The most commonly used contactor in automatic-control systems is the electromagnetic relay. Relays are available in various sizes and ratings for both a-c and d-c operations. When used in control systems, essentially two relays are required, one for positive errors and one for negative errors. Figure C-4 shows two relays arranged for the direct control of a power supply. The relay windings are fed by the error signal; for a positive error, relay A closes and applies a positive restoring power; for a negative error, relay B closes and applies a negative restoring power. The error detector which precedes the relays must be phase-sensitive, *i.e.*, it must be able to supply relay A for positive errors and relay B for negative errors, and it must be able to supply sufficient power to operate the relays. Usually this is not the case, and so a phase-sensitive amplifier is inserted between the error detector and the relays. This amplifier is usually considered part of the controller and not a portion of the error detector. Of course such relay contacts have relatively limited capacity so that relay coils may be utilized to control contactors of considerably larger rating. Figure C-5 is an illustration of such a setup. When error is such as to require clockwise rotation, the normally open contacts of CW close and the normally closed contact of CW is opened, causing current to flow from A to B. For reverse errors, the CCW relay coil is energized, causing associated contactors to force current to flow in the opposite direction through the armature.

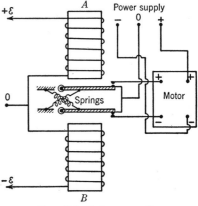

FIG. C-4. Relay controller.

C-6. Amplifier Controllers. In a servomechanism there are normally at least two stages of amplification, one stage in the controller, where it is usually necessary to amplify the error signal in order to obtain sufficient power to actuate the final element in the controller, and a second stage of power amplification in the motor device. This section of the appendix on controllers is concerned only with the amplifiers used in the controller, or first stage of amplification.

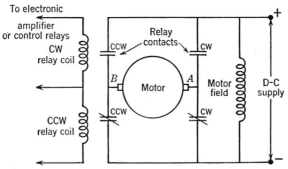

FIG. C-5. Relay controller with contactors.

C-7. Electronic Controller Amplifiers. The versatility and convenience of electron tubes are responsible for their widespread use in servo controllers. In general, electronic amplifiers form only a portion of the controller system, since many servos require more power than can be conveniently delivered by the tubes. If the motoring device requires only small amounts of power of the order of watts as in instrument servomechanisms, then the electronic amplifier may constitute the entire controller, but for systems which require large quantities of power to drive the load, the electronic servo amplifier may feed a rotating amplifier, a magnetic amplifier, or other such device, which in turn supplies power to the motor member.

The design of the electronic servo amplifier depends on the nature of the input error signal and the output requirements. Choice of tubes and detailed circuit design are accomplished by normal electronic-design procedures and are not discussed here. The types of amplifiers which are used may be roughly classified according to the nature of their input-output requirements:

1. D-C input to d-c output
2. D-C input to a-c output
3. A-C input to d-c output
4. A-C input to a-c output

Each of these classes may be further subdivided into single-ended* and phase-sensitive amplifiers.

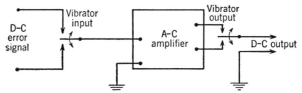

FIG. C-6. D-C amplifier using vibrators.

The general case of single-ended amplifiers may be discussed with a few general comments:

1. For all classes mentioned, special circuit design is usually necessary to control phase shift over the range of frequencies involved. Usually, however, the a-c signal is of constant frequency (60-cycle or 400-cycle), and so the design problems are not too difficult.

2. Classes 2, 3, and 4, are essentially normal amplifiers except that the first stage in 2 may include a "chopper" (vibrator) or a tube with a-c plate supply, and for 3 the output stage includes rectification and possibly filtering.

3. In class 1 the usual stability and drift problems common to d-c amplifiers must be solved. If necessary, a direct-coupled electronic amplifier may be used, but when possible, it seems desirable to use vibrators in conjunction with the tubes. Such an arrangement is shown schematically in Fig. C-6. The two vibrators shown are built in the same vibrator unit and are driven synchronously. The input vibrator chops the d-c signal, thus converting it into a series of pulses which can be amplified by the a-c amplifier, which may be of normal design. The second vibrator is connected to the amplifier output, possibly through a

* A single-ended amplifier, or neutral amplifier, provides an output whose polarity is independent of polarity of input signal.

transformer, and mechanically rectifies the a-c output signal. Vibrator-type d-c amplifiers may be designed to be phase-sensitive by proper selection of the a-c amplifier.

If the amplifier must be phase-sensitive, as is usually the case, then a form of push-pull (identical tubes connected back to back) arrangement is normally desirable. Figure C-7 shows a circuit for producing a

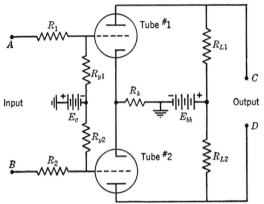

FIG. C-7. Servo amplifier; d-c input to d-c output, phase-sensitive.

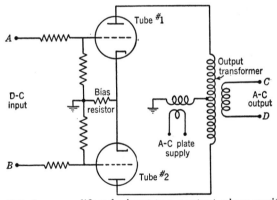

FIG. C-8. Servo amplifier; d-c input to a-c output, phase-sensitive.

reversible-polarity d-c output which is a function of the magnitude and polarity of the d-c input. If the grid bias (Ec) is sufficient to cut off the tubes, then no output is obtained when the input is zero. When input terminal A is positive, tube 1 conducts and output terminal D is positive, while if input terminal B is positive, tube 2 conducts and output terminal C is positive. The cathode resistor R_k serves as a feedback device to improve the amplifier stability.

Figure C-8 shows a circuit arrangement which is phase-sensitive to a d-c input and produces a reversible-phase a-c output. The plates of the tubes are fed from an a-c supply which must also be in phase with the servo-system supply in order to provide a phase reference. Both plates go positive on the same half cycle. When there is no input, both tubes carry the same amount of current so that the output transformer produces zero voltage. If terminal A becomes positive, tube 1 increases conduction while tube 2 carries less current; thus there is a net field coupling the transformer windings, and a net a-c output voltage results. If the transformer winding is properly arranged, the output voltage CD may be in phase with the supply. Then for a positive input on terminal B the output CD would be 180 deg out of phase with the supply.

For a-c input to a-c output, a circuit similar to that in Fig. C-8 may be used, and a more detailed example is shown in Fig. C-9. The oper-

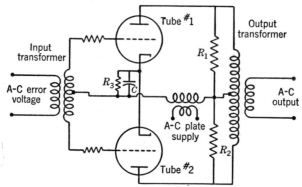

Fig. C-9. Servo amplifier; a-c input to a-c output, phase-sensitive.

ation of the circuit is basically the same as that of Fig. C-8. Resistors R_1 and R_2 serve a dual purpose. They provide a discharge path for the magnetic energy when the tube cuts off and also help in smoothing. However, they affect the time lag in the amplifier response. Capacitors may be used instead of resistors R_1 and R_2 if their effect on the time lag is acceptable. Proper bias is obtained for both tubes by adjustment of the cathode resistor R_3.

If a reversible-polarity d-c output is required with a-c input, a circuit such as is shown in Fig. C-10a or b may be used. Both circuits use the same phase-detection principle; *i.e.*, for an error signal in phase with the plate supply, tube 1 increases conduction, while tube 2 carries less current, and vice versa for an error signal 180 deg out of phase with the plate supply. The circuit of Fig. C-10b requires a plate-supply transformer with two separate secondary windings, while the circuit of Fig. C-10a requires additional resistors and capacitors. Many variations of the above circuits are in practical use in servo systems. A number of companies build plug-in-type servo amplifiers, which are available commercially. The actual amplifier system frequently incorporates compensating networks (phase lag or phase lead), and when compensation is to be included in the design, the amplifier is frequently much more complex than has been shown in the preceding schematic diagrams.

C-8. Magnetic Amplifiers. A magnetic amplifier is a device employing saturable reactors, generally in combination with dry-type rectifiers, to achieve power amplification. Though the use of reactors for amplification purposes is not new, recent developments of high-permeability magnetic materials and gapless construction of magnetic circuits have made the magnetic amplifier entirely suitable for most applications.

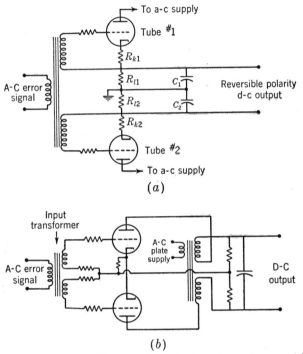

Fig. C-10. Servo amplifiers; a-c input to d-c output, phase-sensitive.

Magnetic amplifiers are often preferred to the electronic type, especially in applications where shock and vibration are serious problems, as they are mechanically sturdy and inherently shockproof. Reactors are particularly well suited for air-borne use, guided missiles, etc., as relatively inexpensive amplifiers can be designed to have very high gain, with low input-power requirements, and to be compact and light in weight.

Other characteristics which favor magnetic amplifiers in many applications are low maintenance, complete isolation of input and output signals, and inherently stable operation when used as a d-c amplifier. They lend themselves to operation in cascade so that multistage application is possible. However, one serious disadvantage in the use of reactors is their relatively sluggish response. Various feedback schemes have been developed and are presently employed to decrease the response time without excessive reduction in amplification.

The basic circuit of a saturable reactor is shown in Fig. C-11. It consists of an iron-cored reactor in series with an a-c supply and load. A separate winding on the iron core is excited from a d-c source. When no current flows in the d-c coil, the magnetic core is unsaturated and so the reactance of the a-c coil is large. Thus the coil absorbs almost all of the a-c supply voltage. If some current is allowed to pass through the d-c winding, the core tends to become saturated, decreasing the effective inductance of the a-c winding so that more of the a-c supply voltage appears across the load. When the d-c current supplied is sufficient

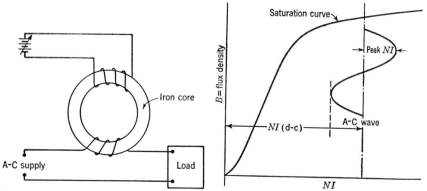

Fig. C-11. Basic circuit of saturable reactor.

Fig. C-12. Magnetic requirements of a saturable reactor.

to saturate the core completely, the reactance of the a-c coil is negligible and essentially all of the a-c voltage appears at the load terminals. Thus the control of d-c current flow may be used to control the flow of power to the load by varying the effective impedance into which the a-c supply circuit works.

Considerable power amplification may be obtained when the d-c winding is used as an input to control the power delivered to the load, as the d-c coil usually consists of many turns of small wire, carries little current, and so absorbs little power. The a-c coil, however, consists of comparatively few turns of large cross section, designed to carry high currents and allow the transfer of large quantities of power to the load.

Actually the simple saturable reactor is not a good amplifier because it has relatively slow response, and because the input-coil power requirement, though small, is still appreciable. These shortcomings of the reactor are due largely to the fact that the d-c coil must supply more ampere turns than the a-c coil in order to maintain saturation. Figure C-12 illustrates this: the ampere turns supplied by the d-c coil must be able to saturate the core to such an extent that the peak NI supplied by the a-c coil on the negative half cycle does not unsaturate the core appreciably.

The response delay of this reactor, as well as of magnetic amplifiers in general, is dependent upon the time lag introduced by the control-field inductance and the lag caused by the a-c windings in series with the load. Over-all design procedures normally provide for an increase in response speed by reducing the delay caused by the control field. Flexibility in

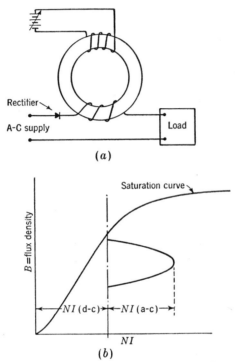

Fig. C-13. Self-saturating magnetic amplifier. (*a*) Basic self-saturating circuit; (*b*) magnetic characteristics.

design of the winding or windings in series with the load is not so great, though over-all speed of response can be improved somewhat by proper design and connection of the a-c winding.

Over-all response times for magnetic amplifiers vary from 0.1 sec to several seconds, most of the delay being contributed by the control-field inductance. To decrease the amplifier time lag, several feedback methods may be used, all of which allow the use of a d-c control winding of fewer turns, thus cutting down the field time constant L/R and at the same time reducing the input-power requirements through the reduction in coil resistance.

C-9. Self-saturating Magnetic Amplifier. The objectionable features of the simple saturable reactor can be largely overcome by using a type of feedback known as self-saturation. In the circuit shown in Fig. C-13a, half-wave rectified power is supplied to the load. (Such operation would not be acceptable for most applications, but it serves to illustrate the principles involved.) The rectifier is placed in series with the a-c source so that the current always flows through the a-c coil in the same direction. Thus the d-c coil merely has to set up the desired condition in the core, and the unidirectional current in the a-c coil completes the saturation. The power requirements of the d-c coil are reduced, permitting greater power amplification, and the d-c coil may be redesigned with a shorter time constant, permitting faster response.

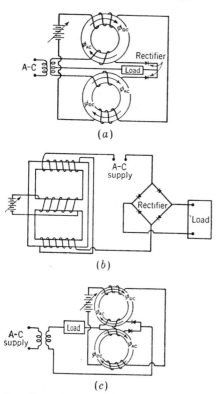

(a)

(b)

(c)

Fig. C-14. Self-saturating magnetic amplifiers. (a) Amplifier with d-c output; (b) amplifier with d-c output; (c) amplifier with a-c output.

The self-saturating circuit can be used to produce full-wave rectification with d-c output as shown in Fig. C-14a. (A second reactor is required, or a three-legged reactor, as shown in Fig. C-14b, can be used.) The operation of the circuit in Fig. C-14a is essentially the same as for Fig. C-13, one-half of the amplifier being effective on each half cycle. An a-c output can also be obtained, as shown in Fig. C-14c. The action of the magnetic circuit is identical with that of Fig. C-14a, but the arrangement of the load circuit is different.

C-10. Phase-sensitive Magnetic Amplifier. None of the preceding circuits is phase-sensitive; *i.e.*, the polarity of the output does not depend on the polarity of the input. Various circuits are available for phase-sensitive magnetic amplifiers, one of which is shown in Fig. C-15. The d-c and a-c windings on the reactors are arranged so that in one reactor the ampere turns aid, while in the other they oppose. Thus, during one-half cycle, one reactor is effectively a short circuit, while the other is a high impedance. The output is then unidirectional, but pulsating. The capacitors across the load provide filtering. The polarity of the output reverses if the d-c input reverses, because such an input variation interchanges the actions of the reactors.

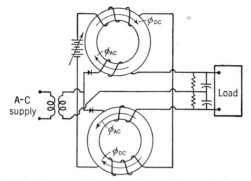

FIG. C-15. Phase-sensitive magnetic amplifier with d-c output.

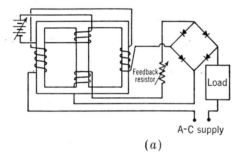

(a)

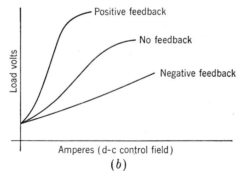

(b)

FIG. C-16. Magnetic amplifier with feedback. (a) Feedback added; (b) characteristics.

Magnetic-amplifier performance may also be adjusted by adding an auxiliary coil serving as feedback winding. This coil is fed from the load (through rectifiers where the output is a-c), as shown in Fig. C-16a. The three-legged reactor is shown as the simplest illustration possible. The response time may be decreased and a more linear relation established between a-c output and d-c input if the feedback is negative.   The power amplification can be increased by providing a positive feedback connection, but the time lag in the response would be increased.   Approximate characteristics of the magnetic amplifier with and without feedback are indicated in Fig. C-16b.

C-11. Biased Magnetic Amplifiers.   Frequently it is desired to set the zero-control-signal magnetic state of the reactor core to some predetermined value which is then altered by the actual control signal. Such an adjustment is called a *bias* and is obtained with a separate coil wound on the reactor core.   The bias is generally introduced to produce an initial amount of d-c saturation so that it is possible to obtain more amplification for weak signals than would be obtained without it.

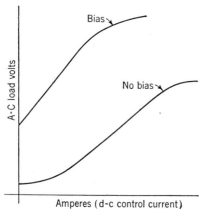

Fig. C-17. Magnetic amplifiers; effect of bias.

Figure C-17 depicts a typical a-c voltage vs. d-c control-field current characteristic for a magnetic amplifier.   When a bias is added to the reactor, the amplifier characteristic will be shifted upward, as shown, so that small variations in control-field current produce relatively large changes in a-c voltage.   The desired high amplification for weak signals is thus obtained.   One apparent disadvantage of this scheme is that the minimum output with zero d-c field current is considerably higher with the bias.   This difficulty is usually overcome by connecting two magnetic amplifiers in balanced or push-pull arrangement, thus allowing the cancellation of the initial voltage obtainable from each.

In general the speed of response and the power amplification of magnetic amplifiers is improved by using high-permeability steels which saturate easily and by using a-c sources of higher than 60-cycle frequency, as much as 400 cycles.   Flexibility in circuit design is provided for by the manufacturer by winding three control coils (all of different numbers of turns) on the reactor core.   Thus a control signal, bias, and feedback may all be used if necessary.

C-12. Rotary or Dynamoelectric Amplifiers.   Where the power required to drive a load is large but only a relatively small amount of power is available as a control signal, rotating or dynamoelectric amplifiers are often a part of the controller.   The rotating amplifier is essentially an electric generator, either a-c or d-c.   It may be driven by an electric motor or by any other convenient means.   In general it comprises only one stage (the output stage) of the controller system and so is usually preceded by a magnetic or electronic amplifier.

Actually any rotating generator is a power amplifier because a small amount of power applied to the generator field controls a large power output from the armature.   But standard d-c or a-c generators usually are not suitable for amplifier use because the field circuits require more power than is normally available, and the response of these generators is often too sluggish to permit desired system performance.   Certain d-c generators, the amplidyne, rototrol, and regulex, are designed to provide a large armature power output for very small field inputs.   These specialized types also provide this amplification with minimum time delay.

C-13. D-C Shunt Generator.   The ordinary d-c shunt generator pictured in Fig. C-18a is used as a rotating amplifier in applications where speed of response is not critical. In discussing the use of the generator as an amplifier it is somewhat easier to refer to the equivalent circuit of the d-c machine.   The equivalent circuit consists of a series inductance and resistance, representative of the shunt-field parameters, and a resistance and leakage inductance (R_a and L_a) in series with the generated voltage in the armature circuit.   Referring to Fig. C-18b, there will be two time delays in the rotating-amplifier response to an input signal: that due to the shunt-, or control-, field inductance and that caused by the armature inductance.

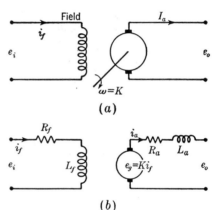

Fig. C-18. D-C shunt generator and its equivalent circuit. (a) Schematic; (b) equivalent circuit.

Response times of a fraction of a second can be realized, but the amplification is not great. Additional gain is possible, however, through the addition of an auxiliary field wound on the same pole structures as the shunt field, provided the added response delay due to such fields can be tolerated.

Rotating amplifiers may be connected in series to obtain high amplification if desired.   (In fact, some special machines incorporate such design principles into a single structure.)   The addition of feedback connections will be found to affect both the response time and the amplification.   In general, negative feedback leads to an often desirable shortening of the response time, but it is also found to decrease the effective amplification.   The inverse is true when positive feedback is used.   The ease of providing external feedback to series-connected rotating amplifiers is apparent in Fig. C-19a.   If an additional control-field winding is available, feedback may be introduced as in Figs. C-19*b* and *c*.

C-14. Amplidyne. The special design features which enable the amplidyne to obtain much greater power amplification than is realizable with ordinary shunt generators of the same size, and to do so with excellent speed of response, are briefly discussed below. The literature should be consulted for a more detailed treatment.

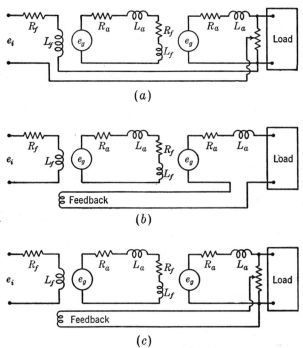

Fig. C-19. Rotating amplifier with various feedback connections. (*a*) Feedback in series with main field; (*b*) feedback to separate control winding (current type); (*c*) feedback to separate control winding (voltage type).

There are several basic differences between conventional d-c generators and amplidynes. First, two or more control (shunt) fields are usually provided, wound of varying numbers of turns, aiding and opposing. Second, two independent brush sets, located perpendicular to each other, are employed rather than one. The output is not taken from the brush set located on or about the mechanical neutral, as is usually done, as these brushes are shorted, but is taken from the second brush set whose axis is perpendicular to the mechanical neutral. Locating the output brushes in this position is necessary in order to get high amplification from the normally small control-field fluxes.

In Fig. C-20a is shown a typical amplidyne. To explain the operation of the amplidyne, refer to the simpler schematic in Fig. C-20b, and assume that the net control-field current produces the flux, Φ_m. This flux will be relatively small because the control fields of amplidynes are wound with relatively few turns and are usually designed to permit direct connection to an electronic amplifier of limited current rating. The voltage, E_g,

induced between the brushes MN is correspondingly small. If these brushes are connected to an external load, a current I_q would flow whose magnitude would be approximately $E_{g1}/(R_a + R_2)$. The magnetic field set up by I_q would be directed along the mechanical neutral perhaps as shown by Φ_q. But in an amplidyne the brushes MN are shorted so that $I_q \approx E_{g1}/R_a$ will be appreciable, thus causing a large armature reaction flux to be established and $\Phi_q \gg \Phi_m$. Use is made of the large flux established by the short-circuit current, by supplying the load from the second brush set OP, geometrically located at right angles to the shorted pair. The voltage induced between brushes OP, E_{g2}, will be much larger than E_{g1}; yet E_{g2} will still be a function of the original control-field flux, Φ_m. It can be shown that the magnitude and polarity of the output voltage will vary with the magnitude and direction of current flow in the control fields (saturation and hysteresis effect neglected).

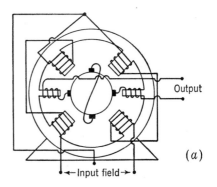

(a)

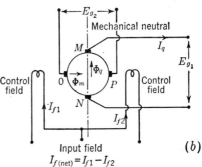

(b)

Fig. C-20. The amplidyne. (a) Sketch of wiring connections; (b) schematic diagram (simplified).

Before the rotating amplifier of Fig. C-20b can operate satisfactorily with any load connected across the brushes OP, a compensating winding must be added to counterbalance the magnetic field which would be set up by the load current. The magnetic field set up by the load current will be directed opposite to the control-field flux as indicated in Fig. C-21a. By proper design of compensating winding the flux set up by the load will be canceled out by the compensating flux, and the net flux in the armature will consist only of Φ_m and Φ_q. Note that when properly compensated $\Phi_C = \Phi_L$ for all values of load current since the compensating winding is connected in series with the load. Exact compensation adjustment is usually accomplished by shunting the compensating winding with a variable resistor and by adjusting this resistance.

Analysis of this type of rotating amplifier is best carried out on the basis of its equivalent circuit shown in Fig. C-21b. All significant time delays are indicated. It should be noted that the short-circuit-axis, or quadrature-axis, parameters may include the resistance and inductance of an auxiliary field that is often added to increase the flux, Φ_q, and produce higher amplification. Though three separate time delays normally are associated with amplidynes, the speed of response is still faster than for conventional d-c generators, primarily because the control-field time constant is much smaller.

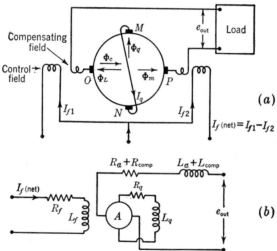

FIG. C-21. Compensated amplidyne. (a) Amplidyne with compensating winding; (b) approximate equivalent circuit.

C-15. Clutches. In many applications the output of a servomechanism is a mechanical motion requiring high momentary accelerations but having relatively small power requirements under other conditions. The use of a motoring device large enough to supply the accelerating power directly is frequently not desirable even aside from economic considerations. Furthermore, the controller needed to activate such a motoring device would probably be required to deliver considerable power. Under such circumstances a clutch mechanism is frequently a satisfactory solution.

For such applications the power source drives a motor, perhaps with inertia to store energy, and the motor is shafted to one section of the clutch. The other section of the clutch is then connected to the load. The controller (of which the clutch is a part) energizes the clutch coil, thus permitting transfer of energy from the drive to the load. Four types of clutches are available for servo-system use:

1. Friction clutches
2. Eddy-current clutches
3. Magnetic-fluid clutches
4. Hydraulic transmissions.

C-16. Friction Clutches. These are basically the same as the friction clutch used in automobiles but are usually actuated electrically, *i.e.*, the friction surfaces are forced together by the action of an electromagnet. The relationship between magnet current and transmitted torque is not linear, and the surfaces tend to bounce or vibrate so that the transmission of power is not always as smooth as might be desired. A section view of a friction clutch is shown in Fig. C-22. Another obvious disadvantage of the friction clutch is that its transmission characteristics vary with use, owing to wearing of the friction surfaces.

For some servo applications the friction clutch is satisfactory. An example of friction clutch use in a servo unit is the servo unit of a Minneapolis-Honeywell type C-1 automatic pilot. The operation of the unit is as follows: The servomotor drives two clutch plates continuously, but the plates are not engaged when the aircraft control surface is holding the airplane on the desired course; instead two brake solenoids lock the output disk of the clutch to maintain that condition. If the course of the aircraft must be corrected, the automatic pilot feeds an electrical signal to the proper operating solenoid, which pushes the motor-driven clutch plate against the output clutch plate and continues to push until the output clutch plate is freed from the braking surface. Then the servomotor drives the aircraft control surface so as to correct the course.

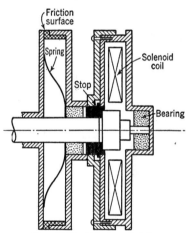

FIG. C-22. Friction clutch.

C-17. Eddy-current Clutches. In an eddy-current clutch, use is made of the fact that a metallic disk rotating in a magnetic field has eddy currents induced in it and electromagnetic forces are set up between the eddy currents and the magnetic field. Thus if an electromagnetic yoke is attached to the shaft of a drive motor which is rotated at constant speed, and if a metal disk is fastened to the load shaft in proper geometric relation to the yoke, power may be transmitted from the driven shaft to the load through the electromagnetic forces.

The magnetic field is obtained by amplifying the error signal and energizing the coils on the magnetic yoke with the resulting current. The magnetic field of the clutch is readily controlled from the error signal, and the transmission of power is thus somewhat smoother than in a friction clutch. Some slippage is inherent, however. A sectional view of an eddy-current clutch is shown in Fig. C-23.

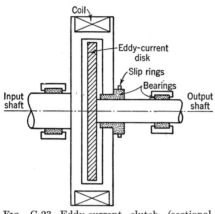

FIG. C-23. Eddy-current clutch (sectional view).

Various mechanical designs are possible with the eddy-current clutch, but in general it is desirable to drive the magnetic structure from the power source so that the low-inertia eddy-current member may be connected to the load shaft. A novel design for an eddy-current-clutch servo has been reported by Gutman.[137,*] With this clutch the drive motor rotates two magnetic structures in opposite directions through a bevel gear. Each magnetic structure has separate coils wound on it and may be magnetized separately. Eddy currents are induced by the rotating field in a metal sleeve, which is connected to the output shaft through a disk. Direction of rotation is controlled by magnetizing the proper magnetic structure.

C-18. Magnetic-fluid Clutches. If finely divided particles of iron are suspended in a light machine oil or silicone oil, a substance is obtained which resembles a heavy oil or light grease (depending on the relative proportions of iron and oil). This substance behaves as a fluid under normal conditions but tends to solidify when subjected to a magnetic field. The solidification is gradual, depending on the strength of the magnetic field, but the substance is essentially a solid when a sufficiently strong field is applied. If the magnetic field is removed, the substance returns to its original fluid condition.

Magnetic fluids of the type described have been developed at the National Bureau of Standards and have been applied to the development of a magnetic-fluid clutch. The design of such a clutch may result in various mechanical forms, and a possible form is shown in Fig. C-24. When current (as from an amplified error signal) is applied to the coil, the magnetic fluid begins to solidify. This causes a drag between the frame supporting the coil structure and the cup connected to the output

---

* Superior numbers, when they appear in the text proper, are the numbers of references given in the Bibliography.

shaft. If a weak magnetic field is applied, there is slippage but power is transmitted, and if a sufficiently strong magnetic field is used, the magnetic fluid solidifies, there is no slippage, and energy transmission is very efficient.

There is a minimum drag through the clutch due to the viscosity of the fluid, but, from this condition up to maximum power transmission, changes in control current cause a very smooth and nearly linear variation in torque. The smoothness of action is further improved by the fact that there seems to be no difference between static and kinetic friction, and thus there is no chattering at low output speeds.

The friction clutch and magnetic-fluid clutch are unidirectional controllers, *i.e.*, the direction of rotation of the output shaft is fixed. How-

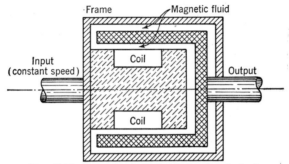

Fig. C-24. Magnetic-fluid clutch (sectional view).

ever, where directional sensitivity is required, two clutches may be used with proper gearing. It is then necessary to use a phase-sensitive preamplifier which energizes the clutch controlling the desired rotational direction.

C-19. Hydraulic Transmission. A very convenient and versatile device for controlling rotational output is a hydraulic transmission. Various types are available, differing considerably in operating principle. For servo-system purposes the transmission is usually driven from a constant-speed source such as an electric motor, and the output speed is controlled through the hydraulic system. In any such transmission it is apparent that there must be two basic mechanical members, a pumping device connected to the driven shaft, and a hydraulic motor connected to the load shaft. There are in general three ways to control the speed of the output shaft: (1) by a mechanical adjustment which alters the displacement per stroke of the pump (or motor); (2) by a by-pass valve which permits the pump to operate at constant volume but controls the amount of fluid which passes through the motor; (3) by a series restriction valve which controls the fluid flow.

Figure C-25 shows a hydraulic transmission which uses the variable-displacement method. The mechanical adjustment which controls the speed of the output shaft is available manually with a vernier adjustment which permits accurate speed setting from maximum speed forward to maximum speed in reverse. A lever controlling this adjustment is also available for use in servo systems.

C-20. Control Valves. In the automatic control of industrial processes, the control instrument generally is an amplifying device which combines the functions of error detector, recorder, and controller into a single unit. Ordinarily a measurement of the controlled variable is taken at various critical points in the process and fed to the process-control instrument. A comparison of the condition of the controlled variable and some reference is then made. Simultaneously with the positioning of a recording

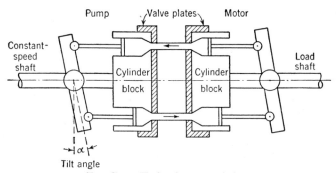

Fig. C-25. Hydraulic transmission.

head along some arbitrary scale to indicate the status of the variable, an error signal (corresponding to the difference between the reference and the measured variable) is fed mechanically, electrically, pneumatically, or hydraulically to some type of valve which is activated to bring about whatever change in power supply is necessary to reduce the error to zero or minimum. The error signal supplied to the valve is often modified by differentiating and integrating mechanisms incorporated into the controller to bring about the desired transient and steady-state response. The flow characteristics of the valve may also be modified to bring about the desired performance.

In this section brief consideration is given to the operation and characteristics of valves which may control the flow of some fluid that directly or indirectly affects the controlled variable. There are a tremendous number of process-control valves and valve types available, but a comprehensive discussion of these is far beyond the scope of this text. The remarks made, therefore, are of a very general nature, and for detailed information the reader is referred to the manufacturer's literature. Control valves, as discussed here, are considered as part of the controller and not as the equivalent of servomotors, since the valve does not supply the power to the controlled variable but, rather, controls the power source. However, the valves will necessarily contain some sort of motoring device since a physical displacement (rotation or translation) is required to change the hydraulic area and so adjust the flow.

C-21. Pneumatically Operated Flow-control Valves. The pneumatically operated diaphragm valve is by far the most commonly used in automatic control. Other types available are hydraulically or electrically operated. Both rotational and translational may be obtained, but in general translational motions are used. Valves are obtainable in a large variety of standard sizes, of various materials and designs.

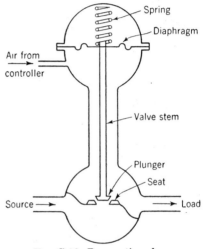

FIG. C-26. Pneumatic valve.

The basic components of a process-control valve are shown in Fig. C-26, which is an amplified sketch of a pneumatic diaphragm valve. The motor portion of the valve is the diaphragm-spring combination, which is designed to provide a displacement proportional to the pneumatic pressure applied from the controller. The valve stem then lifts the plunger from the seat and permits flow from the source to the load. The sketch shows a single-seat arrangement, but double-seat construction is also used.

As previously noted, the valve displacement is proportional to the signal supplied by the controller. This signal (depending on the controller) may be proportional to the error only or may contain a component due to the derivative or integral of the error. In any case, the correction applied depends not solely on the valve displacement but also on the shape of the plunger. Thus the engineer must determine the proper type plunger for the specific application, as well as the size and mechanical characteristics of the valve.

The simplest plunger is a beveled disk, often called a *quick-acting* or *poppet* valve. With this type of valve the area of the valve opening varies in almost direct proportion to the amount the plunger is lifted from the seat. One of the most popular types in present-day application is the *equal-percentage*, or logarithmic, valve. In this type a given lift changes the area of the valve opening as a fixed percentage of the area which existed before the plunger was lifted. Such a characteristic is obtained by shaping the plunger.

It is obvious that for a given lift, each of the valve types discussed would change the flow by a different amount. The poppet valve provides nearly a linear relationship between lift and flow, while the equal-percentage valve provides a logarithmic or nonlinear relationship. It may be said that in general, where line losses are small, a poppet valve is suitable for process control in which the controlled variable is a linear function of fluid flow. Where the process characteristics are nonlinear, the use of the equal-percentage type is popular as it serves to compensate for this nonlinearity.[206]

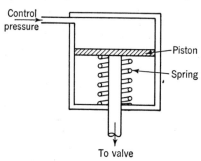

FIG. C-27. Hydraulic piston to operate flow valve.

In those cases where line losses are not small the poppet-valve flow characteristics will deviate considerably from being linear, while the equal-percentage valve will be seen to more nearly provide proportional control action.

C-22. Hydraulically Operated Valves. Most of the remarks in the preceding section also apply to hydraulically operated valves, except that the motoring device is usually not a diaphragm but a piston arrangement such as is shown in Fig. C-27. Reverse action is supplied either by a restoring spring or by a second piston operated in the opposite direction.

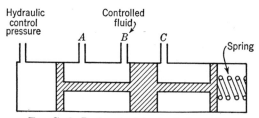

FIG. C-28. Basic principle of selector valve.

For servomechanism systems, hydraulically operated valves may be used as on-off devices or as flow-control devices. In general the valve is hydraulically operated only if the servo system itself is hydraulic; and the following brief discussion is limited to such cases.

The basic valve type for hydraulic on-off servos is the selector valve, which is used to select the pipe line through which the fluid is to flow. The basic principle is illustrated in Fig. C-28, and there are innumerable mechanical designs which provide for multiple selections in various ways. The operating principle of the selector valve as shown in Fig. C-28 is quite simple—for high hydraulic pressure the valve is in the position shown so that the controlled fluid flows in at B and out at A. If the control pressure is decreased, the slide moves to the left, closing B entirely. Further reduction in pressure connects B to C. For simplicity in explanation, Fig. C-28 shows a spring opposing the hydraulic control pressure. In practice a spring may be used, or a second hydraulic control pressure. Such selector valves may also be operated mechanically or electrically.

Where the hydraulic system involves speed control, the valve must be of the flow-control type. The general principles stated for process-control valves apply in this case also, though the mechanical design is

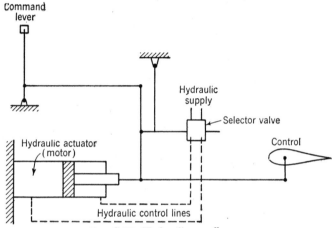

Fig. C-29. Hydraulic on-off servo.

considerably different in order to permit hydraulic control and in order to withstand the higher pressures normally used in hydraulic servo systems.

An illustration of the basic on-off hydraulic servo is shown schematically in Fig. C-29. The operation of the system is as follows: Motion of the command lever operates the selector valve which applies hydraulic pressure to one side of the piston in the hydraulic actuator and at the same time connects the other side of the piston to the return line so that the fluid may be forced out. Motion of the hydraulic motor adjusts the control surface and at the same time gradually restores the selector valve to the neutral position so that the control surface comes to rest at a position corresponding to the command signal. As shown, the system is not a closed loop and is therefore not a servomechanism. When such a system is used in aircraft to control a rudder or aileron, the pilot closes the servo loop through the exercise of judgment and experience, while if an automatic pilot is used, the loop is closed through the gyroscope reference.

C-23. Electrically Controlled Valves.   When high-speed valve action is desired, electrically controlled valves are frequently used.   These are generally of the solenoid type and are ordinarily used in on-off applications, as in the operation of selector valves in hydraulic or pneumatic servos.   Solenoid valves which are properly spring-loaded may be used for proportional flow control, but this is rather rare because the control instruments in common use are predominantly pneumatic in operation rather than electrical, owing largely to cost and maintenance considerations.   The design of the valve itself is not affected by use of a solenoid motor except in so far as mechanical changes may be required to economically incorporate the solenoid device.

APPENDIX D

SERVOMOTORS

D-1. Introduction. The motoring component in an automatic-control system is generally considered to be the device which supplies power to the load. In some control applications this component is not a discrete mechanism; for example, in heating or illumination control the power will probably be supplied from the power company's lines and may be controlled by a saturable reactor or some other suitable device; or in process control the power might be supplied from a steam line of essentially constant pressure, with the flow controlled by a valve. In many other applications, however, the motoring device is a specific piece of equipment such as an electric, hydraulic, or pneumatic motor. Electric motors are generally rotational devices but can be used to produce linear motions by means of proper linkages. Hydraulic motors and pneumatic motors are available in rotational types, and in cylinder types which produce linear displacements directly. This appendix is concerned only with these specific types of servomotors.

In many control systems the physical nature of the servomotor is set by the nature of the application, or the type of power available, or by weight and space limitations. Under such conditions the designer must determine the proper size of motor and may base his specific selection largely on cost, dependability, maintenance features, etc. In other servo systems the selection of the servo motor is based primarily on performance requirements, and the choice of a power-supply system (electric, hydraulic, or pneumatic) may be determined by the type of motor which will give the best performance without making the over-all system too large.

A detailed discussion of the calculations involved in selecting servomotors is beyond the scope of this text, but several interesting articles are available in the literature.[55-60],* However, a brief listing is presented of the basic performance requirements of any servomotor:

1. It must be able to supply the steady-state power requirements of the load, plus any losses in gearing or similar associated equipment.

* Superior numbers, when they appear in the text proper, are the numbers of references given in the Bibliography.

2. It must be able to accelerate itself and the connected load in accordance with given acceleration specifications.

3. It must be able to supply the peak power demanded during possible transient conditions.

4. It must operate at a given velocity or over a given range of velocities.

5. It must be suitable for the specified duty cycle.

The remainder of this appendix is devoted to a discussion of the types of motors available and their characteristics.

D-2. Standard Electric Motors. For some types of servo systems standard electric motors are perfectly acceptable and, from a cost viewpoint, even preferable to special types. This is particularly true for clutch-type servomechanisms where the motor runs at normal speed and is loaded through the clutch. Virtually any type of standard motor may be used, with the choice depending on available power supplies and on speed and torque requirements.

For continuous-control servos requiring speed variations and direction reversals of the motor proper, d-c motors or two-phase motors are most commonly used. If the accelerations required are relatively low, *i.e.*, if high-speed response is not required, standard motors may be used for such applications also. In high-speed servo systems, however, the standard motor is seldom satisfactory, and specially designed servomotors are required.

D-3. Electric Servomotors—General. The servomotor is normally expected to produce rapid accelerations from standstill or near standstill conditions. This requires a motor with high starting torque and low inertia, and the standard electric motor normally does not possess both of these features. The servomotor then differs from standard motors principally in that it has considerably lower inertia and in general a higher starting torque.

Low inertia may be obtained in a number of ways, but the problem of maintaining high starting torque must be met simultaneously, for it is actually the ratio of torque to inertia that is important in most servomotors. The following methods have been used in the design of servomotors:

1. Reduction of armature diameter and increase in the axial length of the armature. The reduction in diameter obviously decreases the inertia but also decreases the lever arm of the conductor. Increasing the length of the armature compensates for the reduced lever arm and provides the desired torque. For example, halving the diameter and doubling the armature length theoretically increases the torque-to-inertia ratio by a factor of 8. This cannot be fully realized, of course, because the change in dimensions also affects flux densities and current densities, but the improvement is considerable.

2. The torque of d-c motors and of a-c commutator motors can be increased by using compensating windings designed to permit greater peak armature currents.

3. For small power requirements—up to perhaps 30 watts—the moving parts may be reduced to the armature conductors alone, thus tremendously reducing the inertia. This is done by using a fixed field system, with fixed central core and the armature conductors located in the annular ring between field and core as in an instrument movement.

4. To obtain very low inertia in induction motors, the rotor may be made in the shape of a cup and mounted in a frame consisting of a fixed field structure and a fixed central core. This is the so-called "drag-cup" motor.

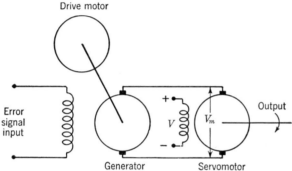

Fig. D-1. Armature-controlled d-c servomotor.

5. Standard induction motors usually have low starting torques, with maximum torque near rated speed. This is done by making the armature reactance high with respect to its resistance. If the reactance-to-resistance ratio is decreased, maximum torque occurs at reduced speeds. For the ratio of unity the starting torque is very nearly maximum. Thus by controlling the armature resistance or reactance, high starting torques may be obtained.

Direct-current motors usually are lighter for the same power output and have higher starting and reversing torques than a-c motors. On the other hand, a-c motors are used extensively in servo applications because they are simple, reliable, and economical, give rapid response, and present no commutator problems.

D-4. D-C Servomotors with Armature Control. If a d-c shunt-wound servomotor is operated with a fixed field excitation and controlled armature input as from a standard d-c generator (Ward-Leonard connection) or from an amplidyne, the circuit used would be similar to that shown in Fig. D-1. The usual shunt-motor equations apply.

$$V_m = E_m + I_a R_a$$
$$E_m = K_1 \times \text{rpm}$$
$$T_m = \text{torque} = K_2 I_a$$

from which

$$V_m = K_1 \times \text{rpm} + \frac{T_m R_a}{K_2}$$

and

$$T_m = \left(\frac{V_m - K_1 \times \text{rpm}}{R_a} \right) K_2$$

If the motor torque (T_m) is plotted as a function of speed from this equation, the curves of Fig. D-2 result. These curves indicate that the motor is equivalent to a device which produces a constant torque at all speeds coupled to a viscous-friction damper that requires a driving torque proportional to speed. Thus the armature-controlled d-c motor inherently provides a certain amount of damping, and although the available torque is reduced at high speeds, the damping tends to improve the system stability.

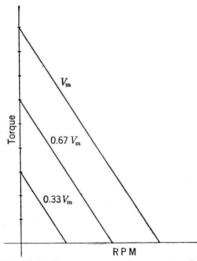

Fig. D-2. Torque vs. speed curves for d-c armature-controlled motor.

The curves of Fig. D-2 are idealized, of course, since the effects of armature reaction, and brush and bearing friction are neglected in the equations. Armature reaction reduces the torque output at high armature currents, but its effect can be reduced by designing the motor to have high reluctance in the armature-reaction axis or by the use of compensating windings. The friction normally has a viscous and a coulomb component. The former would cause a slight change in the slope of the torque-speed curves, while the latter would lower the torque at all speeds by the same amount. In a well-designed servomotor, bearing and brush friction are both very low.

The armature control method has some definite advantages and disadvantages. The motor inherently has little time delay because the armature inductance is low (and can be made smaller with compensating windings), while the torque may be made very large by supplying transient currents which are several times normal full-load current. This combination provides very fast response. On the other hand, armature control requires large currents and large amounts of power from the control device at a low-impedance level. If the motor-generator set indicated in Fig. D-1 is not acceptable, thyratron circuits may often be used.

D-5. D-C Motors with Field Control. Figure D-3a shows the basic circuit for field control of a d-c shunt motor. The armature is excited from a constant-current source, while the error signal energizes the field through a phase-sensitive amplifier. The torque equation is $T_m = KI_f$. Curves of motor torque as a function of speed are shown in Fig. D-3b

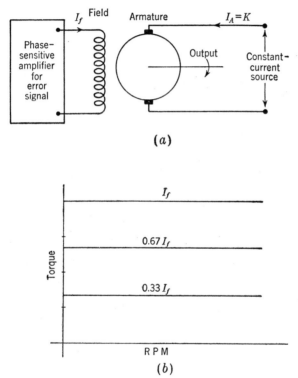

(a)

(b)

Fɪɢ. D-3. Field-controlled d-c servomotor. (a) Basic circuit for field control; (b) torque vs. speed curves.

for the condition of constant armature current. Such a system has no inherent damping, and other means must be provided to supply it. If a constant-current source is not readily available, a constant-voltage supply with series dropping resistor may be used with reasonably good results.

Many d-c motors designed for field-control applications have split-field windings which are able to carry full armature current so that a thyratron circuit as shown in Fig. D-4 may be used. The tubes both conduct simultaneously, supplying about half of their maximum current. The fields are then balanced and opposing so that no torque results. Application of a control voltage increases one tube current while decreasing the other by an equal amount. Thus a net field results, and torque is supplied, while the armature current remains constant.

Field-controlled motors usually have high-impedance inputs which make them suitable for control by thyratrons or vacuum tubes, but this impedance is frequently largely inductive, which causes a time delay in the response and may adversely affect stability. Another difficulty with field control lies in the fact that the armature back emf may cause large changes in armature current and thus invalidate the constant-armature-current assumption. If this happens, it is necessary to increase the field current to decrease the motor speed, which is often undesirable.

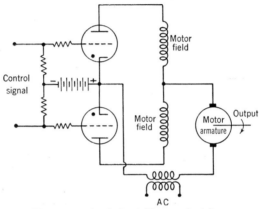

Fig. D-4. Thyratron circuit for field control of d-c servomotor.

Properly designed motors, however, make it possible to obtain satisfactory performance.

D-6. D-C Motors with Permanent-magnet Fields. Because of the development of Alnico permanent magnets, it has been possible to build motors and generators with permanent-magnet fields, having good performance characteristics. The motors are usually small, seldom larger than several hundred watts, but generators have been built with capacities of several kilowatts. The motors have approximately the same characteristics as a shunt-wound motor. They are readily reversed by reversing the armature supply, and their speed is easily controlled. Some care must be taken to prevent heavy overloading, or high peak armature currents, since the permanent-magnet field may be weakened or demagnetized by such currents.

D-7. D-C Series and Split-series Motors. Series motors have high starting torque and poor speed regulation with torque. This high negative slope of the torque-speed characteristic is equivalent to a high viscous damping and contributes materially to servo stability but also adds to velocity errors. Higher torques can be obtained on reversals with a series motor than with other types of motors. In general, a straight-series motor has the disadvantage of being a unidirectional device unless some type of switching is used that reverses either the armature or the field connections, but not both. Series motors with such change of connections made by a relay have been used in some cases to obtain bidirectional control, an example being a radar trainer integrator servo.

Split-series motors are characterized by high starting torque and have the advantage of bidirectional control with a small number of control elements. Figure D-5a shows a relay control circuit for a separately controlled armature motor, and Fig. D-5b shows a relay control circuit for a split-series motor. It is seen that only half as many relay contacts

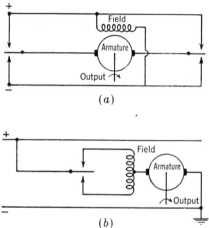

FIG. D-5. Relay control of motors. (a) Separately controlled armature; (b) split-series motor.

are required for the split-series motor. Because the split-series motor can utilize only one-half of the field-winding space at one instant, its design is generally not so compact as that of a straight-series motor of the same rating. Comparing motors wound on the same frame, a split-series motor will have a lower field flux and a lower torque rating than a straight-series motor.

D-8. A-C Two-phase Motors. The a-c motors used for servomotors are predominantly two-phase induction motors, since this is the only type of a-c motor which provides ready speed and torque control plus reversibility with simple circuitry and without switching devices. The basic circuit is indicated in Fig. D-6. The two field currents must be 90 deg out of phase, and torque is obtained by varying the magnitude of the control-field voltage. Directional control is obtained by phase reversal in the control field. If a two-phase supply is not available, the necessary 90-deg relationship can be obtained from a single-phase supply by means of a series capacitor in the reference field circuit or by a phase-shifting circuit in the amplifier.

A normal two-phase motor will not start if only one phase is energized, but if started it continues to run as a single-phase motor when the second phase is deenergized. A two-phase servomotor must not only refuse to start on single phase but must also stop quickly if one phase is deenergized. This feature is obtained partly by adjusting the rotor reactance-to-resistance ratio and partly by proper design of other features.

D-9. Hydraulic and Pneumatic Motors. These may be roughly subdivided into two classes, linear actuators (also called cylinders or jacks), and rotational motors.

The linear actuators are piston devices. They may be obtained in a variety of power capacities with a wide range of stroke lengths. Speed of action can usually be adjusted to meet any reasonable specifications. The devices are relatively simple mechanically, with the pneumatic cylin-

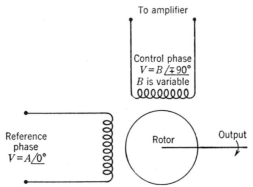

To amplifier

Control phase
$V = B\,\underline{/\mp 90°}$
B is variable

Reference phase
$V = A\,\underline{/0°}$

Rotor

Output

Fig. D-6. Basic two-phase servomotor circuit.

der usually involving fewer parts and being faster acting. The hydraulic jack, however, can be locked in place, since the hydraulic fluid is practically incompressible, while the pneumatic cylinder must be pressure-locked. Both types are used in aircraft servos. Hydraulics are more commonly used, but pneumatic systems have been featured in some of the most modern aircraft. In either the hydraulic or the pneumatic types reversible action is readily provided by proper design.

Rotary hydraulic and pneumatic motors are available in unidirectional or reversible types, and in a wide range of ratings, both fractional and integral horsepower. They may be designed as low-speed or high-speed devices. In general, they have good torque characteristics and are very light in weight considering their power ratings. The rotors have comparatively low inertia, providing a high torque-to-inertia ratio, which is frequently important in systems having high acceleration requirements. The hydraulic motor is more efficient, but the pneumatic motor is more suitable for applications where there is a fire or explosion hazard. Speed control is readily accomplished in either type by valve adjustments.

APPENDIX E

COMPENSATING DEVICES

E-1. Introduction. The need for compensating devices, and the manner in which they alter system performance, has been discussed at some length in the text. This appendix, after a brief summary of the material previously presented in the text, discusses some of the devices which are used for compensation purposes.

Performance specifications for a servomechanism system usually include requirements as to: (1) speed of response, including acceleration performance; (2) maximum overshoot and oscillatory characteristics; (3) steady-state errors. If a given system does not meet specifications, improvement is usually obtained by gain adjustment and compensation. Increasing the gain makes system response faster and decreases steady-state errors but makes the system more oscillatory. The oscillatory conditions thus obtained are compensated for by damping devices; viscous friction, derivative devices, or phase-lead devices which accomplish an approximate differentiation. If the steady-state errors cannot be sufficiently reduced by such methods, it is necessary to insert an integrating device in the system. This device may perform a true integration or an approximate integration, the designer's choice depending largely on the steady-state error specifications. Insertion of an integrator usually makes the system sluggish and may affect the oscillatory conditions so that damping devices may also be required.

E-2. Viscous Dampers. In general, viscous damping is not frequently used in servo systems, especially if they are velocity systems, because the viscous damper dissipates appreciable power which must be supplied by the servo drive. When used, the viscous damper is essentially a dashpot device. Such types will not be discussed here.

There are several devices which have viscous-damping characteristics without the objectionable power-consumption characteristics. Several of these are discussed briefly here; they are electric motors which have viscous-damping characteristics, and certain rotational types of viscous dampers.[160],*

---

* Superior numbers, when they appear in the text proper, are the numbers of references given in the Bibliography.

When a d-c shunt motor is armature-controlled, its performance characteristics exhibit viscous-damping features. For a constant applied armature voltage, the shaft torque decreases as the speed increases. This is equivalent to a constant-torque motor coupled to a viscous damper, since the retarding torque of the damper increases linearly with the speed and subtracts from the torque of a constant-torque motor to produce an equivalent torque which decreases linearly with speed. This is a convenient way to obtain damping and does not dissipate power, but unfortunately the amount of damping (determined by the slope of the torque-speed curve) is fixed by the motor design and cannot be increased. It

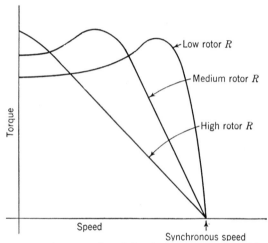

Fɪɢ. E-1. Torque vs. speed curves of an induction motor as affected by rotor resistance.

can be decreased by inserting resistance in series with the armature, but a decrease is not usually wanted, and such manipulation also decreases the available torque.

The torque-speed characteristics of induction motors as a function of rotor resistance are shown in Fig. E-1. It may be seen that the starting torque increases as the rotor resistance is increased, and this feature is usually desired in induction motors for servo use. It may also be seen that for high rotor resistance the torque-speed curve of the induction motor is quite similar to that of the armature-controlled d-c motor, and thus the servo induction motor produces equivalent viscous damping.

The rotor resistance of a squirrel-cage induction motor is fixed by design, and thus for such motors the viscous damping is not variable. If a wound-rotor motor is available, however, the damping may be changed over a reasonable range, though at the expense of available starting torque.

Another method for varying the damping of a two-phase induction motor is to introduce a d-c current into one of the windings in addition to the a-c signal. This d-c component produces eddy-current braking effects which are equivalent to viscous damping.

A mechanical device which provides viscous damping for rotational systems without the large power consumption of dashpot-type devices is shown in Fig. E-2a. A container filled with a fluid suitable for viscous damping is fastened to a shaft. In the fluid is a mass mounted on the shaft by means of a ball bearing. The shaft is attached to the output, or drive motor, of the servo. When the output moves, the shaft rotates but a drag is produced between the cover and the mass through the viscous fluid, thus tending to damp the system during transient periods. If the system is driven at constant velocity, very little loss is incurred in

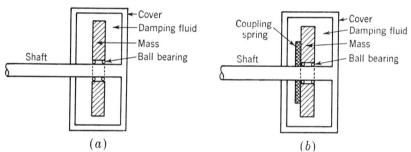

FIG. E-2. Friction dampers. (a) Rotational viscous damper; (b) spring-coupled viscous damper.

the damper because the mass attains essentially the same velocity as the cover owing to the viscous drag.

The inertia, J, is an important factor in such a damper and according to Hall[160] must be at least six times the system inertia to limit the peak overshoot to four-thirds when no other damping is present in the system. The viscous drag produced is $T_a = F_a\omega$, where F_a is the viscous-friction coefficient, and ω is the velocity of the cover relative to the damper mass. In this expression the coefficient F_a must be selected and then obtained by choice of a fluid and the mechanical design of the damper.

The relatively large mass required for damping with the viscous damper is frequently undesirable. A worth-while reduction in the damping mass may be obtained by using a coil spring to couple the mass to the damper shaft as shown in Fig. E-2b. The spring applies an additional retarding torque to the output shaft during position or velocity changes, and since this torque is also applied to the damping mass, the mass is accelerated and the viscous damping changes more rapidly.

It is apparent that the damping mass, spring, and fluid combination may form an overdamped, underdamped, or critically damped system.

For best performance as a servo damper, the unit should be under-damped. The design of such a unit is obviously more difficult than that of the previously described viscous damper, but the reduction in inertia is frequently worth while. For the equations needed in design, the reader is referred to the article by Hall.[160]

E-3. Derivative Dampers—Phase-lead Devices. It has been shown in the text that the transient response of a servomechanism can be improved by adding to the error signal an additional signal which is proportional to the time derivative of the error, or to the time derivative of the output. In terms of the frequency-response analysis this corresponds to adding a signal which leads the error signal in time phase. In general the transient response can be improved by an anticipatory signal whether such signal is a true derivative or only an approximate derivative.

Derivative damping signals are used in many high-performance auto-matic-control systems and may take various physical forms. In electri-cal servos, networks are placed in series with the controller channel to differentiate the error signal, or networks may be placed in subordinate feedback loops to accomplish the same purpose. Various electromagnetic and electromechanical devices are also used in electrical servos, some of which will be discussed here. In nonelectrical systems, such as pneu-matically operated process-control instruments, derivative signals are obtained by nonelectrical means. These will also be discussed briefly.

The text contains considerable discussion on series and feedback phase-lead networks for d-c systems, and since specific design of such networks is different for each application, no further discussion is contained in this appendix. For a more detailed discussion of the subject the reader is referred to the work of A. C. Hall.[45]

Output derivative feedback may be obtained by gearing a d-c tachome-ter to the load shaft. The tachometer produces a voltage proportional to the time rate of change of output position. This voltage is then fed back to a convenient point in the controller. In some systems the com-mutator ripple produced by a d-c tachometer is objectionable, and so an a-c tachometer is used and its output rectified.

Most a-c-operated servos utilize two-phase servomotors and operate at 60 cycles or 400 cycles, which frequently is said to be the carrier. One phase of the motor is always excited at rated voltage and is called the reference phase. The second, or control, phase requires a carrier shifted 90 deg from the reference and is energized only when an error exists. The data-transmission system which detects the error is normally a syn-chro generator–control transformer unit operating at carrier frequency and expressing the error as an amplitude modulation. If the system is to be energized from a single-phase source, a quadrature voltage must be set up.   This may be done in either the reference phase or the control phase, but methods for accomplishing this will not be discussed.

The modulated signals are of the suppressed-carrier type, and the compensation problem is to produce a positive phase shift in the modulation envelope.   In terms of electrical networks capable of accomplishing this, two general approaches to the problem are used.   The first of these is to demodulate the signal, pass the resultant signal through a d-c compensating network, and remodulate the carrier with the output of the d-c network.   The second method uses well-known communication-circuit techniques in designing filter and phase-shift networks which suppress the carrier and produce equal attenuation in the upper and lower sidebands.   The mathematical procedures involved are only slightly more complex than for d-c phase-lead circuits, and for further discussion the reader is referred to the literature.[161-166]

The following methods may be used to accomplish derivative compensation without the design of special a-c phase-shift networks:

1. Demodulate the error signal with any suitable demodulator, phase-shift the resulting signal with a d-c derivative network, and remodulate.

2. Drive a low-inertia two-phase servomotor with the error signal by coupling into the control channel at some convenient point.   The motor velocity is then proportional to the error signal.   Drive an a-c tachometer of the two-phase induction type from the servomotor.   The tachometer output voltage is then proportional to the motor velocity and is thus a derivative of the error.   Feed back the tachometer voltage.

3. A third method is the use of a resonant-type electromagnetic filter suggested by McDonald.[163]   This device consists of a torque motor coupled to an induction pick-off.   The unit includes a spring device, a damper, and additional inertia, all adjustable so that the unit may be tuned to resonance in the range of the desired signal frequency with suitable damping.   The torque motor is driven from the error signal, and the induction pick-off produces an approximate derivative signal which is then fed back into the controller.

When it is desired to obtain the derivative compensation for an a-c servo by means of an electrical network, a special design is required for each new system.   The following is an abbreviated list of the types of networks which have been used successfully:

1. Parallel T (symmetrical)
2. Parallel T (nonsymmetrical)
3. Bridged parallel T
4. Wien bridge
5. Bridged T
6. Series-resonant RLC networks

Output derivative compensation may be obtained for a-c servos by gearing a tachometer to the load shaft. The tachometer must be of the induction type in order that the velocity signal be of carrier frequency. Induction tachometers are basically two-phase machines with squirrel-cage rotor of low resistance. One phase is energized at carrier frequency and induces eddy currents in the rotor. The second phase is used as a voltage pick-off. When the rotor is at standstill, the magnetic field of the eddy currents does not link the pick-off phase and no voltage is induced. When the rotor moves, it shifts the space alignment of the eddy-current field, which induces a voltage in the pick-off phase that is directly proportional to rotor velocity.

E-4. Pneumatic Derivative Devices. The use of derivative devices in pneumatically operated automatic-control systems is not uncommon.

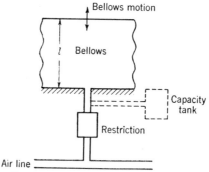

Fɪɢ. E-3. Pneumatic derivative device.

A good example is the derivative component in automatic process controllers. The derivative device in general consists of a bellows with a restriction in the air line which feeds it as shown in Fig. E-3. It is readily seen that the length of the bellows, l, depends on the internal pressure, P. Any change in length of the bellows is proportional to the change in pressure, $\Delta l \propto \Delta P$. If there is a change in air pressure in the line, the restriction (which may be a capillary tube or a needle valve, etc.) prevents P from following the line pressure immediately and the rate of flow through the restriction is proportional to the pressure difference between the line and the bellows. It is readily seen that the pressure drop across the restriction changes as the line pressure changes, and therefore this pressure drop is proportional to the rate of change of line pressure.

The pressure drop across the restriction changes as the pressure inside the bellows builds up. If the volume of the bellows is small, the pressure builds up rapidly and the pressure drop across the restriction is not maintained. To adjust this, a capacity tank may be attached to the bellows side of the restriction as shown in Fig. E-3.

In terms of an electrical analogue, the restriction may be considered as a resistance, and the volume of the bellows plus capacity tank may be considered as a capacitance. Thus the pneumatic combination is seen to have a "time constant" equivalent to the RC time constant of an electrical network. This time constant may be adjusted by varying either the restriction or the volume.

The application of such a pneumatic derivative device in practical pneumatic controllers is accomplished by various mechanical linkages. A discussion of these is beyond the scope of this text, and the reader is referred to the literature.[43,44]

E-5. Integrators—Phase-lag Devices. When the steady-state error of a servo system must be corrected, it is frequently necessary to use integral or phase-lag compensation. A discussion of electrical networks used for integrating is omitted from this appendix because the discussion in the text proper is thought adequate. Only two types of integral devices are discussed here—electric motors and pneumatic controller integrators.

E-6. Electric Motors as Integrators. In terms of the mathematical notation an integrative device is one for which $\theta_o = K \int_0^t \theta_i \, dt$. It is readily shown that this characteristic is possessed by an electric motor for which the output velocity is directly proportional to the applied voltage.

If

$$\theta_i = V \text{ (input volts)}$$

and

$$\frac{d\theta_o}{dt} = \text{rpm}$$

where rpm $= KV$, then

$$\frac{d\theta_o}{dt} = KV$$

and

$$\theta_o = \int_0^t KV \, dt$$

Thus a mechanical output signal (rotation of motor shaft) may be made proportional to the time integral of an input-voltage signal. The voltage input is usually obtained from some amplifier stage in the controller, and if an electrical output signal is desired, the motor may be geared to a potential divider or some similar device.

E-7. Pneumatic Integrator. The pneumatic devices used for integration in process controllers are basically the same in construction as the pneumatic derivative device shown in Fig. E-3. This combination may be used to integrate as well as differentiate, and the only practical differences are the choice of time constant and the mechanical linkages used.

It should be noted that the pressure drop across the restriction causes a flow of air into (or out of) the bellows. The total volume of air displaced is then proportional to the integral of the pressure drop across the restriction over the time period when such pressure drop exists. Furthermore, the flow of air to the bellows causes a displacement which in general is proportional to the volume of air involved. The displacement of the bellows is then a mechanical signal proportional to the time integral of the pressure difference between line and bellows.

APPENDIX F

BIBLIOGRAPHY

1. HAZEN, H. L., Theory of Servomechanisms, *J. Franklin Inst.*, 1934.
2. AHRENDT, W. R., and J. F. TAPLIN, "Automatic Feedback Control," McGraw-Hill Book Company, Inc., New York, 1951.
3. GARDNER, M. F., and J. L. BARNES, "Transients in Linear Systems," John Wiley & Sons, Inc., New York, 1942.
4. CHURCHILL, R. V., "Modern Operational Mathematics in Engineering," McGraw-Hill Book Company, Inc., New York, 1944.
5. GOLDMAN, S., "Transformation Calculus and Electrical Transients," Prentice-Hall, Inc., New York, 1949.
6. THOMSON, W. T., "Laplace Transformation," Prentice-Hall, Inc., New York, 1950.
7. DEN HARTOG, J. P., "Mechanical Vibrations," McGraw-Hill Book Company, Inc., New York, 1940.
8. TIMOSHENKO, S., "Vibration Problems in Engineering," D. Van Nostrand Company, Inc., New York 1937.
9. SKILLING, H. H., "Transient Electric Currents," McGraw-Hill Book Company, Inc., New York, 1937.
10. FREBURG, C. R., The Solution of Vibration Problems by the Use of Electric Models, *Purdue Univ. Eng. Bull.* 92, 1944.
11. FROST, S., Compact Analog Computer for Obtaining a Solution to Differential Equations, *Electronics*, 1948.
12. HRONES, J. A., and J. B. RESWICK, The Electronic Analogue, *Machine Design*, September, 1949.
13. ECKMAN, D. P., "Industrial Process Control," John Wiley & Sons, Inc., New York, 1945.
14. PASCHKIS, V., and H. D. BAKER, A Method for Determining Unsteady-state Heat Transfer by Means of an Electric Analogy, *Trans. ASME*, 1942.
15. HORNFECK, A. J., Response Characteristics of Thermometer Elements, *Trans. ASME*, 1949.
16. MASON, C. E., Quantitative Analysis of Process Lags, *Trans. ASME*, 1938.
17. MCCANN, G. D., C. H. WILTS, and B. J. LOCANTHI, Electronic Techniques Applied to Analog Methods of Computation, *Proc. IRE*, 1949.
18. HIGGINS, S. P., and R. M. HUTCHINSON, Laboratory Analogs for Electric Furnaces, *Paper 48, IIRD, 3, ASME* meeting, Sept. 13-17, 1948.
19. ECKMAN, D. P., and W. H. WANNAMAKER, Electrical Analogy Method for Fundamental Investigations in Automatic Control, *Trans. ASME*, 1945.
20, 21. MCCANN, G. D., and S. W. HERWALD, Dimensionless Analysis of Servomechanisms by Electrical Analogy (2 parts), *Trans. AIEE*, 1946, 1947.
22. MCCANN, G. D., S. HERWALD, H. S. KIRSCHBAUM, Electrical Analogy Methods Applied to Servomechanism Problems, *Trans. AIEE*, 1946.

23. McCANN, G. D., and C. H. WILTS, Application of Electrical Analogy Computers to Heat Transfer and Fluid Flow Problems, *J. Applied Mechanics*, September, 1949.

24. HARDER, E. L., Solution of the General Voltage Regulator Problem by Electrical Analogy, *Trans. AIEE*, 1947.

25. PHILBRICK, G. A., Designing Industrial Controllers by Analogs, *Electronics*, 1948.

26. RAGAZZINI, J. R., R. H. RANDALL, and F. A. RUSSELL, Analysis of Problems in Dynamics by Electronic Circuits, *Proc. IRE*, 1947.

27. LAUER, H., R. LESNICK, and L. E. MATSON, "Servomechanism Fundamentals," McGraw-Hill Book Company, Inc., New York, 1947.

28. BROWN, G. S., Transient Behavior and Design of Servomechanisms, *NDRC paper*, 1943.

29. JAMES, H. M., N. B. NICHOLS, and R. S. PHILLIPS, "Theory of Servomechanisms," McGraw-Hill Book Company, Inc., New York, 1947.

30. HARRIS, H., The Analysis and Design of Servomechanisms, *OSRD* 454.

31. BROWN, G. S., and D. P. CAMPBELL, "Principles of Servomechanisms," John Wiley & Sons, Inc., New York, 1948.

32. WEISS, H. K., Constant Speed Control Theory, *J. Aeronaut. Sci.*, 1939.

33. BROWN, G. S., and A. C. HALL, Dynamic Behavior and Design of Servomechanisms, *Trans. ASME*, 1946. OLDENBOURG, R. C., and H. SARTORIUS, "The Dynamics of Automatic Controls" (translation), American Society of Mechanical Engineers, 1948.

34. CLARKE, J. G., Differentiating and Integrating Circuits, *Electronics*, November, 1944.

35. DRAPER, C. S., and W. McKAY, "Instrument Analysis," unpublished notes.

36. MITCHELL, K., Estimation of the Effect of a Parameter Change on the Roots of Stability Equations, *Aeronaut. Quart.*, May, 1949.

37. McCANN, G. D., W. D. OSBON, and H. S. KIRSCHBAUM, General Analysis of Speed Regulators under Impact Load, *Trans. AIEE*, 1947.

38. DRAPER, C. S., and G. P. BENTLEY, Design Factors Controlling the Dynamic Performance of Instruments, *Trans. ASME*, 1940.

39. DRAPER, C. S., and G. V. SCHIESTETT, General Principles of Instrument Analysis, *Instruments*, 1939.

40. MASON, C. E., and G. A. PHILBRICK, Automatic Control in the Presence of Process Lags, *Trans. ASME*, 1940.

41. SPITZGLASS, A. F., Quantitative Analysis of Single Capacity Processes (2 parts), *Trans. ASME*, 1938, 1940.

42. ZIEGLER, J. G., and N. B. NICHOLS, Process Lags in Automatic Control Circuits, *Trans. ASME*, 1942.

43. TIVY, V. V., Air Operated Controllers, *Trans. ASME*, 1946.

44. TIVY, V. V., The Derivative Controller, *Petroleum Processing*, July, 1948.

45. HALL, A. C., Application of Circuit Theory to the Design of Servomechanisms, *J. Franklin Inst.*, 1946.

46. TSCHUDI, E. W., Transfer Functions for RC and RL Equalizer Networks, *Electronics*, May, 1949.

47. CHESTNUT, H., Obtaining Attenuation–Frequency Characteristics for Servomechanisms, *Gen. Elec. Rev.*, December, 1947.

48. BLACK, H. S., Stabilized Feedback Amplifiers, *Bell System Tech. J.*, 1934.

49. NYQUIST, H., Regeneration Theory, *Bell System Tech. J.*, 1932.

50. BODE, H. W., "Network Analysis and Feedback Amplifier Design," D. Van Nostrand Company, Inc., New York, 1945.

51. MacColl, L. A., "Fundamental Theory of Servomechanisms," D. Van Nostrand Company, Inc., New York, 1945.
52. Harris, H., The Frequency Response of Automatic Control Systems, *Trans. AIEE*, 1946.
53. Ansoff, H. I., Stability of Linear Oscillating Systems with Constant Time Lag, *J. Applied Mechanics*, June, 1949.
54. Mulligan, J. H., Jr., The Effect of Pole and Zero Location on the Transient Response of Linear Dynamic Systems, *Proc. IRE*, May, 1949.
55. Edwards, R. S., Selecting Electric Servomotors, *Machine Design*, January, 1949.
56. Edwards, R. S., A Comparison of Small and Medium Power Electric Servomotors, *Instruments*, 1948.
57. Harris, H., A Comparison of Two Basic Servomechanism Types, *Trans. AIEE*, 1947.
58. Newton, G. C., Jr., What Size Motor? *Machine Design*, November, 1950.
59. Newton, G. C., Jr., Comparison of Hydraulic and Electric Servomotors, *Proc. Natl. Ind. Hydraulics Conf.*, 1949.
60. Blackburn, J. F., "Components Handbook," McGraw-Hill Book Company, Inc., New York, 1949.
61. McDonald, D., Stabilizing Servomechanisms, *Electronics*, November, 1948.
62. Kessler, W. J., Transient Response Equalization through Steady State Methods, *Proc. IRE*, 1949.
63. Nadler, M., The Synthesis of Electric Networks According to Prescribed Transient Conditions, *Proc. IRE*, 1949.
64. Schwartz, G. J., The Application of Lead Networks and Sinusoidal Analysis to Automatic Control Systems, *Trans. AIEE*, 1947.
65. Whiteley, A. L., Theory of Servo Systems, with Particular Reference to Stabilization, *J. Inst. Elec. Engrs. (London)*, 1946.
66. Whiteley, A. L., Fundamental Principles of Automatic Regulators and Servomechanisms, *J. Inst. Elec. Engrs. (London)*, 1947, part IIa.
67. Ferrell, E. B., The Servo as a Transmission Problem, *Proc. IRE*, 1945.
68. Chestnut, H., and R. W. Mayer, Comparison of Steady State and Transient Performance of Servomechanisms, *Trans. AIEE*, 1949.
69. Graham, R. E., Linear Servo Theory, *Bell System Tech. J.*, 1946.
70. Weiss, H. K., Analysis of Relay Servomechanisms, *J. Aeronaut. Sci.*, 1946.
71. Kahn, D. A., An Analysis of Relay Servomechanisms, *Trans. AIEE*, 1949.
72. Kochenburger, R. J., A Frequency Response Method for Analyzing and Synthesizing Contactor Servomechanisms, *Trans. AIEE*, 1949.
73. Rogers, T. A., and W. C. Hurty, Relay Servomechanisms—The Shunt Motor Servo with Inertia Load, *Trans. ASME*, 1950.
74. Evans, W. R., Graphical Analysis of Control Systems, *Trans. AIEE*, 1948.
75. Evans, W. R., Control System Synthesis by Root Locus Method, *Trans. AIEE*, 1950.
76. Profos, P., A New Method for the Treatment of Regulation Problems, *Sulzer Tech. Rev.*, 1945.
77. Herwald, S. W., Forms and Principles of Servomechanisms, *Westinghouse Engr.*, 1946.
78. Marcy, H. T., M. Yachter, and J. Zauderer, Instrument Inaccuracies in Feedback Control Systems with Particular Reference to Backlash, *Trans. AIEE*, 1949.
79. Johnson, T. C., Selsyn Design and Application, *Trans. AIEE*, 1945.
80. Linville, T. M., and J. S. Woodward, Selsyn Instruments for Position Systems, *Elec. Eng.*, 1934.

81. CHESTNUT, H., Electrical Accuracy of Selsyn Generator–Control Transformer System, *Trans. AIEE*, 1946.
82. EXLINE, P. G., Pressure Responsive Elements, *Trans. ASME*, 1938.
83. OPLINGER, K. A., Gyroscopes and Their Applications, *Machine Design*, July, 1948.
84. HOTTENROTH, F. W., JR., Electric Control Devices for Aircraft, *Trans. AIEE*, 1945 suppl.
85. HOTTENROTH, F. W., JR., Preferred Practices for Electric Control Devices for Aircraft, *Trans. AIEE*, 1945.
86. KONET, H., Electrically Operated Gyroscopic Instruments, *Trans. AIEE*, 1944.
87. YOUNG, C. M., E. E. LYNCH, E. R. BOYNTON, Electrical Control in Automatic Pilots, *Trans. AIEE*, 1944.
88. ROMAN, W. G., Electronic Regulators and Regulating Systems, *Machine Design*, December, 1949.
89. OWEN, J. C., Automatic Pilots, *Elec. Eng.*, 1948.
90. LEAR, W. P., Remote and Automatic Electric Controls for Aircraft, *J. Franklin Inst.*, 1944.
91. ROBINETTE, W. C., A Packaged Servomechanism, *Electronics*, 1948.
92. GORMAN, W. J., JR., Utilizing Selsyns in Machines, *Machine Design*, 1948.
93. MEREDITH, F. W., The Modern Autopilot, *J. Roy. Aeronaut. Soc.*, 1949.
94. FEISS, R., Modern Control Dynamics and Stability Criteria as Applied to Gyroscopic Speed Detectors with Hydraulic Drive, *Trans. ASME*, 1949.
95. ROBINETTE, W. C., A New Servomechanism Theory—The Synthesis of Automatic Control Systems, *Instruments*, 1946.
96. SMITH, E. S., "Automatic Control Engineering," McGraw-Hill Book Company, Inc., New York, 1944.
97. PETERS, J. C., Measurement and Control of Process Variables, *Chem. & Met. Eng.*, 1943.
98. ECKMAN, D. P., "Principles of Industrial Process Control," John Wiley & Sons, Inc., New York, 1945.
99. HANNA, C. R., W. D. OSBON, and R. A. HARTLEY, Tracer Controlled Position Regulator for Propeller Milling Machine, *Trans. AIEE*, 1945.
100. MORTON, H. E., and O. G. RUTEMILLER, Application of Electrical Equipment for Ship Propeller Milling Machine, *Trans. AIEE*, 1945.
101. HALPERT, P., and O. E. ESVAL, Electric Automatic Pilots for Aircraft, *Trans. AIEE*, 1944.
102. ESVAL, O. E., The Gyrosyn Compass, *Trans. AIEE*, 1944.
103. ZIEBOLZ, H., "Relay Devices and Their Application to the Solution of Mathematical Equations" (2 vols), Askania Regulator Co., Chicago, 1940.
104. WARD, E. E., Feedback Amplifiers and Servo Systems, *Wireless Engr.*, 1950.
105. SCHREINER, K. E., High Performance Demodulator for Servomechanisms, *Proc. Natl. Electronics Conf.*, 1946.
106. EDWARDS, F. E., JR., Electronic Circuits for the Control of Clutch Type Servomechanisms, *Proc. Natl. Electronics Conf.*, 1948.
107. TERMAN, F. E., "Radio Engineering," 3d ed., McGraw-Hill Book Company, Inc., New York, 1947.
108. BOYAJIAN, A. O., Theory of DC Excited Iron Core Reactors and Regulators, *Trans. AIEE*, 1924.
109. LAMM, A. UNO, Some Fundamentals of a Theory of the Transductor or Magnetic Amplifier, *Trans. AIEE*, 1947.
110. KIRSCHBAUM, H. L., and E. L. HARDER, A Balanced Amplifier Using Biased Saturable Core Reactors, *Trans. AIEE*, 1947.

111. HEDSTROEM, S. E., L. F. BORG, Transductor Fundamentals, *Electronics*, 1948.
112. CROW, L. R., "Saturating Core Devices," Edwards Bros., Inc., Ann Arbor, Mich., (litho.).
113. FITZGERALD, A. S., Magnetic Amplifier Circuits—Neutral Type, *J. Franklin Inst.*, 1947.
114. FITZGERALD, A. S., Some Notes on Design of Magnetic Amplifiers, *J. Franklin Inst.*, 1947.
115. FITZGERALD, A. S., Magnetic Amplifiers—Neutral Type, *J. Franklin Inst.*, 1947.
116. "Magnetic Amplifier Design Handbook," Vickers, Inc., St. Louis, Mo., 1949.
117. McCLURE, F. N., Application of Magnetic Amplifiers, AIEE Great Lakes District meeting, 1950 (conference paper).
118. OGLE, H. M., The Amplistat and Its Application (3 parts), *Gen. Elec. Rev.*, 1950.
119. BLACK, A. O., Influence of Core Material on Magnetic Amplifier Design, *Proc. Natl. Electronics Conf.*, 1948.
120. VER PLANCK, D. W., An Analysis of Magnetic Amplifiers with Feedback, *Proc. Natl. Electronics Conf.*, 1948.
121. VER PLANCK, D. W., L. A. FINZI, and D. C. BEAUMARIAGE, Analytical Determination of Characteristics of Magnetic Amplifiers with Feedback, *Trans. AIEE*, 1949.
122. JOHNSON, W. C., B. C. MERRELL, and R. E. ALLEY, JR., Universal Curves for D.C. Controllable Reactors, *Trans. AIEE*, 1949.
123. Bibliography on Transductors—Magnetic Amplifiers, *Instruments*, April, 1948.
124. MILNES, A. G., Magnetic Amplifiers, *J. Inst. Elec. Engrs. (London)*, 1949, part I.
125. GALE, H. M., and P. D. ATKINSON, A Theoretical and Experimental Study of the Series Connected Magnetic Amplifier, *J. Inst. Elec. Engrs. (London)*, 1949, part I.
126. DORNHOEFER, W. J., Self Saturation in Magnetic Amplifiers, *Trans. AIEE*, 1949.
127. FORMAHLS, W. H., Rototrol—A Versatile Electric Regulator, *Westinghouse Engr.*, 1942.
128. ALEXANDERSON, E. F., M. A. EDWARDS, and K. K. BOWMAN, The Amplidyne Generator—A Dynamo-electric Amplifier for Power Control, *Gen. Elec. Rev.*, 1940.
129. ALEXANDERSON, E. F., The Amplidyne System of Control, *Proc. IRE*, 1944.
130. BOWERS, J. L., Fundamentals of the Amplidyne Generator, *Trans. AIEE*, 1945.
131. LIWSCHITZ, M. M., The Multi-stage Rototrol, *Trans. AIEE*, 1947.
132. KIMBALL, A. W., Two Stage Rototrol for Low Energy Regulating Systems, *Trans. AIEE*, 1947.
133. SANDERS, R. M., The Dynamo Electric Amplifier—Class A Operation, *Trans. AIEE*, 1949.
134. LITMAN, B., An Analysis of Rotating Amplifiers, *Trans. AIEE*, 1949.
135. "Instruction Book—Minneapolis-Honeywell Type C-1 Autopilot."
136. JAESCHE, R. L., Eddy Current Clutches for Variable Speed Drive, *Machine Design*, 1947.
137. GUTMAN, A. S., Designing an Eddy Current Servo Clutch, *Machine Design*, 1950.
138. RABINOW, J., The Magnetic Fluid Clutch, *Trans. AIEE*, 1948.
139. BETTIS, E. S., and E. R. MANN, A Servo Employing the Magnetic Fluid Clutch, *Rev. Sci. Instruments*, 1949.
140. ELBERTY, R. S., Clutches—Characteristics and Design of Magnetic Fluid Types, *Machine Design*, 1949.
141. NELSON, G., Magnetic Fluid Clutch in Servo Application, *Electronics*, 1949.
142. PARZIALE, A. J., and P. D. TILTON, Characteristics of Some Magnetic Fluid Clutch Servomechanisms, *Trans. AIEE*, 1950.

143. NEWTON, G. C., JR., Hydraulic Variable Speed Transmissions as Servomotors, *J. Franklin Inst.*, 1947.
144. NEWTON, G. C., JR., and W. T. WHITE, Laboratory Aids for Electromechanical System Development, *Trans. AIEE*, 1947.
145. HANNAH, M. R., Frequency Response Measurements on a Hydraulic Power Unit, *Trans. AIEE*, 1948.
146. NICHOLS, N. B., and J. G. ZIEGLER, Process Control Valves, *Machine Design*, 1949.
147. LINDEROTH, L. S., JR., Selecting Hydraulic Pressure Control Valves, *Machine Design*, 1948.
148. ZIEBOLZ, H., Designing Hydraulic Servos, *Machine Design*, 1947.
149. ZIEBOLZ, H., Designing Pneumatic and Electric Servos, *Machine Design*, 1947.
150. KIDD, W. H., and G. A. PHILBRICK, "The Control Valve in Operation," The Foxboro Co., Foxboro, Mass.
151. ROSS, S. D., Valve Characteristics in Automatic Control, *Ind. Eng. Chem.*, 1946.
152. DICKEY, P. S., and H. L. COPLIN, A Study of Damper Characteristics, *Trans. ASME*, 1942.
153. CONWAY, H. G., "Fluid Pressure Mechanisms," Pitman Publishing Corp., New York, 1949.
154. ECKMAN, D. P., "Industrial Instrumentation," John Wiley & Sons, Inc., New York, 1950.
155. RHODES, T. J., "Industrial Instruments for Measurement and Control," McGraw-Hill Book Company, Inc., New York, 1941.
156. ROBERTS, C. C., Control Instruments, *Machine Design*, 1949.
157. KOOPMAN, R. J. W., Operating Characteristics of Two Phase Servo Motors, *Trans. AIEE*, 1949.
158. LEBENBAUM, P., JR., The Design of DC Motors for Use in Automatic Control Systems, *Trans. AIEE*, 1949.
159. KRONACHER, G., Static Accuracy Performance of the Selsyn Generator–Control Transformer System, *Trans. AIEE*, 1950.
160. HALL, A. C., Damper Stabilized Instrument Servomechanisms, *Trans. AIEE*, 1949.
161. SOBSZYK, A., Carrier Frequency Servomechanisms (3 parts), *J. Franklin Inst.*, 1948.
162. NOTTHOFF, A. P., JR., Phase Lead for AC Servo Systems with Compensation for Carrier Frequency Changes, *Trans. AIEE*, 1950.
163. McDONALD, D., Improvements in the Characteristics of AC Lead Networks for Servomechanisms, *Trans. AIEE*, 1950.
164. WHITE, C. F., Transfer Characteristics of a Bridged Parallel T Network, *Naval Research Lab. Rept. R-3167*.
165. TUTTLE, W. M., Bridged T and Parallel T Null Circuits for Measurements at Radio Frequencies, *Proc. IRE*, 1940.
166. HASTINGS, A. E., Analysis of a Resistance-capacitance Parallel T Network and Applications, *Proc. IRE*, 1946.
167. STANTON, L., Theory and Application of Parallel T Resistance-capacitance Frequency Selective Networks, *Proc. IRE*, 1946.
168. PETERS, J. C., Experimental Studies of Automatic Control, *Trans. ASME*, 1942.
169. ZIEGLER, J. G., and N. B. NICHOLS, Optimum Settings for Automatic Controllers, *Trans. ASME*, 1942.
170. PETERS, J. C., Getting the Most from Automatic Control, *Ind. Eng. Chem.*, 1941.
171. KELLER, E. G., Resonance Theory of Series Non-linear Control Circuits, *J. Franklin Inst.*, 1938.

172. MINORSKY, N., Control Problems, *J. Franklin Inst.*, 1941.

173. WINSON, J. W., The Flutter of Servo-controlled Aircraft, *J. Aeronaut. Sci.*, 1949.

174. McCANN, G. D., F. C. LINDVALL, and C. H. WILTS, The Effect of Coulomb Friction on the Performance of Servomechanisms, *Trans. AIEE*, 1948.

175. HUREWICZ, W., and N. B. NICHOLS, Servos with Torque Saturation (2 parts), *Radiation Lab. Rept.* 555 592.

176. HERR, D. L., and I. GERST, The Analysis and Optimum Synthesis of Linear Servomechanisms, *Trans. AIEE*, 1947.

177. HAZEN, H. L., Design and Test of a High Performance Servomechanism, *J. Franklin Inst.*, 1934.

178. MITEREFF, S. D., Principles Underlying the Rational Solution of Automatic Control Problems, *Trans. ASME*, 1935.

179. CHESTNUT, H., and R. W. MAYER, Comparison of Steady State and Transient Performance of Servomechanisms, *Trans. AIEE*, 1949.

180. THOMAS, C. H., and E. C. EASTON, Graphical Determination of Transfer Function Loci for Servomechanism Components and Systems, *Trans. AIEE*, 1949.

181. McCANN, G. D., C. H. WILTS, and B. N. LOCANTHI, Application of the California Institute of Technology Electronic Analogue Computer to Non-linear Mechanics and Servomechanisms, *Trans. AIEE*, 1949.

182. HAZEN, H. L., J. J. JAEGER, and G. S. BROWN, An Automatic Curve Follower, *Rev. Sci. Instruments*, 1936.

183. MACNEE, A. B., An Electronic Differential Analyzer, *Proc. IRE*, 1949.

184. GUND, R. A., Automatic Temperature Control for Aircraft, *Trans. AIEE*, 1945.

185. BERRY, T. M., Polarized Light Servo System, *Trans. AIEE*, 1944.

186. SMITH, E. S., Automatic Regulators, Their Theory and Application, *Trans. ASME*, 1936.

187. MOOG, W. C., The Frequency Response Method of Control Analysis, *Instruments*, 1947.

188. CREDE, C. E., Determining Moment of Inertia, *Machine Design*, 1948.

189. FRY, M., Designing Computing Mechanisms, *Machine Design*, January, 1946.

190. RESTEMEYER, W. E., Operational Methods in Servomechanism Design, *J. Aeronaut. Sci.*, 1945.

191. McDONALD, D., Analog Computers for Servo Problems, *Rev. Sci. Instruments*, 1950.

192. KRON, G., Tensorial Analysis of Control Systems, *J. Applied Mechanics*, 1948.

193. WALTERS, E. R., and J. B. REA, Determination of Frequency Characteristics from Response to Arbitrary Input, *J. Aeronaut. Sci.*, 1950.

194. IVANOFF, A., Theoretical Foundations of the Automatic Regulation of Temperature, *J. Inst. Fuel*, 1934.

195. PRINZ, D. G., Contributions to the Theory of Automatic Controllers and Followers, *J. Sci. Instruments*, 1934.

196. HANNA, C. R., and L. B. LYNN, Gyroscopic Stabilizer for Tanks, *Elec. Eng.*, 1944.

197. ANDRESEN, J., Electrical Pickoffs for Instrumentation of Pilotless Aircraft, *Instruments*, 1950.

198. KOOPMAN, R. J. W., Frequency Response of Instruments, *Instruments*, 1950.

199. SEACORD, C. L., JR., Application of Frequency Response Analysis to Aircraft and Autopilot Stability, *J. Aeronaut. Sci.*, 1950.

200. McDONALD, D., Electromechanical Lead Network for AC Servomechanisms, *Rev. Sci. Instruments*, 1949.

201. DUTILH, J. R., Theory of Non-linear Servomechanisms, *Radio franc.*, 1950.

202. GREENWOOD, I. A., JR., J. V. HOLDAM, JR., and D. MacRAE, JR., "Electronic Instruments," McGraw-Hill Book Company, Inc., New York, 1948.

203. MARCY, H. T., Parallel Circuits in Servomechanisms, *Trans. AIEE*, 1946.

204. MASON, C. E., Quantitative Analysis of Process Lags, *Trans. ASME*, 1938.

205. HARDER, E. L., and J. T. CARLETON, New Techniques on the Anacom—Electric Analog Computer, *Trans. AIEE*, 1950.

206. NICHOLS, N. B., and J. G. ZIEGLER, Process Control Valves, *Machine Design*, January, 1949.

INDEX